Carnegie Learning Algebra I

Student Skills Practice

4th Edition

David Dengler
Sandy Bartle Finocchi
William S. Hadley
Mary Lou Metz

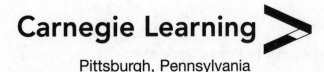
Carnegie Learning

Pittsburgh, Pennsylvania

Carnegie Learning >

501 Grant St., Suite 1075
Pittsburgh, PA 15219
Phone 888.851.7094
Customer Service Phone 888.851.7094, option 3

www.carnegielearning.com

Printing History
First Edition 2012
Second Edition 2014
Third Edition 2015
Fourth Edition 2016

ISBN: 978-1-60972-153-4

Printed in the United States of America by Cenveo Corporation
1 2 3 4 5 6 7 8 9 CC 18 17 16

Name _____ Date _____

A Picture Is Worth a Thousand Words
Understanding Quantities and Their Relationships

Vocabulary

Write a definition for each term in your own words.

1. independent quantity

2. dependent quantity

Problem Set

Determine the independent and dependent quantities in each scenario.

1. Selena is driving to visit her grandmother who lives 325 miles away from Selena's home. She travels an average of 60 miles per hour.

   Independent quantity: time (hours)

   Dependent quantity: distance (miles)

2. Benjamin works at a printing company. He is making T-shirts for a high school volleyball team. The press he runs can imprint 3 T-shirts per minute with the school's mascot.

3. On her way to work each morning, Sophia purchases a small cup of coffee for $4.25 from the coffee shop.

4. Phillip enjoys rock climbing on the weekends. At some of the less challenging locations he can climb upwards of 12 feet per minute.

5. Jose prefers to walk to work when the weather is nice. He walks the 1.5 miles to work at a speed of about 3 miles per hour.

6. Gavin works for a skydiving company. Customers pay $200 per jump to skydive in tandem skydives with Gavin.

Choose the graph that best models each scenario.

7. Kylie is filling her backyard pool to get ready for the summer. She is using a garden hose to fill the pool at a rate of 14 gallons per minute.

Graph A   Graph B   Graph C

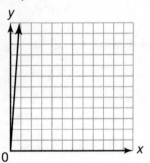 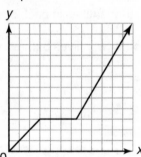 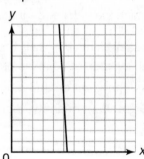

Graph A

8. Hector is training to participate in competitive trampoline. In his best jump, he can reach a maximum height of about 9 meters and can spend about 2 seconds in the air performing tricks.

Graph A   Graph B   Graph C

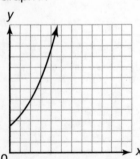 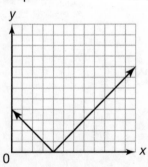 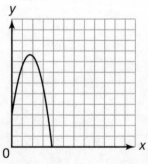

Name _____ Date _____

9. Jasmine is saving for college. She has invested $500 in a mutual fund that is expected to earn an average of 7% annually.

Graph A

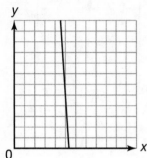

Graph B

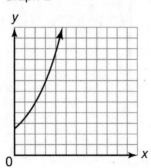

Graph C

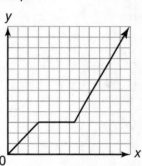

10. Each day Maria starts her walk to school at 7:45 AM. At 7:50 AM she stops at her friend Jenna's house. Jenna is usually late and Maria must wait at least 5 minutes for her to get ready. At 7:55 AM Maria and Jenna leave Jenna's house and arrive at school at 8:10 AM.

Graph A

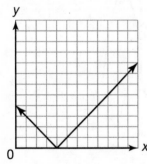

Graph B

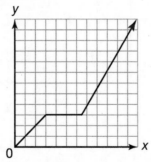

Graph C

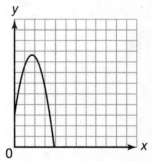

11. Marcus is at the top of an observation tower. He drops an action figure with a parachute attached and watches it descend to the ground.

Graph A

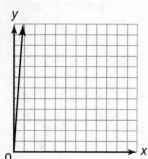

Graph B

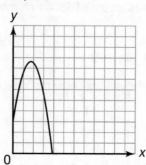

Graph C

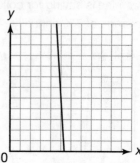

12. Janelle holds a raffle to raise money for a children's hospital. Participants who enter the raffle guess the number of peanuts in a jar. Janelle records the number of peanuts each participant guesses and the number of peanuts their guess is off by.

Graph A

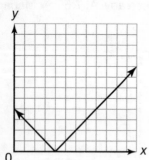

Graph B

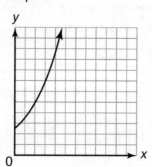

Graph C

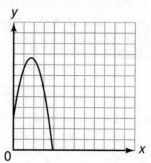

Name _____ Date _____

Label the axes of the graph that models each scenario with the independent and dependent quantities.

13. Madison enjoys bicycling for exercise. Each Saturday she bikes a course she has mapped out around her town. She averages a speed of 12 miles per hour on her journey.

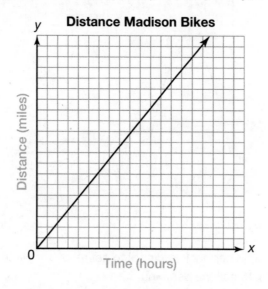

Distance Madison Bikes

Distance (miles)

Time (hours)

14. Natasha is filling the bathtub with water in order to give her dog Buster a bath. The faucet fills the tub at an average rate of 12 gallons per minute.

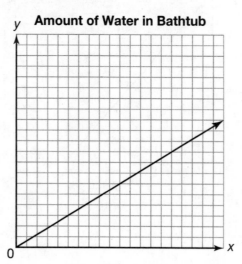

Amount of Water in Bathtub

15. Marcus throws a football straight up into the air. After it reaches its maximum height of 20 feet, it descends back to the ground.

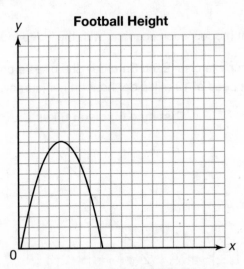

Football Height

16. Chloe is using a pump to drain her backyard pool to get ready for winter. The pump removes the water at an average rate of 15 gallons per minute.

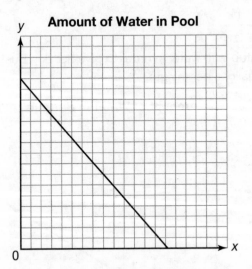

Amount of Water in Pool

Name _____ Date _____

17. Jermaine is saving money to purchase a used car. He places $850 dollars in a savings account that earns 1.65% interest annually.

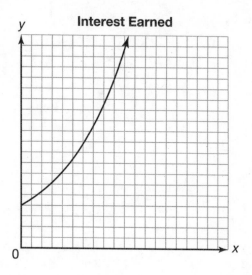

18. Zachary enjoys hiking. On the first day of his latest hiking trip, he hikes through flat terrain for about 8 miles. On the second day, he hikes through very steep terrain for about 3 miles. On the third day he hikes through some hilly terrain for about 6 miles.

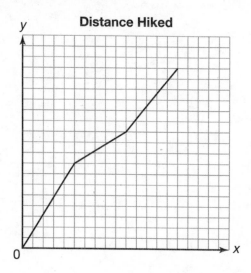

Name _____ Date _____

A Sort of Sorts
Analyzing and Sorting Graphs

Vocabulary

Match each definition to its corresponding term.

1. A graph with no breaks in it	**a.** discrete graph
2. The mapping between a set of inputs and a set of outputs	**b.** continuous graph
3. The set of all input values of a relation	**c.** relation
4. The set of all output values of a relation	**d.** function
5. A graph of isolated points	**e.** domain
6. A visual method used to determine whether a relation represented as a graph is a function	**f.** range
7. A relation between a given set of elements for which each input value there exists exactly one output value	**g.** Vertical Line Test

Problem Set

Each pair of graphs has been grouped together. Provide a rationale to explain why these graphs may have been grouped together.

1. Graph A

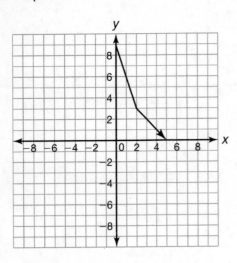

Graph B

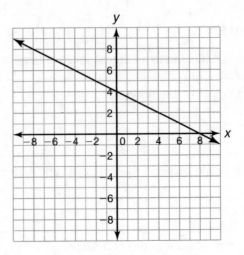

Answers will vary.

Both graphs are always decreasing from left to right. Both graphs are functions. Both graphs are made up of straight lines.

2. Graph A

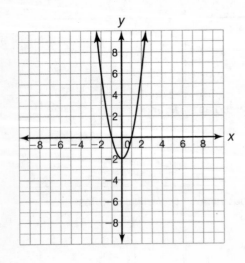

Graph B

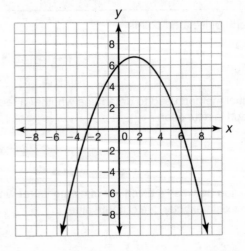

Name _____ Date _____

3. Graph A

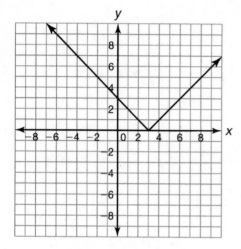

Graph B

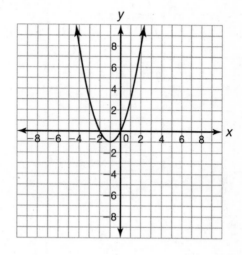

4. Graph A

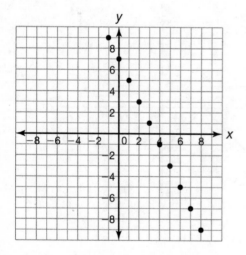

Graph B

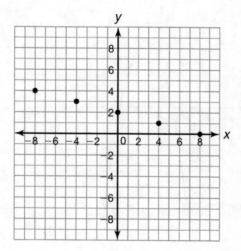

5. Graph A

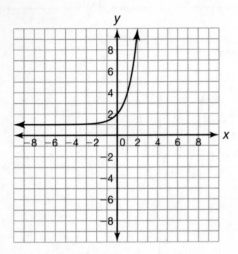

Graph B

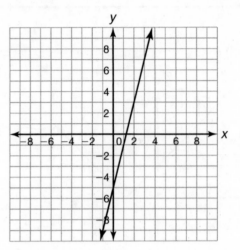

6. Graph A

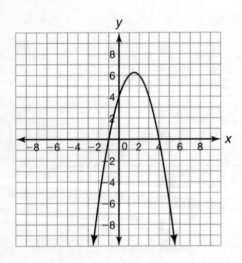

Graph B

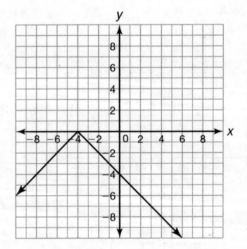

Name _____ Date _____

Determine whether the graph is discrete or continuous.

7.

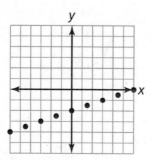

The graph is discrete.

8.

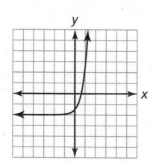

9.

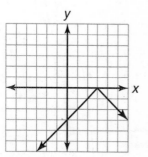

10.

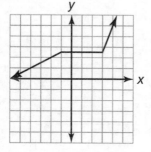

11.

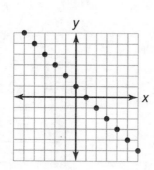

12.

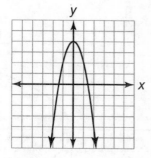

Determine if each graph represents a function by using the Vertical Line Test.

13.

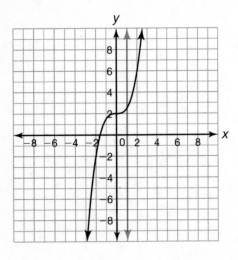

Yes. The graph is a function.

14.

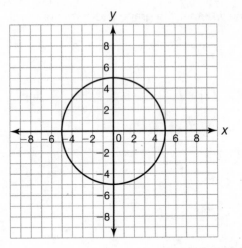

15.

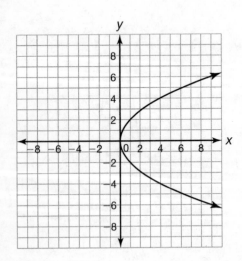

16.

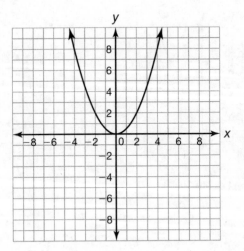

Name _____ Date _____

17.

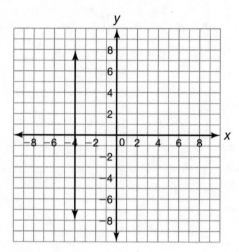

18.

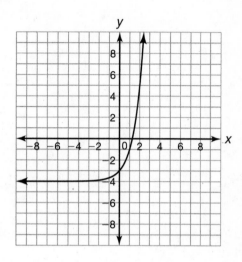

Name _____ Date _____

There Are Many Ways to Represent Functions
Recognizing Algebraic and Graphical Representations of Functions

Vocabulary

Choose the term from the box that best completes each statement.

function notation	increasing function	exponential functions
function family	linear functions	linear absolute value functions
absolute maximum	quadratic functions	constant function
linear piecewise functions	decreasing function	absolute minimum

1. _____ is a way to represent equations algebraically that makes it more efficient to recognize the independent and dependent variables.

2. The family of _____ includes functions of the form $f(x) = a \cdot b^x$, where a and b are real numbers, and b is greater than 0 but is not equal to 1.

3. The family of _____ includes functions that have an equation that changes for different parts, or pieces, of the domain.

4. When both the independent and dependent variables of a function increase across the entire domain, the function is called an _____.

5. A function has an _____ if there is a point on its graph that has a y-coordinate that is greater than the y-coordinates of every other point on the graph.

6. A _____ is a group of functions that share certain characteristics.

7. The family of _____ includes functions of the form $f(x) = a|x + b| + c$, where a, b, and c are real numbers, and a is not equal to 0.

8. When the dependent variable of a function decreases as the independent variable increases across the entire domain, the function is called a _____.

9. The family of _____ includes functions of the form $f(x) = ax^2 + bx + c$, where a, b, and c are real numbers, and a is not equal to 0.

10. The family of _____ includes functions of the form $f(x) = ax + b$, where a and b are real numbers, and a is not equal to 0.

11. If the dependent variable of a function does not change or remains constant over the entire domain, then the function is called a _____.

12. A function has an _____ if there is a point on its graph that has a y-coordinate that is less than the y-coordinates of every other point on the graph.

Problem Set

Rewrite each function using function notation.

1. Rewrite the function $y = 3x - 8$ using function notation so that the dependent quantity, defined as f, is a function of the independent quantity x.

$f(x) = 3x - 8$

2. Rewrite the function $y = 3x^2 + 6x - 1$ using function notation so that the dependent quantity, defined as C, is a function of the independent quantity x.

3. Rewrite the function $y = 3^x + 8$ using function notation so that the dependent quantity, defined as P, is a function of the independent quantity x.

4. Rewrite the function $l = |n - 2|$ using function notation so that the dependent quantity, defined as L, is a function of the independent quantity n.

5. Rewrite the function $d = -\frac{1}{2}m + 5$ using function notation so that the dependent quantity, defined as A, is a function of the independent quantity m.

6. Rewrite the function $c = 2\pi r^2$ using function notation so that the dependent quantity, defined as C, is a function of the independent quantity r.

Name _____ Date _____

Choose the graph that represents each function. Use your graphing calculator.

7. $f(x) = \frac{2}{3}x + 2$

Graph A

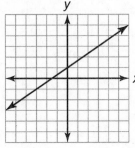

Graph B

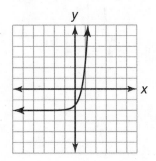

Graph C

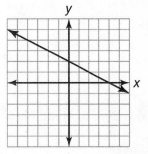

Graph A

8. $f(x) = -x^2 + 4$

Graph A

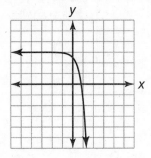

Graph B

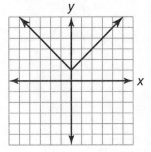

Graph C

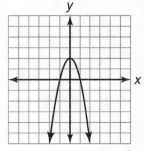

9. $f(x) = 2^x + 5$

Graph A

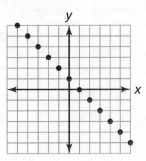

Graph B

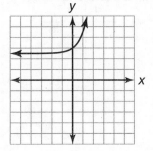

Graph C

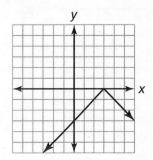

10. $f(x) = |x - 6|$

Graph A   Graph B   Graph C

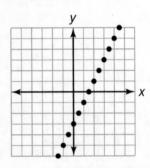   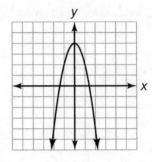   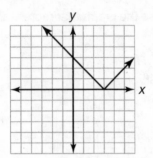

11. $f(x) = 2x - 6$, where x is an integer

Graph A   Graph B   Graph C

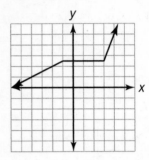   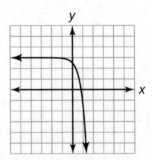   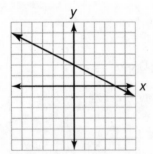

12. $f(x) = -4$

Graph A   Graph B   Graph C

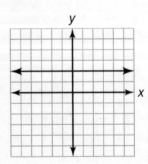   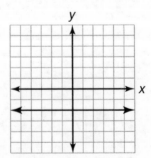   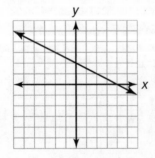

Name _____ Date _____

Determine whether each graph represents an increasing function, a decreasing function, a constant function, or a combination of increasing and decreasing functions.

13.

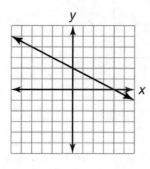

The graph represents an increasing function.

14.

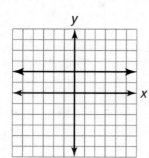

15.

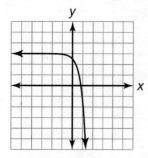

16.

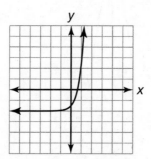

17.

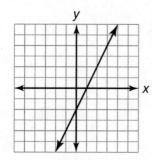

18.

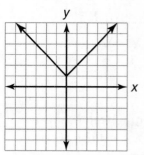

Determine whether each graph represents a function with an absolute minimum, an absolute maximum, or neither.

19.

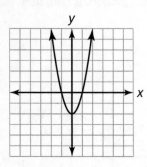

The graph represents a function with an absolute minimum.

20.

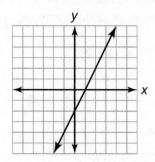

21.

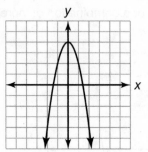

22.

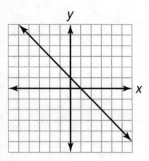

23.

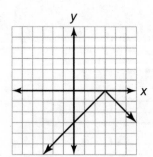

24.

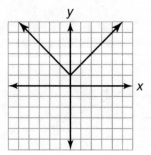

Name _____ Date _____

Determine whether each graph represents a linear function, a quadratic function, an exponential function, a linear absolute value function, a linear piecewise function, or a constant function.

25.

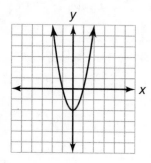

The graph represents an exponential function.

26.

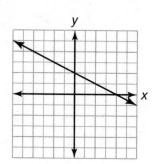

27.

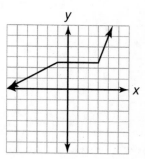

28.

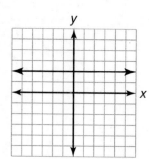

29.

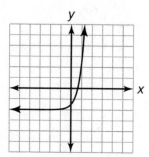

30.

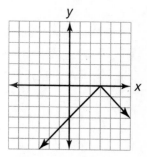

Name _____ Date _____

Function Families for 200, Alex...
Recognizing Functions by Characteristics

Vocabulary

Choose the appropriate function family or families to complete each sentence based on the given characteristic(s).

linear functions	quadratic functions
exponential functions	linear absolute value functions

1. The graph of this function family is a straight line. The function family is _____.

2. The graph of this function family has an increasing interval and a decreasing interval. The function family is _____.

3. The graph of this function family has an absolute minimum. The function family is _____.

4. The graph of this function family is decreasing over the entire domain. The function family is _____.

5. The graph of this function family forms a V shape. The function family is _____ _____.

6. The graph of this function family has an increasing interval and a decreasing interval and forms a U shape. The function family is _____.

7. The graph of this function family does not have an absolute maximum or absolute minimum and is a smooth curve. The function family is _____.

8. The graph of this function family has an absolute maximum or absolute minimum and is made up straight lines. The function family is _____.

9. The graph of this function family contains straight lines and does not have an absolute maximum or absolute minimum. The function family is _____.

10. The graph of this function family decreases over the entire domain and is a smooth curve. The function family is _____.

Problem Set

Create an equation and sketch a graph for a function with each set of given characteristics. Use values that are any real numbers between −10 and 10.

1. Create an equation and sketch a graph that:
   - is a smooth curve,
   - is continuous,
   - has a minimum, and
   - is quadratic.

   Answers will vary.

   $f(x) = x^2$

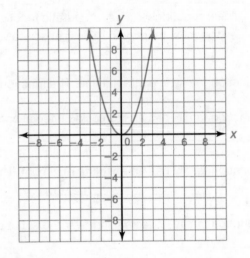

2. Create an equation and sketch a graph that:
   - is linear,
   - is discrete, and
   - is decreasing across the entire domain.

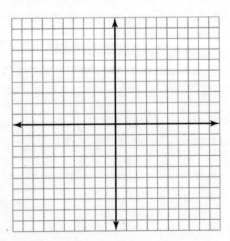

Name _____ Date _____

3. Create an equation and sketch a graph that:
   - is a smooth curve,
   - is increasing across the entire domain,
   - is continuous, and
   - is exponential.

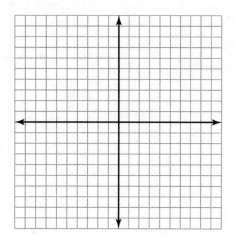

4. Create an equation and sketch a graph that:
   - has a maximum,
   - is continuous, and
   - is a linear absolute value function.

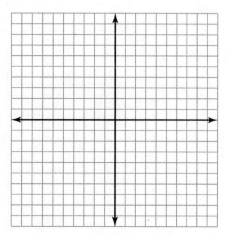

5. Create an equation and sketch a graph that:
 - is linear,

 - is continuous,

 - is neither increasing nor decreasing across the entire domain, and

 - does not pass through the origin.

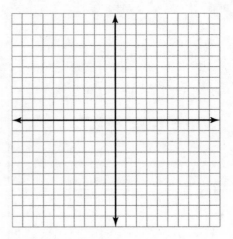

6. Create an equation and sketch a graph that:
 - is discrete,

 - has a maximum,

 - does not pass through the origin, and

 - is quadratic.

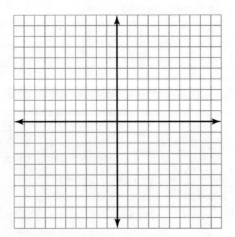

Name _____ Date _____

Choose the function family represented by each graph.

linear function	quadratic function	exponential function
linear absolute value function	linear piecewise function	

7.

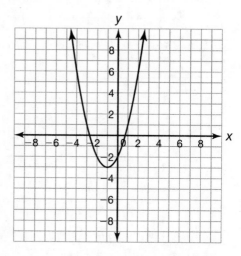

8.

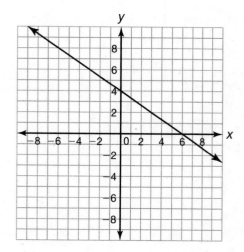

The graph represents a quadratic function.

9.

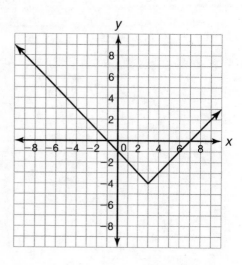

10.

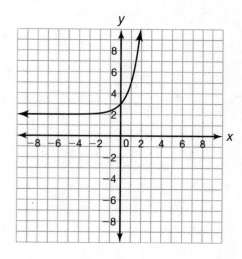

11.

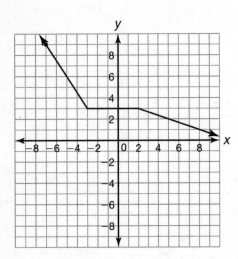

12.

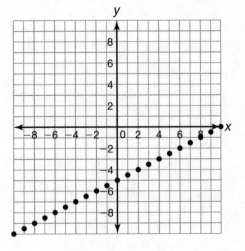

Name _____ Date _____

The Plane!
Modeling Linear Situations

2

Vocabulary

Define each term in your own words.

1. first differences

2. solution

3. intersection point

Problem Set

Identify the independent and dependent quantities in each problem situation. Then write a function to represent the problem situation.

1. Nathan is riding his scooter to school at a rate of 6 miles per hour.

The distance Nathan travels depends on the time. Distance, D, is the dependent quantity and time, t, is the independent quantity.

$D(t) = 6t$

2. Sophia is walking to the mall at a rate of 3 miles per hour.

3. Mario is stuffing envelopes with invitations to the school's Spring Carnival. He stuffs 5 envelopes each minute.

2

4. Shanise plays on the varsity soccer team. She averages 4 goals per game.

5. The football booster club sells hot chocolate during the varsity football games. Each cup of hot chocolate costs $2.

6. The basketball booster club sells t-shirts at the varsity basketball games. Each t-shirt costs $12.

Use each scenario to complete the table of values and calculate the unit rate of change.

7. Miguel is riding his bike to lacrosse practice at a rate of 7 miles per hour.

	Independent Quantity	Dependent Quantity
Quantity	Time	Distance
Units	hours	miles
Expression	t	$7t$
	0	0
	0.5	3.5
	1	7
	1.5	10.5
	2	14

(0.5, 3.5) and (1, 7)

$$\frac{7-3.5}{1-0.5}=\frac{3.5}{0.5}$$
$$=\frac{7}{1}$$

The unit rate of change is 7.

Name _____ Date _____

8. Jada is walking to school at a rate of 2 miles per hour.

	Independent Quantity	Dependent Quantity
Quantity		
Units		
Expression		
	0.25	
	0.5	
	1	
	1.25	
	1.5	

9. Noah is stuffing envelopes with invitations to the school's Harvest Festival. He stuffs 4 envelopes each minute.

	Independent Quantity	Dependent Quantity
Quantity		
Units		
Expression		
	5	
	10	
	15	
	20	
	25	

10. Terell plays on the varsity basketball team. He averages 12 points per game.

	Independent Quantity	Dependent Quantity
Quantity		
Units		
Expression		
	1	
	3	
	5	
	7	
	9	

11. The volleyball boosters sell bags of popcorn during the varsity matches to raise money for new uniforms. Each bag of popcorn costs $3.

	Independent Quantity	Dependent Quantity
Quantity		
Units		
Expression		
	5	
	10	
	15	
	20	
	25	

Name _____ Date _____

12. The football boosters sell hooded sweatshirts to raise money for new equipment. Each sweatshirt costs $18.

	Independent Quantity	Dependent Quantity
Quantity		
Units		
Expression		
	5	
	10	
	20	
	30	
	40	

Identify the input value, the output value, and the rate of change for each function.

13. Belinda is making greeting cards. She makes 4 cards per hour. The function $C(t) = 4t$ represents the total number of cards Belinda makes as a function of time.

The input value is t.

The output value is $4t$.

The rate of change is 4.

14. Owen is riding his bike to his friend's house at a rate of 6 miles per hour. The function $D(t) = 6t$ represents the distance Owen rides as a function of time.

15. Rochelle is shopping for earrings. Each pair of earrings costs $15 dollars. The function $C(e) = 15e$ represents the total cost of the earrings as a function of the number of pairs of earrings Rochelle buys.

16. Lavon is driving to visit a college campus. He is traveling 65 miles per hour. The function $D(t) = 65t$ represents the total distance he travels as a function of time.

17. Kiana is selling coupon books to raise money for her school. Each coupon book cost $35. The function $M(b) = 35b$ represents the total amount of money raised as a function of the number of coupon books sold.

18. Cisco mows lawns in his neighborhood to earn money. He earns $16 for each lawn. The function $A(m) = 16m$ represents the total amount of money earned as a function of the number of lawns mowed.

2

Name _____ Date _____

Solve each function for the given input value. The function $A(t) = 7t$ represents the total amount of money in dollars Carmen earns babysitting as a function of time in hours.

19. $A(3) =$ _____

$A(3) = 7(3)$

$\quad = 21$

Carmen earns $21 when she babysits for 3 hours.

20. $A(2) =$ _____

21. $A(5) =$ _____

22. $A(4.5) =$ _____

23. $A(3.5) =$ _____

24. $A(6) =$ _____

2

Use the graph to determine the input value for each given output value. The function $D(t) = 40t$ represents the total distance traveled in miles as a function of time in hours.

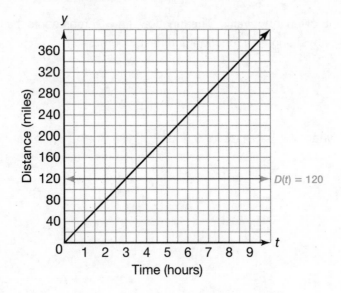

25. $D(t) = 120$

  $t = 3$

26. $D(t) = 320$

27. $D(t) = 240$

28. $D(t) = 160$

29. $D(t) = 80$

30. $D(t) = 400$

Name _____ Date _____

What Goes Up Must Come Down
Analyzing Linear Functions

2

Problem Set

Complete the table to represent each problem situation.

1. A hot air balloon cruising at 1000 feet begins to ascend. It ascends at a rate of 200 feet per minute.

	Independent Quantity	Dependent Quantity
Quantity	Time	Height
Units	minutes	feet
	0	1000
	2	1400
	4	1800
	6	2200
	8	2600
Expression	t	$200t + 1000$

2. A bathtub contains 10 gallons of water. The faucet is turned on and fills the tub at a rate of 5.25 gallons per minute.

	Independent Quantity	Dependent Quantity
Quantity		
Units		
	0	
	1	
	3	
		36.25
		46.75
Expression		

3. A helicopter flying at 4125 feet begins its descent. It descends at a rate of 550 feet per minute.

	Independent Quantity	Dependent Quantity
Quantity		
Units		
	0	
	1	
	2	
		2475
		1925
Expression		

Name _____ Date _____

4. A fish tank filled with 12 gallons of water is drained. The water drains at a rate
   of 1.5 gallons per minute.

	Independent Quantity	Dependent Quantity
Quantity		
Units		
	0	
	1	
	3	
		4.5
		1.5
Expression		

5. A submarine is traveling at a depth of −300 feet. It begins ascending at a rate of 28 feet per minute.

	Independent Quantity	Dependent Quantity
Quantity		
Units		
	0	
	2	
	4	
		−132
		−76
Expression		

6. A free-diver is diving from the surface of the water at a rate of 15 feet per minute.

	Independent Quantity	Dependent Quantity
Quantity		
Units		
	0	
	1	
	2	
		−45
		−60
Expression		

Identify the input value, the output value, the *y*-intercept, and the rate of change for each function.

7. A hot air balloon at 130 feet begins to ascend. It ascends at a rate of 160.5 feet per minute. The function $f(t) = 160.5t + 130$ represents the height of the balloon as it ascends.

   The input value is *t*, time in minutes. The output value is $f(t)$, height in feet.

   The *y*-intercept is 130. The rate of change is 160.5.

8. A backyard pool contains 500 gallons of water. It is filled with additional water at a rate of 6 gallons per minute. The function $f(t) = 6t + 500$ represents the volume of water in the pool as it is filled.

9. A submarine is diving from the surface of the water at a rate of 17 feet per minute. The function $f(t) = -17t$ represents the depth of the submarine as it dives.

Name _____ Date _____

10. A helicopter flying at 3505 feet begins its descent. It descends at a rate of 470 feet per minute. The function $f(t) = -470t + 3505$ represents the height of the helicopter as it descends.

11. A bathtub contains 5 gallons of water. The faucet is turned on and water is added to the tub at a rate of 4.25 gallons per minute. The function $f(t) = 4.25t + 5$ represents the volume of water in the bathtub as it is filled.

12. A free-diver is diving from the surface of the water at a rate of 8 feet per minute. The function $f(t) = -8t$ represents the depth of the diver.

Sketch the line for the dependent value to estimate each intersection point.

13. $f(x) = -40x + 1200$ when $f(x) = 720$ **14.** $f(x) = 6x + 15$ when $f(x) = 75$

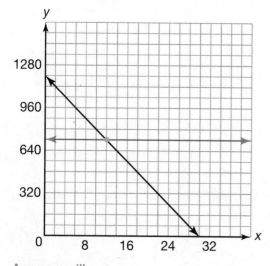

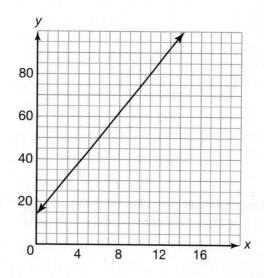

Answers will vary.

$f(x) = 720$ at $x = 12$

15. $f(x) = -2x + 5$ when $f(x) = -7$

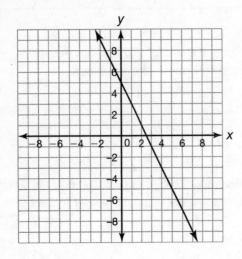

16. $f(x) = 4x - 7$ when $f(x) = 8$

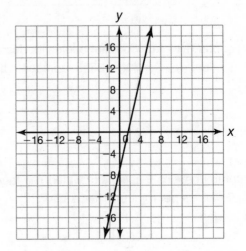

17. $f(x) = -200x + 2400$ when $f(x) = 450$

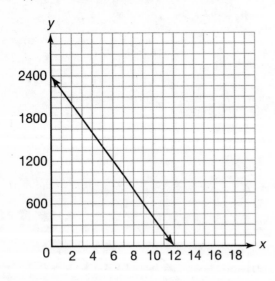

18. $f(x) = 12x + 90$ when $f(x) = 420$

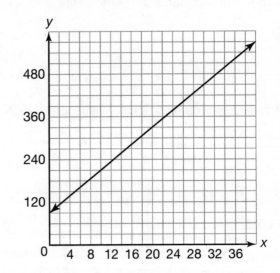

Name _____ Date _____

Substitute and solve for x to determine the exact value of each intersection point.

19. $f(x) = -40x + 1200$ when $f(x) = 720$

$f(x) = -40x + 1200$
$720 = -40x + 1200$
$-480 = -40x$
$12 = x$

20. $f(x) = 6x + 15$ when $f(x) = 75$

21. $f(x) = -2x + 5$ when $f(x) = -7$

22. $f(x) = 4x - 7$ when $f(x) = 8$

23. $f(x) = -200x + 2400$ when $f(x) = 450$

24. $f(x) = 12x + 90$ when $f(x) = 420$

2

Name _____ Date _____

Scouting for Prizes!
Modeling Linear Inequalities

Vocabulary

Define the term in your own words.

1. solve an inequality

Problem Set

Carlos works at an electronics store selling computer equipment. He can earn a bonus if he sells
$10,000 worth of computer equipment this month. So far this month, he has sold $4000 worth of
computer equipment. He hopes to sell additional laptop computers for $800 each to reach his goal.
The function $f(x) = 800x + 4000$ represents Carlos's total sales as a function of the number of laptop
computers he sells.

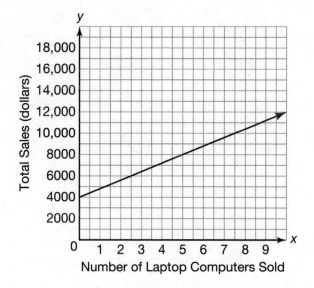

Use the graph to write an equation or inequality to determine the number of laptop computers Carlos would need to sell to earn each amount.

1. at least $10,000

Carlos would need to sell at least 8 laptop computers.

$x \geq 8$

2. less than $7000

3. less than $6000

4. at least $9000

5. more than $12,000

6. exactly $8000

Elena works at the ticket booth of a local playhouse. On the opening night of the play, tickets are $10 each. The playhouse has already sold $500 worth of tickets during a presale. The function $f(x) = 10x + 500$ represents the total sales as a function of tickets sold on opening night.

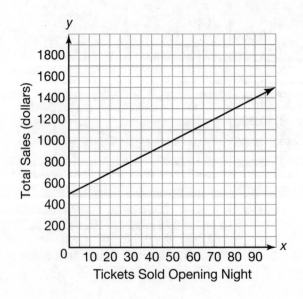

Name _____ Date _____

Use the graph of the function to answer each question. Graph each solution on the number line.

7. How many tickets must Elena sell in order to make at least $1000?

Elena must sell at least 50 tickets. $x \geq 50$

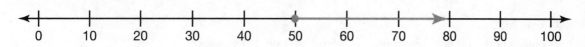

8. How many tickets must Elena sell in order to make less than $800?

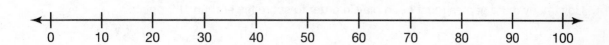

9. How many tickets must Elena sell in order to make at least $1200?

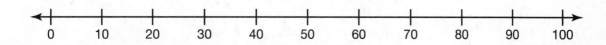

10. How many tickets must Elena sell in order to make exactly $1400?

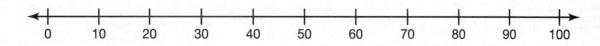

11. How many tickets must Elena sell in order to make less than $600?

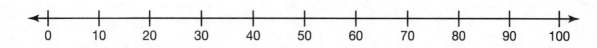

12. How many tickets must Elena sell in order to make exactly $900?

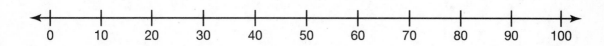

Leon plays on the varsity basketball team. So far this season he has scored a total of 52 points. He scores an average of 13 points per game. The function $f(x) = 13x + 52$ represents the total number of points Leon will score this season. Write and solve an inequality to answer each question.

13. How many more games must Leon play in order to score at least 117 points?

$f(x) = 13x + 52$

$117 \le 13x + 52$

$65 \le 13x$

$5 \le x$

Leon must play in 5 or more games to score at least 117 points.

14. How many more games must Leon play in order to score fewer than 182 points?

15. How many more games must Leon play in order to score more than 143 points?

Name _____ Date _____

16. How many more games must Leon play in order to score at least 100 points?

17. How many more games must Leon play in order to score fewer than 85 points?

18. How many more games must Leon play in order to score more than 200 points?

Draw an oval on the graph to represent the solution to each question. Write the corresponding inequality statement.

19. A hot air balloon at 4000 feet begins its descent. It descends at a rate of 200 feet per minute. The function $f(x) = -200x + 4000$ represents the height of the balloon as it descends. How many minutes have passed if the balloon is below 3000 feet?

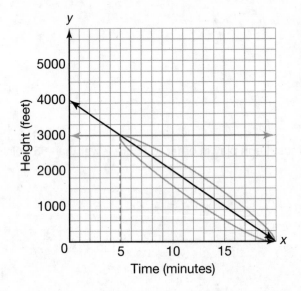

More than 5 minutes have passed if the balloon is below 3000 feet.

$x > 5$

20. A bathtub filled with 55 gallons of water is drained. The water drains at a rate of 5 gallons per minute. The function $f(x) = -5x + 55$ represents the volume of water in the tub as it drains. How many minutes have passed if the tub still has more than 20 gallons of water remaining in it?

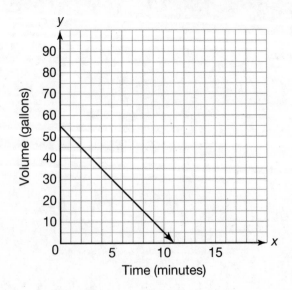

Name _____ Date _____

21. Lea is walking to school at a rate of 250 feet per minute. Her school is 5000 feet from her home. The function $f(x) = 250x$ represents the distance Lea walks. How many minutes have passed if Lea still has more than 2000 feet to walk?

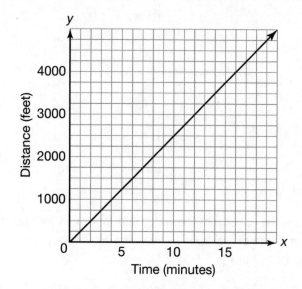

22. Franco is riding his bike to school at a rate of 600 feet per minute. His school is 9000 feet from his home. The function $f(x) = 600x$ represents the distance Franco rides. How many minutes have passed if Franco has less than 3000 feet left to ride?

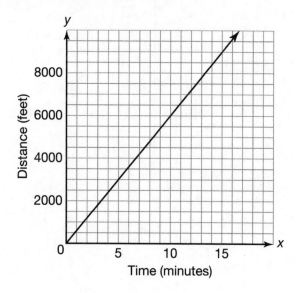

23. A submarine is diving from the surface of the water at a rate of 20 feet per minute. The function $f(x) = -20x$ represents the depth of the submarine as it dives. How many minutes have passed if the submarine is at least 160 feet below the surface?

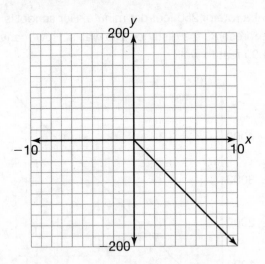

24. A scuba diver is diving from the surface of the water at a rate of 14 feet per minute. The function $f(x) = -14x$ represents the depth of the diver as he dives. How many minutes have passed if the diver is less than 42 feet below the surface?

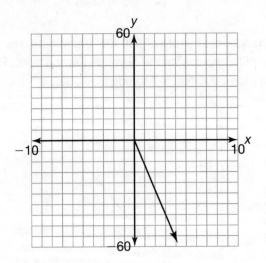

Name _____ Date _____

We're Shipping Out!
Solving and Graphing Compound Inequalities

2

Vocabulary

Match each definition to its corresponding term.

1. compound inequality

    a. a solution of a compound inequality in the form $a < x < b$, where a and b are any real numbers

2. solution of a compound inequality

    b. an inequality that is formed by the union, "or," or the intersection, "and," of two simple inequalities

3. conjunction

    c. the part or parts of the solutions that satisfy both of the inequalities

4. disjunction

    d. a solution of a compound inequality in the form $x < a$ or $x > b$, where a and b are any real numbers

Problem Set

Write each compound inequality in compact form.

1. All numbers less than or equal to 22 and greater than -4

    $22 \geq x > -4$

2. All numbers less than 55 and greater than 45

3. All numbers greater than or equal to 0 and less than or equal to 6

4. All numbers greater than 10 and less than 1000

5. All numbers less than or equal to 87 and greater than or equal to 83

6. All numbers greater than -1 and less than or equal to 39

Write an inequality for each graph.

7.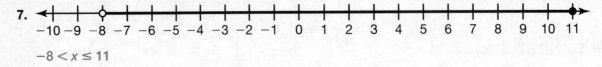

$-8 < x \le 11$

8.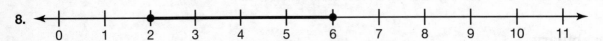

9.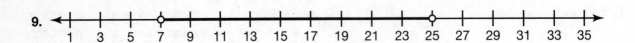

10.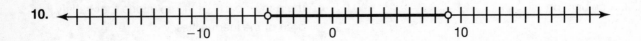

11.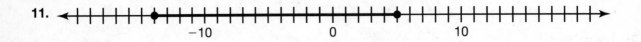

12.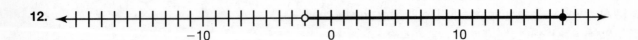

Graph each inequality.

13. $45 < x < 75$

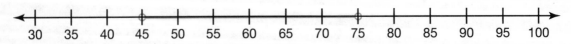

14. $-5 < x < 5$

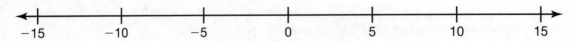

15. $-13 \le x \le 5$

Name _____ Date _____

16. $-6 \leq x < 19$

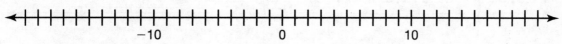

17. $-35 \leq x \leq 50$

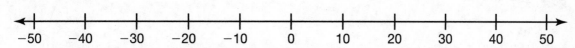

18. $-5 < x \leq 45$

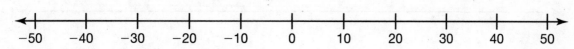

Write a compound inequality for each situation.

19. The flowers in the garden are 6 inches or taller *or* shorter than 3 inches.

$x \geq 6$ or $x < 3$

20. People with a driver's license are at least 16 years old *and* no older than 85 years old.

21. Kyle's car gets more than 31 miles per gallon on the highway *or* 26 miles or less per gallon in the city.

22. The number of houses that will be built in the new neighborhood must be at least 14 and no more than 28.

23. At the High and Low Store, they sell high-end items that sell for over $1000 and low-end items that sell for less than $10.

24. The heights of the twenty tallest buildings in New York City range from 229 meters to 381 meters.

Represent the solution to each part of the compound inequality on the number line. Then write the final solution that is represented by each graph.

25. $x > 2$ and $x \leq 7$

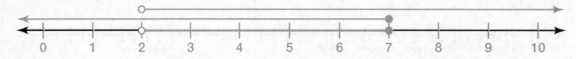

$2 < x \leq 7$

26. $x > 10$ or $x > 6$

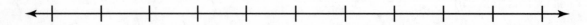

27. $x \geq 5$ or $x < 3$

28. $x > 4$ and $x < 3$

29. $x \leq -1$ or $x > 0$

Name _____ Date _____

30. $8 > x \geq -8$

31. $x \leq 9$ and $x \geq 2$

32. $x > -11$ or $x \leq -11$

Solve each compound inequality. Then graph and describe the solution.

33. $-3 < x + 7 \leq 17$

$$-3 < x + 7 \leq 17$$
$$-3 - 7 < x + 7 - 7 \leq 17 - 7$$
$$-10 < x \leq 10$$

```
◄──○──────────────┼──────────────◆──►
  -10             0               10
```

Solution: $-10 < x \leq 10$

34. $4 \leq 2x + 2 < 12$

35. $x + 5 > 14$ or $3x < 9$

36. $-5x + 1 \geq 16$ or $x - 6 \leq -8$

Name _____ Date _____

37. $28 \le \frac{7}{8}x < 42$

38. $-2x + 5 \le 9$ or $-x - 13 > -31$

2

Name _____ Date _____

Play Ball!
Absolute Value Equations and Inequalities

Vocabulary

Define each term in your own words.

1. opposites

2. absolute value

Give an example of each term.

3. linear absolute value equation

4. linear absolute value inequality

Match each equivalent compound inequality to its corresponding absolute value inequality.

5. $|ax + b| < c$ a. $-c < ax + b < c$

6. $|ax + b| \leq c$ b. $ax + b < -c$ or $ax + b > c$

7. $|ax + b| > c$ c. $-c \leq ax + b \leq c$

8. $|ax + b| \geq c$ d. $ax + b \leq -c$ or $ax + b \geq c$

Problem Set

Evaluate each absolute value.

1. $|3| = 3$ 2. $|-3| =$ 3. $\left|\dfrac{1}{4}\right| =$

4. $\left|-\dfrac{1}{4}\right| =$ 5. $|3.7| =$ 6. $|-3.7| =$

Determine the number of solutions for each equation. Then calculate the solution.

7. $x = -9$

There is only one solution.

$x = -9$

8. $|x| = -6$

9. $|x| = 4$

10. $|-x| = -8$

11. $|x| = 0$

12. $|-x| = 15$

Solve each linear absolute value equation.

13. $|x + 9| = 2$

$(x + 9) = 2$ $-(x + 9) = 2$

$x + 9 - 9 = 2 - 9$ $x + 9 = -2$

$x = -7$ $x + 9 - 9 = -2 - 9$

$x = -11$

14. $|x + 4| = 10$

15. $|x - 12| = 5$

16. $|2x - 6| = 18$

Name _____ Date _____

17. $|3x + 1| = -9$

18. $|5x + 1| = 14$

Solve each linear absolute value equation.

19. $|x| - 8 = 25$

$$|x| - 8 = 25$$
$$|x| - 8 + 8 = 25 + 8$$
$$|x| = 33 \qquad\qquad\qquad -(x) = 33$$
$$x = 33 \qquad\qquad\qquad x = -33$$

20. $|x + 3| - 7 = 40$

21. $2|x - 6| = 48$

2

22. $3|x + 8| = 36$

23. $5|x| + 4 = 79$

24. $2|x| - 5 = 11$

Solve each linear absolute value inequality. Graph the solution on the number line.

25. $|x + 5| < 2$

$(x + 5) < 2$ $-(x + 5) < 2$

$x + 5 - 5 < 2 - 5$ $x + 5 > -2$

$x < -3$ $x + 5 - 5 > -2 - 5$

$x > -7$

Name _____ Date _____

26. $|x - 3| \leq 6$

27. $2|x - 1| < 14$

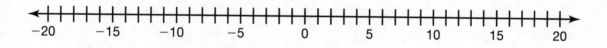

28. $3|x + 4| \geq 9$

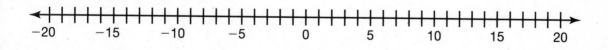

29. $2|x - 1| - 8 \leq 10$

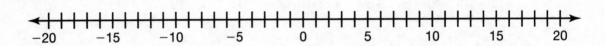

30. $3|x + 2| + 5 \geq 23$

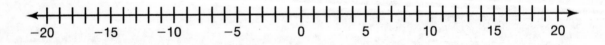

Name _____ Date _____

Graph the function that represents each problem situation.
Draw an oval on the graph to represent the answer.

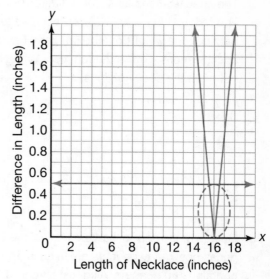

Length of Necklace (inches)

31. A jewelry company is making 16-inch bead necklaces.
The specifications allow for a difference of 0.5 inch.
The function $f(x) = |x - 16|$ represents the difference
between the necklaces manufactured and the
specifications. Graph the function. What necklace
lengths meet the specifications?

The necklaces can be between 15.5 and 16.5 inches
long to meet the specifications.

32. Julian is cutting lengths of rope for a class project.
Each rope length should be 10 inches long. The
specifications allow for a difference of 1 inch. The
function $f(x) = |x - 10|$ represents the difference
between the rope lengths cut and the specifications.
Graph the function. What rope lengths meet the
specifications?

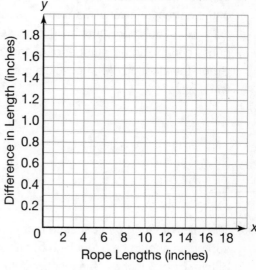

Rope Lengths (inches)

33. A snack company is filling bags with pita chips sold
by weight. Each bag should contain 8 ounces of chips.
The specifications allow for a difference of 0.25 ounce.
The function $f(x) = |x - 8|$ represents the difference
between the weight of a bag of chips and the
specifications. Graph the function. What weights meet
the specifications?

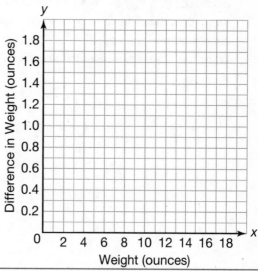

Weight (ounces)

34. A cereal company is filling boxes with cereal sold by weight. Each box should contain 32 ounces of cereal. The specifications allow for a difference of 0.5 ounce. The function $f(x) = |x - 32|$ represents the difference between the weight of a box of cereal and the specifications. Graph the function. What weights do not meet the specifications?

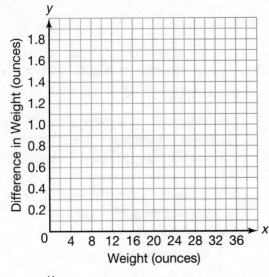

35. Guests at the school harvest festival are asked to guess how many peanuts are in a jar. The jar contains 260 peanuts. All guests within 10 peanuts of the correct answer win a prize. The function $f(x) = |x - 260|$ represents the difference between a guess and the actual number of peanuts in the jar. Graph the function. What possible guesses will not win a prize?

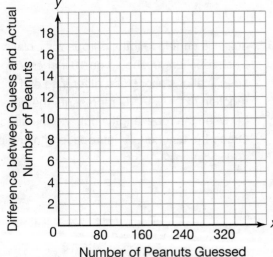

36. The rules of an art contest state that sculptures submitted should be 3 feet high but allow for a difference of 6 inches. The function $f(x) = |x - 3|$ represents the difference between a sculpture that is submitted and the specifications. Graph the function. What heights do not meet the specifications?

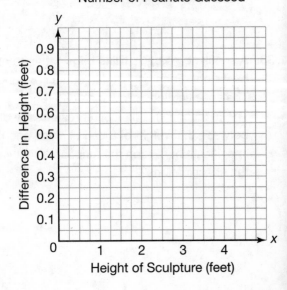

Name _____ Date _____

Choose Wisely!
Understanding Non-Linear Graphs and Inequalities

Problem Set

Choose the function that represents each problem situation.

1. Tonya is walking to school at a rate of 3 miles per hour.

   A $f(x) = 3x^2$ **B** $f(x) = 3x$ **C** $f(x) = 3^x$

   B $f(x) = 3x$

2. Guests at a craft fair are asked to guess how many beads are in a jar. The jar contains 220 beads. All guests within 10 beads of the correct answer win a prize.

   A $f(x) = |x - 220|$ **B** $f(x) = 220 - x$ **C** $f(x) = 220^x$

3. Mario buys a car for \$25,000. Each year the car loses $\frac{1}{6}$ of its value.

   A $f(x) = 25{,}000 - \frac{1}{6}x$ **B** $f(x) = \frac{1}{6}x^2 + 25{,}000$ **C** $f(x) = 25{,}000\left(\frac{5}{6}\right)^x$

4. A bathtub filled with 50 gallons of water is drained. The water drains at a rate of 5 gallons per minute.

   A $f(x) = 50 - 5x$ **B** $f(x) = 5x^2 - 50$ **C** $f(x) = 50 - 5^x$

5. Rodell throws a football straight up with a speed of 25 feet per second. The acceleration of the ball due to gravity is 32 feet per second.

   A $f(x) = -32x + 25$ **B** $f(x) = -32x^2 + 25x$ **C** $f(x) = |32x - 25|$

6. A pasta company is filling boxes with pasta sold by weight. Each box should contain 16 ounces of pasta. The specifications allow for a difference of 0.5 ounce.

   A $f(x) = 16x - 0.5$ **B** $f(x) = 16x^2 - 0.5x$ **C** $f(x) = |x - 16|$

Graph the function that represents each problem situation. Use the graph to answer the question.

7. A fish tank filled with 20 gallons of water is drained. The water drains at a rate of 4 gallons per minute. The function $f(x) = 20 - 4x$ represents the volume of water in the fish tank as it drains. Graph the function. How many minutes does it take for half of the water to drain from the tank?

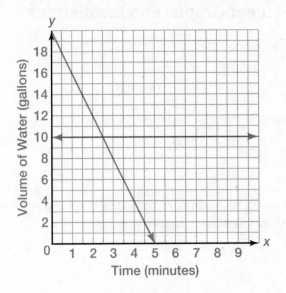

After 2.5 minutes, half of the water in the tank (10 gallons) will be drained.

8. A pasta company is filling boxes with pasta sold by weight. Each box should contain 32 ounces of pasta. The specifications allow for a difference of 1.5 ounces. The function $f(x) = |x - 32|$ represents the difference between the weight of a box of pasta and the specifications. Graph the function. What weights meet the specifications?

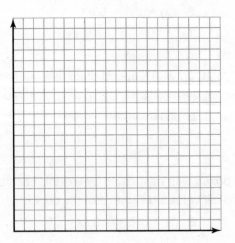

Name _____ Date _____

9. Ronna buys a car for \$20,000. Each year the car loses $\frac{1}{4}$ of its value. The function $f(x) = 20{,}000\left(\frac{3}{4}\right)^x$ represents the value of the car over time. Graph the function. Ronna wants to eventually sell the car and make at least \$10,000 in the sale. Estimate the number of years Ronna can own the car before she must resell and still make at least \$10,000.

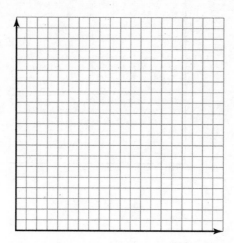

10. Serena is driving to her aunt's house at a rate of 55 miles per hour. The function $f(x) = 55x$ represents the distance Serena travels over time. Graph the function. Estimate how long it will take Serena to get to her aunt's house which is 192 miles away.

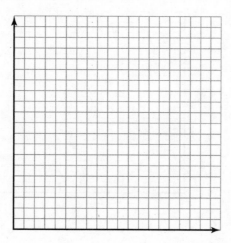

11. Hector throws a softball straight up with a speed of 50 feet per second. The acceleration of the ball due to gravity is 32 feet per second. The function $f(x) = -32x^2 + 50x$ represents the height of the softball as it travels up in the air and back to the ground. Graph the function. Estimate the length of time the softball is in the air.

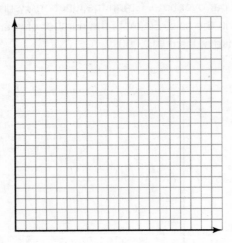

12. Guests at a craft fair are asked to guess how many beads are in a jar. The jar contains 180 beads. All guests within 20 beads of the correct answer win a prize. The function $f(x) = |x - 180|$ represents the difference between a guess and the actual number of beads in the jar. Graph the function. What possible guesses will win a prize?

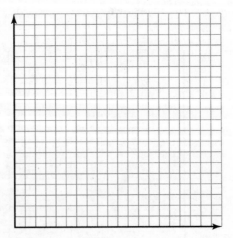

Name _____ Date _____

Is It Getting Hot in Here?
Modeling Data Using Linear Regression

Vocabulary

Choose the term that best completes each sentence.

linear regression	line of best fit	linear regression equation
significant digits	correlation coefficient	

1. The equation that describes a line of best fit is called a _____.

2. Decimal digits that carry meaning contributing to a number's precision are _____.

3. _____ models the relationship between two variables in a data set by producing a line of best fit.

4. A _____ is a line that best approximates the linear relationship between two variables in a data set.

5. The _____ indicates how closely data points are to forming a straight line.

Problem Set

Use your calculator to determine the linear regression equation and the correlation coefficient for each given set of data. Then use the equation to make the prediction.

1. The table shows the attendance for the varsity football games at Pedro's high school. Predict the attendance for Game 9.

Game	Attendance
1	2000
2	2132
3	2198
4	2301
5	2285
6	2401

$f(x) = 73x + 1963, r \approx 0.9694$

Game 1 is represented by $x = 1$, so Game 9 is represented by $x = 9$.

$f(x) = 73x + 1963$

$f(9) = 73(9) + 1963$

$f(9) = 2620$

The attendance during Game 9 will be 2620 people.

Name _____ Date _____

2. The table shows the attendance for the annual spring concert at Eva's high school for 6 years. Predict the attendance in 2016.

Year	Attendance
2007	789
2008	805
2009	773
2010	852
2011	884
2012	902

3. The table shows the average gas price for 6 months. Predict the average gas price for August.

Month	Price of Gas (dollars)
January	$3.15
February	$3.22
March	$3.19
April	$3.28
May	$3.35
June	$3.32

Name _____ Date _____

4. The table shows monthly record sales of a recording artist over 6 months. Predict the record sales total for December.

Monthly	Record Sales (CDs)
January	60,000
February	54,000
March	58,000
April	46,000
May	43,000
June	30,000

5. The table shows the number of miles Kata traveled for work each year for 6 years. Predict the number of miles Kata will travel in 2014.

Year	Miles Traveled
2006	8300
2007	7550
2008	8005
2009	7600
2010	6935
2011	6405

Name _____ Date _____

6. The table shows the number of songs downloaded for a recording artist over 6 months. Predict the number of songs that will be downloaded in November.

Month	Songs Downloaded
January	15,302
February	16,783
March	18,204
April	17,899
May	20,345
June	24,980

Name _____ Date _____

Tickets for Sale
Standard Form of Linear Equations

Vocabulary

Define each term in your own words.

1. standard form

2. slope-intercept form

Problem Set

Define variables and write an expression to represent each situation.

1. A farmer's market sells apples for $0.75 per pound and oranges for $0.89 per pound. Write an expression to represent the total amount the farmer's market can earn selling apples and oranges.

a = pounds of apples
b = pounds of oranges
$0.75a + 0.89b$

2. A photo printing website sells 8 × 10 prints for $4.99 and 3 × 5 prints for $1.99. Write an expression to represent the total amount the website can earn selling 8 × 10 and 3 × 5 prints.

3. A movie theater sells tickets for matinee showings for $7.00 and evening showings for $10.50. Write an expression that represents the total amount the theater can earn selling tickets.

4. A bakery sells muffins for $1.25 each and scones for $1.75 each. Write an expression that represents the total amount the bakery can earn selling muffins and scones.

5. A florist sells daisies for $8.99 a dozen and roses for $15.99 a dozen. Write an expression that represents the total amount the florist can earn selling daisies and roses.

6. The hockey booster club is selling winter hats for $12 each and sweatshirts for $26 each. Write an expression that represents the total amount the booster club can earn selling hats and sweatshirts.

Define variables and write an equation to represent each situation.

7. A florist sells carnations for $10.99 a dozen and lilies for $12.99 a dozen. During a weekend sale, the florist's goal is to earn $650. Write an equation that represents the total amount the florist would like to earn selling carnations and lilies during the weekend sale.

c = carnations

f = lilies

$10.99c + 12.99f = 650$

8. A bakery sells bagels for $0.85 each and muffins for $1.10 each. The bakery hopes to earn $400 each day from these sales. Write an equation that represents the total amount the bakery would like to earn selling bagels and muffins each day.

9. A farmer's market sells oranges for $0.79 per pound and peaches for $1.05 per pound. The farmer's market hopes to earn $325 each day from these sales. Write an equation to represent the total amount the farmer's market would like to earn selling oranges and peaches each day.

Name _____ Date _____

10. The high school soccer booster club sells tickets to the varsity matches for $4 for students and $8 for adults. The booster club hopes to earn $200 at each match. Write an equation to represent the total amount the booster club would like to earn from ticket sales at each match.

11. An electronics store sells DVDs for $15.99 and Blu-ray discs for $22.99. The store hopes to earn $2000 each week from these sales. Write an equation to represent the total amount the store would like to earn each week.

12. Ling is selling jewelry at a craft fair. She sells earrings for $5 each and bracelets for $7 each. She hopes to earn $300 during the fair. Write an equation to represent the total amount Ling would like to earn during the fair.

The basketball booster club runs the concession stand during a weekend tournament. They sell hamburgers for $2.50 each and hot dogs for $1.50 each. They hope to earn $900 during the tournament. The equation $2.50b + 1.50h = 900$ represents the total amount the booster club hopes to earn. Use this equation to determine each unknown value.

13. If the booster club sells 315 hamburgers during the tournament, how many hot dogs must they sell to reach their goal?

$$2.50b + 1.50h = 900$$
$$2.50(315) + 1.50h = 900$$
$$787.50 + 1.50h = 900$$
$$1.50h = 112.50$$
$$h = 75$$

The booster club must sell 75 hot dogs to reach their goal.

14. If the booster club sells 420 hot dogs during the tournament, how many hamburgers must they sell to reach their goal?

15. If the booster club sells 0 hot dogs during the tournament, how many hamburgers must they sell to reach their goal?

16. If the booster club sells 0 hamburgers during the tournament, how many hot dogs must they sell to reach their goal?

17. If the booster club sells 281 hamburgers during the tournament, how many hot dogs must they sell to reach their goal?

Name _____ Date _____

18. If the booster club sells 168 hot dogs during the tournament, how many hamburgers must they sell to reach their goal?

Determine the *x*-intercept and the *y*-intercept of each equation.

19. $20x + 8y = 240$

$$20x + 8y = 240$$
$$20x + 8(0) = 240$$
$$20x = 240$$
$$x = 12$$

$$20x + 8y = 240$$
$$20(0) + 8y = 240$$
$$8y = 240$$
$$y = 30$$

The *x*-intercept is (12, 0) and the *y*-intercept is (0, 30).

20. $15x + 3y = 270$

21. $y = 8x + 168$

22. $y = -4x + 52$

23. $14x + 25y = 342$

24. $y = 6x + 291$

Determine the *x*-intercept and *y*-intercept. Then graph each equation.

25. $5x + 6y = 90$ **26.** $12x - 9y = 36$

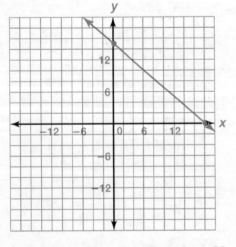
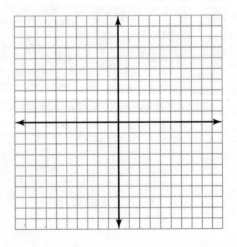

$5x + 6y = 90$	$5x + 6y = 90$
$5x + 6(0) = 90$	$5(0) + 6y = 90$
$5x = 90$	$6y = 90$
$x = 18$	$y = 15$

Name _____ Date _____

27. $y = 3x - 15$

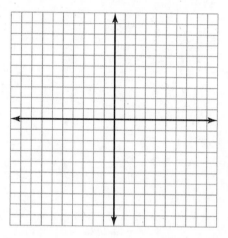

28. $y = -30x + 180$

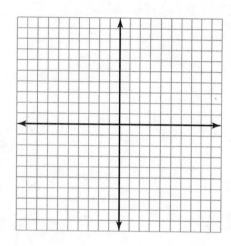

29. $6x + 13y = 57$

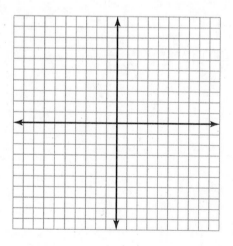

30. $y = 3x - 41$

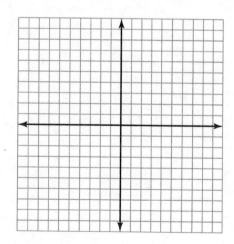

3

Name _____ Date _____

Cool As A Cucumber or Hot Like A Tamale!
Literal Equations in Standard Form and Slope-Intercept Form

Vocabulary

Define the term in your own words.

1. literal equations

Problem Set

Convert between degrees Fahrenheit and degrees Celsius using the literal equation given. If necessary, round the answer to the nearest hundredth.

$$C = \frac{5}{9}(F - 32)$$

1. 72°F

$C = \frac{5}{9}(F - 32)$

$C = \frac{5}{9}(72 - 32)$

$C = \frac{5}{9}(40)$

$C \approx 22.22$

72°F ≈ 22.22°C

2. −11°F

3. 102.6°F

4. 25°C

5. 42°C

6. −3.4°C

Convert each equation from standard form to slope-intercept form.

7. $4x + 6y = 48$

$$4x + 6y = 48$$
$$4x - 4x + 6y = -4x + 48$$
$$\frac{6y}{6} = \frac{-4x + 48}{6}$$
$$y = -\frac{4}{6}x + 8$$
$$y = -\frac{2}{3}x + 8$$

8. $3x - 5y = 25$

9. $-4x + 9y = 45$

10. $6x - 2y = -52$

11. $-x - 8y = 96$

12. $12x + 28y = -84$

Name _____ Date _____

Convert each equation from slope-intercept form to standard form.

13. $y = 5x + 8$

$$y = 5x + 8$$

$$-5x + y = 5x - 5x + 8$$

$$-5x + y = 8$$

14. $y = -4x + 2$

15. $y = \frac{2}{3}x - 6$

16. $y = -\frac{1}{2}x - 3$

17. $y = -5x - 13$

18. $y = \frac{3}{4}x + 10$

Solve each equation for the variable indicated.

19. The formula for the area of a triangle is $A = \frac{1}{2}bh$. Solve the equation for h.

$$A = \frac{1}{2}bh$$

$$(2)A = 2\left(\frac{1}{2}bh\right)$$

$$2A = bh$$

$$\frac{2A}{b} = \frac{bh}{b}$$

$$\frac{2A}{b} = h$$

20. The formula for the area of a trapezoid is $A = \frac{1}{2}(b_1 + b_2)h$. Solve the equation for b_1.

21. The formula for the area of a circle is $A = \pi r^2$. Solve the equation for r.

Name _____ Date _____

22. The formula for the volume of a cylinder is $V = \pi r^2 h$. Solve the equation for h.

23. The formula for the volume of a pyramid is $V = \frac{1}{3}lwh$. Solve the equation for w.

24. The formula for the volume of a sphere is $V = \frac{4}{3}\pi r^3$. Solve the equation for r.

Name _____ Date _____

A Growing Business
Combining Linear Equations

Problem Set

Write a linear function in two different ways to represent each problem situation.

1. Mei paints and sells ceramic vases for $35 each. Each month she typically breaks 3 vases in the kiln.
    Write a linear function that represents the total amount Mei earns each month selling vases taking
    into account the value of the vases she breaks.

    $f(x) = 35(x - 3)$
    $f(x) = 35x - 105$

2. Isabel makes and sells fruit pies at her bakery for $12.99 each. Each month she gives away 4 pies as
    samples. Write a linear function that represents the total amount Isabel earns each month selling fruit
    pies taking into account the value of the pies she gives away as samples.

3. Mattie sells heads of lettuce for $1.99 each from a roadside farmer's market stand. Each week she
    loses 2 heads of lettuce due to spoilage. Write a linear function that represents the total amount
    Mattie earns each week selling heads of lettuce taking into account the value of the lettuce she loses
    due to spoilage.

4. Carlos prints and sells T-shirts for $14.99 each. Each month 5 T-shirts are misprinted and cannot be
    sold. Write a linear equation that represents the total amount Carlos earns each month selling T-shirts
    taking into account the value of the T-shirts that cannot be sold.

5. Odell prints and sells posters for $20 each. Each month 1 poster is misprinted and cannot be sold.
    Write a linear equation that represents the total amount Odell earns each month taking into account
    the value of the poster that cannot be sold.

6. Emilio builds and sells homemade wooden toys for $40 each. Each month he donates 3 toys to a children's hospital. Write a linear equation that represents the total amount Emilio earns each month selling toys taking into account the toys he donates.

Write a linear function to represent each problem situation.

7. A cereal manufacturer has two production lines. Line A produces a variety of cereal that is sold for $3 per box. Line A typically produces 4 boxes per day that do not meet company standards and cannot be sold. Line B produces a variety of cereal that is sold for $2 per box. Line B typically produces 6 boxes per day that do not meet company standards and cannot be sold. Line A and Line B produce the same total number of boxes each day.

The linear functions $a(x) = 3(x - 4)$ and $b(x) = 2(x - 6)$ represent the total amount each line can produce taking into account the boxes that do not meet company standards and cannot be sold. Write a linear function that represents the total number of boxes the lines can produce combined.

Line A: $\frac{1}{2}x$ $\qquad\qquad\qquad\qquad$ $a(x) = 3\left(\frac{1}{2}x - 4\right)$

Line B: $\frac{1}{2}x$ $\qquad\qquad\qquad\qquad$ $b(x) = 2\left(\frac{1}{2}x - 6\right)$

$c(x) = a(x) + b(x)$

$\qquad = 3\left(\frac{1}{2}x - 4\right) + 2\left(\frac{1}{2}x - 6\right)$

$\qquad = \frac{3}{2}x - 12 + \frac{2}{2}x - 12$

$\qquad = \frac{5}{2}x - 24$

The linear function $c(x) = \frac{5}{2}x - 24$ represents the total number of boxes that Line A and Line B can produce combined.

Name _____ Date _____

8. A pretzel manufacturer has two production lines. Line A produces a variety of pretzel that is sold for $2.40 per bag. Line A typically produces 3 bags per day that do not meet company standards and cannot be sold. Line B produces a variety of pretzel that is sold for $3.60 per bag. Line B typically produces 4 bags per day that do not meet company standards and cannot be sold. Line A produces 3 times as many bags as Line B each day.

The linear functions $a(x) = 2.4(x - 3)$ and $b(x) = 3.6(x - 4)$ represent the total number of bags each line can produce taking into account the bags that do not meet company standards and cannot be. Write a linear function that represents the total number of bags the lines can produce combined.

9. Carlos has a roadside stand that sells peaches. He sells his peaches for $1.99 per pound. He typically loses 5 pounds per week to spoilage. Hector also has a roadside stand that sells peaches. He sells his peaches for $2.49 per pound. He typically only loses 1 pound per week to spoilage. Carlos' stand sells twice as many peaches per week as Hector's stand.

The linear functions $c(x) = 1.99(x - 5)$ and $h(x) = 2.49(x - 1)$ represent the total amount each stand can earn taking into account the peaches lost to spoilage. Write a linear function that represents the total amount that Carlos and Hector can earn combined.

10. A lamp manufacturer has two production lines. Line A produces a lamp model that is sold for $24.99 each. Line A typically produces 2 lamps per day that do not meet company standards and cannot be sold. Line B produces a lamp model that is sold for $34.99 each. Line B typically produces 1 lamp per day that does not meet company standards and cannot be sold. Line A produces half as many lamps as Line B each day.

The linear functions $a(x) = 24.99(x - 2)$ and $b(x) = 34.99(x - 1)$ represent the total number of lamps each line can produce taking into account the lamps that do not meet company standards and cannot be sold. Write a linear function that represents the total number of lamps the lines can produce combined.

11. A jean manufacturer has two production lines. Line A produces a style that is sold for $42 each. Line A typically produces 2 pairs per day that do not meet company standards and cannot be sold. Line B produces a style that can be sold for $65 each. Line B typically produces 3 pairs per day that do not meet company standards and cannot be sold. Line A produces three times as many pairs of jeans as Line B each day.

The linear functions $a(x) = 42(x - 2)$ and $b(x) = 65(x - 3)$ represent the total number of pairs of jeans that each line can produce taking into account the jeans that do not meet company standards and cannot be sold. Write a linear function that represents the total number of pairs of jeans the lines can produce combined.

Name _____ Date _____

12. Jada makes and sells handmade puzzles for $32 each. Each month she donates 2 puzzles to a retirement community. Ronna also makes and sells handmade puzzles for $28 each. Each month she donates 2 puzzles to a childcare center. Jada and Ronna make the same number of puzzles each month.

The linear functions $j(x) = 32(x - 2)$ and $r(x) = 28(x - 2)$ represent the total amount each girl can earn taking into account the puzzles that are donated and not sold. Write a linear function that represents the total amount Jada and Ronna can earn combined.

Name _____ Date _____

Is There a Pattern Here?
Recognizing Patterns and Sequences

Vocabulary

Choose the term that best completes each statement.

| sequence | term of a sequence | infinite sequence | finite sequence |

1. A sequence which terminates is called a(n) _____.

2. A(n) _____ is an individual number, figure, or letter in a sequence.

3. A(n) _____ is a pattern involving an ordered arrangement of numbers, geometric figures, letters, or other objects.

4. A sequence which continues forever is called a(n) _____.

Problem Set

Describe each given pattern. Draw the next two figures in each pattern.

1.

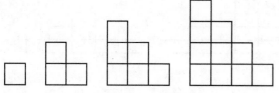

The second figure has 2 more squares than the first, the third figure has 3 more squares than the second, and the fourth figure has 4 more squares than the third.

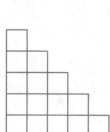 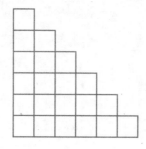

2.

3. ◯ ◯◯◯ ◯◯◯◯◯

4.

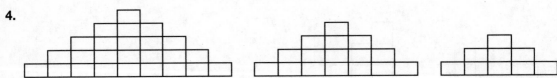

5.

Name _____ Date _____

6.

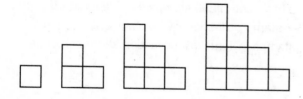

Write a numeric sequence to represent each given pattern or situation.

7. The school cafeteria begins the day with a supply of 1000 chicken nuggets. Each student that passes through the lunch line is given 5 chicken nuggets. Write a numeric sequence to represent the total number of chicken nuggets remaining in the cafeteria's supply after each of the first 6 students pass through the line. Include the number of chicken nuggets the cafeteria started with.

1000, 995, 990, 985, 980, 975, 970

8. Write a numeric sequence to represent the number of squares in each of the first 7 figures of the pattern.

9. Sophia starts a job at a restaurant. She deposits $40 from each paycheck into her savings account. There was no money in the account prior to her first deposit. Write a numeric sequence to represent the amount of money in the savings account after Sophia receives each of her first 6 paychecks.

10. Write a numeric sequence to represent the number of blocks in each of the first 5 figures of the pattern.

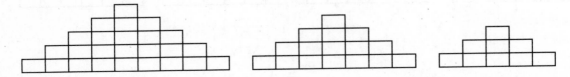

11. Kyle is collecting canned goods for a food drive. On the first day he collects 1 can. On the second day he collects 2 cans. On the third day he collects 4 cans. On each successive day, he collects twice as many cans as he collected the previous day. Write a numeric sequence to represent the total number of cans Kyle has collected by the end of each of the first 7 days of the food drive.

12. Write a numeric sequence to represent the number of line segments in each of the first 7 figures of the pattern.

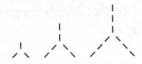

13. For her 10th birthday, Tameka's grandparents give her a set of 200 stamps. For each birthday after that, they give her a set of 25 stamps to add to her stamp collection. Write a numeric sequence consisting of 7 terms to represent the number of stamps in Tameka's collection after each of her birthdays starting with her 10th birthday.

Name _____ Date _____

14. Write a numeric sequence to represent the number of squares in each of the first 6 figures of the pattern.

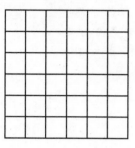 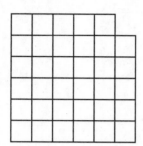 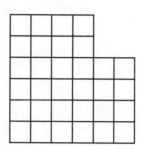 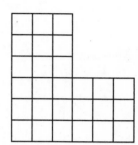

15. Leonardo uses 3 cups of flour in each cake he bakes. He starts the day with 50 cups of flour. Write a numeric sequence to represent the amount of flour remaining after each of the first 7 cakes Leonardo bakes. Include the amount of flour Leonardo started with.

4

16. Write a numeric sequence to represent the number of triangles in each of the first 7 figures of the pattern.

Name _____ Date _____

The Password Is . . . Operations!
Arithmetic and Geometric Sequences

Vocabulary

Describe each given sequence using the terms arithmetic sequence, common difference, geometric sequence, and common ratio as they apply.

1. 10, 20, 30, 40, . . .

2. 1, 2, 4, 8, . . .

Problem Set

Determine the common difference for each arithmetic sequence.

1. 1, 5, 9, 13, . . .
$d = 5 - 1$
$d = 4$

2. 10, 3, −4, −11, . . .

3. 10.5, 13, 15.5, 18, . . .

4. $\frac{1}{3}, \frac{2}{3}, 1, \frac{4}{3}, \ldots$

5. 95, 91.5, 88, 84.5, . . .

6. 170, 240, 310, 380, . . .

7. 1250, 1190, 1130, 1070, . . .   **8.** −4.8, −6.0, −7.2, −8.4, . . .

9. $8\frac{1}{2}$, 9, $9\frac{1}{2}$, 10, . . .   **10.** −28, −13, 2, 17, . . .

Determine the common ratio for each geometric sequence.

11. 5, 10, 20, 40, . . .   **12.** 2, 8, 32, 128, . . .
$r = 10 \div 5$
$r = 2$

13. 3, −6, 12, −24, . . .   **14.** 800, 400, 200, 100, . . .

15. 10, −30, 90, −270, . . .   **16.** 64, −32, 16, −8, . . .

17. 5, 40, 320, 2560, . . .   **18.** 45, 15, 5, $\frac{5}{3}$, . . .

19. 0.2, −1, 5, −25, . . .   **20.** 150, 30, 6, 1.2, . . .

Name _____ Date _____

Determine the next 3 terms in each arithmetic sequence.

21. 8, 14, 20, 26, _32_, _38_, _44_, . . .

22. 90, 75, 60, 45, _____, _____, _____, . . .

23. −24, −14, −4, 6, _____, _____, _____, . . .

24. $\frac{3}{5}, \frac{4}{5}, 1, \frac{6}{5}$, _____, _____, _____, . . .

25. 20, 11, 2, −7, _____, _____, _____, . . .

26. 12, 16.5, 21, 25.5, _____, _____, _____, . . .

27. −101, −112, −123, −134, _____, _____, _____, . . .

28. 3.8, 5.1, 6.4, 7.7, _____, _____, _____, . . .

29. −500, −125, 250, 625, _____, _____, _____, . . .

30. 24.5, 20.7, 16.9, 13.1, _____, _____, _____, . . .

Determine the next 3 terms in each geometric sequence.

31. 3, 9, 27, 81, _243_, _729_, _2187_, . . .

32. 512, 256, 128, 64, _____, _____, _____, . . .

33. 5, −10, 20, −40, _____, _____, _____, . . .

34. 3000, 300, 30, 3, _____, _____, _____, . . .

35. 2, −2, 2, −2, _____, _____, _____, . . .

36. 0.2, 1.2, 7.2, 43.2, _____, _____, _____, . . .

37. −8000, 4000, −2000, 1000, _____, _____, _____, . . .

38. 0.1, 0.4, 1.6, 6.4, _____, _____, _____, . . .

39. 156.25, 31.25, 6.25, 1.25, _____, _____, _____, . . .

40. 7, −21, 63, −189, _____, _____, _____, . . .

Determine whether each given sequence is arithmetic, geometric, or neither. For arithmetic and geometric sequences, write the next 3 terms of the sequence.

41. 4, 8, 12, 16, . . .

The sequence is arithmetic. The next 3 terms are 20, 24, and 28.

42. 2, 4, 7, 11, . . .

43. 3, 12, 48, 192, . . .

44. 9, −18, 36, −72, . . .

45. 1.1, 1.11, 1.111, 1.1111, . . .

4

46. 4, −8, −20, −32, . . .

47. 7.5, 11.6, 15.7, 19.8, . . .

48. 1, −4, 9, −16, . . .

49. 5, −20, 80, −320, . . .

50. 9.8, 5.6, 1.4, −2.8, . . .

Name _____ Date _____

The Power of Algebra Is a Curious Thing
Using Formulas to Determine Terms of a Sequence

Vocabulary

Choose the term that best completes each statement.

| index | explicit formula | recursive formula |

1. A(n) _____ expresses each term of a sequence based on the preceding term of the sequence.

2. The _____ is the position of a term in a sequence.

3. A(n) _____ calculates each term of a sequence using the term's position in the sequence.

Problem Set

Determine each unknown term in the given arithmetic sequence using the explicit formula.

1. Determine the 20th term of the sequence
   1, 4, 7, . . .

   $a_n = a_1 + d(n - 1)$

   $a_{20} = 1 + 3(20 - 1)$

   $a_{20} = 1 + 3(19)$

   $a_{20} = 1 + 57$

   $a_{20} = 58$

2. Determine the 30th term of the sequence
   $-10, -15, -20, . . .$

3. Determine the 25th term of the sequence
   3.3, 4.4, 5.5, . . .

4. Determine the 50th term of the sequence
   100, 92, 84, . . .

5. Determine the 42nd term of the sequence 12.25, 14.50, 16.75, . . .

6. Determine the 28th term of the sequence −242, −251, −260, . . .

7. Determine the 34th term of the sequence −76.2, −70.9, −65.6, . . .

8. Determine the 60th term of the sequence 10, 25, 40, . . .

9. Determine the 57th term of the sequence 672, 660, 648, . . .

10. Determine the 75th term of the sequence −200, −100, 0, . . .

Determine each unknown term in the given geometric sequence using the explicit formula. Round the answer to the nearest hundredth when necessary.

11. Determine the 10th term of the sequence 3, 6, 12, . . .

$$g_n = g_1 \cdot r^{n-1}$$
$$g_{10} = 3 \cdot 2^{10-1}$$
$$g_{10} = 3 \cdot 2^9$$
$$g_{10} = 3 \cdot 512$$
$$g_{10} = 1536$$

12. Determine the 15th term of the sequence 1, −2, 4, . . .

Name _____ Date _____

13. Determine the 12th term of the sequence 5, 15, 45, . . .

14. Determine the 16th term of the sequence 9, 18, 36, . . .

15. Determine the 20th term of the sequence 0.125, −0.250, 0.500, . . .

16. Determine the 18th term of the sequence 3, 9, 27, . . .

17. Determine the 14th term of the sequence −4, 8, −16, . . .

18. Determine the 10th term of the sequence 0.1, 0.5, 2.5, . . .

19. Determine the 12th term of the sequence 4, 5, 6.25, . . .

20. Determine the 10th term of the sequence 5, −25, 125, . . .

Determine whether each sequence is arithmetic or geometric. Then, use the appropriate recursive formula to determine the unknown term(s) in the sequence.

21. 4, 8, 16, 32, _____64_____, . . .

The sequence is geometric.

$g_n = g_{n-1} \cdot r$

$g_5 = g_4 \cdot 2$

$g_5 = 32 \cdot 2$

$g_5 = 64$

22. 16, 30, 44, 58, _____, . . .

23. 2, −6, 18, _____, 162, _____, . . .

24. 7.3, 9.4, 11.5, _____, 15.7, _____, . . .

25. 320, 410, 500, _____, _____, . . .

Name _____ Date _____

26. 7, 21, 63, _____, 567, _____, . . .

27. −68, −83, −98, _____, _____, _____, . . .

28. −5, 20, −80, _____, _____, _____, . . .

Determine the unknown term in each arithmetic sequence using a graphing calculator.

29. Determine the 20th term of the sequence 30, 70, 110, . . .

$a_{20} = 790$

30. Determine the 25th term of the sequence −25, −50, −75, . . .

31. Determine the 30th term of the sequence 16, 24, 32, . . .

32. Determine the 35th term of the sequence 120, 104, 88, . . .

33. Determine the 30th term of the sequence 350, 700, 1050, . . .

34. Determine the 22nd term of the sequence 0, −45, −90, . . .

35. Determine the 24th term of the sequence 6.8, 9.5, 12.2, . . .

36. Determine the 36th term of the sequence 189, 200, 211, . . .

37. Determine the 20th term of the sequence 2500, 3100, 3700, . . .

38. Determine the 50th term of the sequence −97, −94, −91, . . .

Name _____ Date _____

Thank Goodness Descartes Didn't Drink Some Warm Milk!
Graphs of Sequences

Problem Set

Complete the table for each given sequence then graph each sequence on the coordinate plane.

1. $a_n = 15 + 3(n - 1)$

Term Number (n)	Value of Term (a_n)
1	15
2	18
3	21
4	24
5	27
6	30
7	33
8	36
9	39
10	42

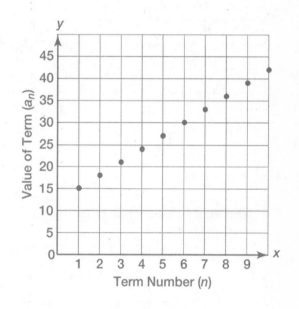

2. $g_n = 3 \cdot 2^{n-1}$

Term Number (n)	Value of Term (g_n)
1	
2	
3	
4	
5	
6	
7	
8	
9	
10	

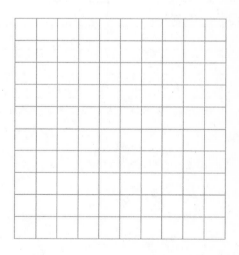

3. $a_n = 50 + (-8)(n - 1)$

Term Number (n)	Value of Term (a_n)
1	
2	
3	
4	
5	
6	
7	
8	
9	
10	

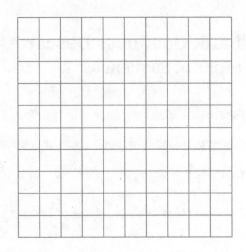

4. $g_n = 3 \cdot (-2)^{n-1}$

Term Number (n)	Value of Term (g_n)
1	
2	
3	
4	
5	
6	
7	
8	
9	
10	

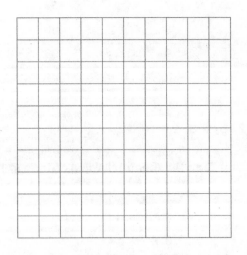

Name _____ Date _____

5. $a_n = -24 + 6(n - 1)$

Term Number (n)	Value of Term (a_n)
1	
2	
3	
4	
5	
6	
7	
8	
9	
10	

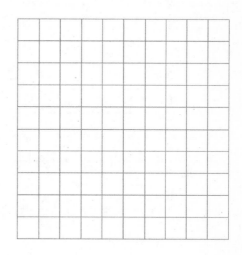

6. $g_n = -1 \cdot 2^{n-1}$

Term Number (n)	Value of Term (g_n)
1	
2	
3	
4	
5	
6	
7	
8	
9	
10	

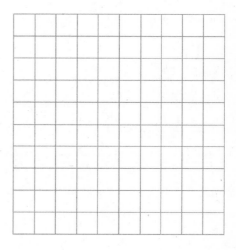

7. $a_n = 75 + 25(n - 1)$

Term Number (n)	Value of Term (a_n)
1	
2	
3	
4	
5	
6	
7	
8	
9	
10	

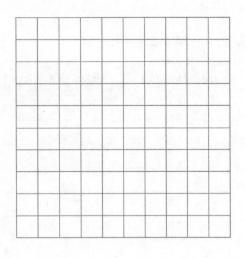

8. $g_n = 32{,}000 \cdot (0.5)^{n-1}$

Term Number (n)	Value of Term (g_n)
1	
2	
3	
4	
5	
6	
7	
8	
9	
10	

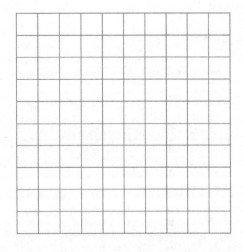

Name _____ Date _____

9. $a_n = 400 + (-80)(n - 1)$

Term Number (n)	Value of Term (a_n)
1	
2	
3	
4	
5	
6	
7	
8	
9	
10	

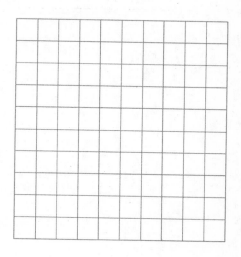

4

10. $g_n = 2 \cdot (-3)^{n-1}$

Term Number (n)	Value of Term (g_n)
1	
2	
3	
4	
5	
6	
7	
8	
9	
10	

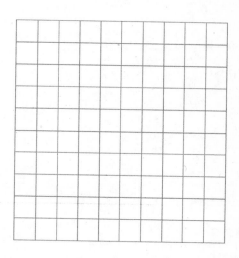

4

Name _____ Date _____

Well, Maybe It *Is* a Function!
Sequences and Functions

Problem Set

Write each arithmetic sequence as a linear function. Graph the function for all integers, *n*, such that $1 \leq n \leq 10$.

1. $a_n = 16 + 5(n - 1)$

$a_n = 16 + 5(n - 1)$

$f(n) = 16 + 5(n - 1)$

$f(n) = 16 + 5n - 5$

$f(n) = 5n + 16 - 5$

$f(n) = 5n + 11$

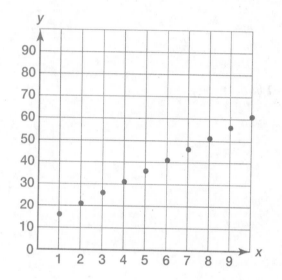

2. $a_n = -50 + 15(n - 1)$

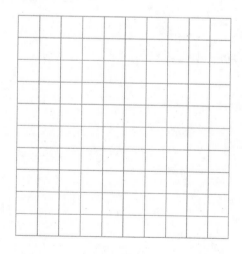

3. $a_n = 100 + (-20)(n - 1)$

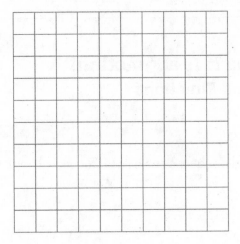

4. $a_n = -9 + (-7)(n - 1)$

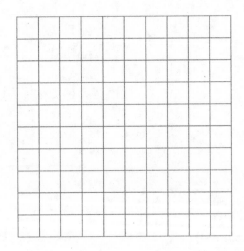

5. $a_n = 550 + (-50)(n - 1)$

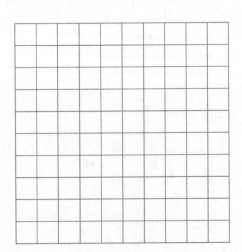

Name _____ Date _____

6. $a_n = 3 + \left(-\dfrac{3}{5}\right)(n - 1)$

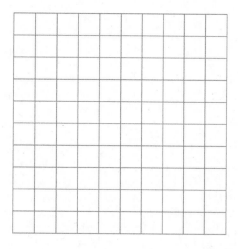

Write each geometric sequence as an exponential function. Graph the function for all integers, *n*, such that $1 \leq n \leq 10$.

7. $g_n = 5 \cdot 2^{n-1}$

$g_n = 5 \cdot 2^{n-1}$

$f(n) = 5 \cdot 2^{n-1}$

$f(n) = 5 \cdot 2^n \cdot 2^{-1}$

$f(n) = 5 \cdot 2^{-1} \cdot 2^n$

$f(n) = 5 \cdot \dfrac{1}{2} \cdot 2^n$

$f(n) = \dfrac{5}{2} \cdot 2^n$

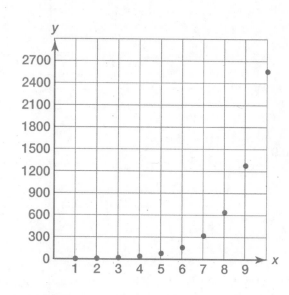

8. $g_n = -3 \cdot 3^{n-1}$

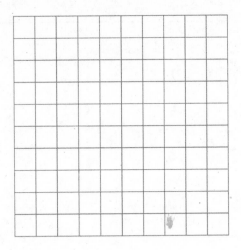

9. $g_n = 20 \cdot 2.5^{n-1}$

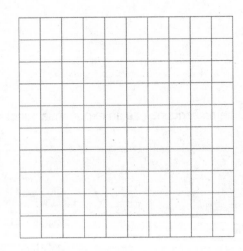

10. $g_n = 900 \cdot 0.9^{n-1}$

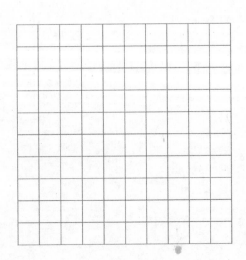

Name _____ Date _____

11. $g_n = -0.5 \cdot 2^{n-1}$

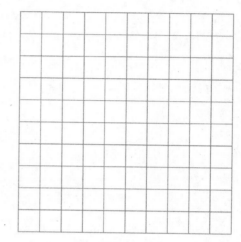

12. $g_n = 1250 \cdot 1.25^{n-1}$

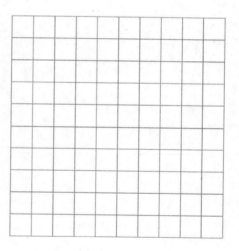

4

Name _____ Date _____

Go for the Curve!
Comparing Linear and Exponential Functions

Vocabulary

Describe each type of account as simple interest or compound interest based on the scenario given. Explain your reasoning.

1. Andrew deposits $300 into an account that earns 2% interest each year. After the first year, Andrew has $306 in the account. After the second year, Andrew has $312 in the account, and after the third year, Andrew has $318 in the account.

2. Marilyn deposits $600 in an account that earns 1.5% interest each year. After the first year, Marilyn has $609 in the account. After the second year, Marilyn has $618.14 in the account, and after the third year, Marilyn has $627.41 in the account.

Problem Set

Write a function to represent each problem situation.

1. Nami deposits $500 into a simple interest account. The interest rate for the account is 3%. Write a function that represents the balance in the account as a function of time t.

   $P(t) = P_0 + (P_0 \cdot r)t$
   $P(t) = 500 + (500 \cdot 0.03)t$
   $P(t) = 500 + 15t$

2. Carmen deposits $1000 into a simple interest account. The interest rate for the account is 4%. Write a function that represents the balance in the account as a function of time t.

3. Emilio deposits $250 into a simple interest account. The interest rate for the account is 2.5%. Write a function that represents the balance in the account as a function of time t.

4. Vance deposits $1500 into a simple interest account. The interest rate for the account is 5.5%. Write a function that represents the balance in the account as a function of time t.

5. Perry deposits $175 into a simple interest account. The interest rate for the account is 4.25%. Write a function that represents the balance in the account as a function of time t.

6. Julian deposits $5000 into a simple interest account. The interest rate for the account is 2.75%. Write a function that represents the balance in the account as a function of time t.

5

Sherwin deposits $500 into a simple interest account. The interest rate for the account is 3.75%. The function $P(t) = 500 + 18.75t$ represents the balance in the account as a function of time. Determine the account balance after each given number of years.

7. 3 years

$P(t) = 500 + 18.75t$

$P(3) = 500 + 18.75(3)$

$P(3) = 556.25$

In 3 years, the account balance will be $556.25.

8. 2 years

9. 10 years

10. 15 years

Name _____ Date _____

11. 50 years

12. 75 years

Hector deposits $400 into a simple interest account. The interest rate for the account is 5.25%. The function $P(t) = 400 + 21t$ represents the balance in the account as a function of time. Determine the number of years it will take for the account balance to reach each given amount.

13. $505

$P(t) = 400 + 21t$

$505 = 400 + 21t$

$105 = 21t$

$5 = t$

It will take 5 years for the account balance to reach $505.

14. $610

15. $1450

16. $2500

17. double the original deposit

18. triple the original deposit

5

Write a function to represent each problem situation.

19. Ronna deposits $500 into a compound interest account. The interest rate for the account is 4%.

$P(t) = P_0 \cdot (1 + r)^t$

$P(t) = 500 \cdot (1 + 0.04)^t$

$P(t) = 500 \cdot 1.04^t$

20. Leon deposits $250 into a compound interest account. The interest rate for the account is 6%.

21. Chen deposits $1200 into a compound interest account. The interest rate for the account is 3.5%.

22. Serena deposits $2700 into a compound interest account. The interest rate for the account is 4.25%.

23. Shen deposits $300 into a compound interest account. The interest rate for the account is 1.75%.

24. Lea deposits $450 into a compound interest account. The interest rate for the account is 5.5%.

Name _____ Date _____

Cisco deposits $500 into a compound interest account. The interest rate for the account is 3.25%. The function $P(t) = 500 \cdot 1.0325^t$ represents the balance in the account as a function of time. Determine the account balance after each given number of years.

25. 2 years

    $P(t) = 500 \cdot 1.0325^t$

    $P(2) = 500 \cdot 1.0325^2$

    $P(2) \approx 533.03$

    In 2 years, the account balance will be $533.03.

26. 4 years

27. 15 years

28. 20 years

29. 50 years

30. 65 years

Mario deposits $1000 into a compound interest account. The interest rate for the account is 5%. The function $P(t) = 1000 \cdot 1.05^t$ represents the balance in the account as a function of time. Use a graphing calculator to estimate the number of years it will take for the account balance to reach each given amount.

31. $1500

    It will take about 8.3 years for the account balance to reach $1500.

32. $4000

33. $6000

34. $10,000

35. double the original amount   **36.** triple the original amount

Use the simple and compound interest formula to complete each table. Round to the nearest cent.

37. Teresa has $300 to deposit into an account. The interest rate available for the account is 4%.

Quantity	Time	Simple Interest Balance	Compound Interest Balance
Units	years	dollars	dollars
Expression	t	$300 + 12t$	$300 \cdot 1.04^t$
	0	300.00	300.00
	2	324.00	324.48
	6	372.00	379.60
	10	420.00	444.07

38. Ye has $700 to deposit into an account. The interest rate available for the account is 6%.

Quantity	Time	Simple Interest Balance	Compound Interest Balance
Units			
Expression			
	0		
	3		
	10		
	20		

Name _____ Date _____

39. Pablo has $1100 to deposit into an account. The interest rate available for the account is 3.5%.

Quantity	Time	Simple Interest Balance	Compound Interest Balance
Units			
Expression			
	0		
	5		
	10		
	30		

40. Ty has $525 to deposit into an account. The interest rate available for the account is 2.5%.

Quantity	Time	Simple Interest Balance	Compound Interest Balance
Units			
Expression			
	0		
	10		
	20		
	50		

5

41. Xavier has $2300 to deposit into an account. The interest rate available for the account is 3.75%.

Quantity	Time	Simple Interest Balance	Compound Interest Balance
Units			
Expression			
	0		
	2		
	5		
	15		

42. Denisa has $100 to deposit into an account. The interest rate available for the account is 6.25%.

Quantity	Time	Simple Interest Balance	Compound Interest Balance
Units			
Expression			
	0		
	5		
	15		
	30		

Name _____ Date _____

Downtown and Uptown
Graphs of Exponential Functions

Vocabulary

Define the term in your own words.

1. horizontal asymptote

Problem Set

Write a function that represents each population as a function of time.

1. Blueville has a population of 7000. Its population is increasing at a rate of 1.4%.

$P(t) = P_0 \cdot (1 + r)^t$

$P(t) = 7000 \cdot (1 + 0.014)^t$

$P(t) = 7000 \cdot 1.014^t$

2. Youngstown has a population of 12,000. Its population is increasing at a rate of 1.2%.

3. Greenville has a population of 8000. Its population is decreasing at a rate of 1.75%.

4. North Park has a population of 14,000. Its population is decreasing at a rate of 3.1%.

5. West Lake has a population of 9500. Its population is increasing at a rate of 2.8%.

6. Springfield has a population of 11,500. Its population is decreasing at a rate of 1.25%.

Waynesburg has a population of 16,000. Its population is increasing at a rate of 1.5%. The function $P(t) = 16,000 \cdot 1.015^t$ represents the population as a function of time. Determine the population after each given number of years. Round your answer to the nearest whole number.

7. 1 year

$P(t) = 16,000 \cdot 1.015^t$

$P(1) = 16,000 \cdot 1.015^1$

$P(1) = 16,240$

The population after 1 year will be 16,240.

8. 3 years

9. 5 years

10. 10 years

11. 20 years

12. 50 years

Name _____ Date _____

Morristown has a population of 18,000. Its population is decreasing at a rate of 1.2%. The function, $P(t) = 18,000 \cdot 0.988^t$ represents the population as a function of time. Use a graphing calculator to estimate the number of years it will take for the population to reach each given amount.

13. 17,000

It will take about 4.7 years for the population to reach 17,000.

14. 15,000

15. half

16. one-third

17. 0

18. 10,000

Complete each table and graph the function. Identify the *x*-intercept, *y*-intercept, asymptote, domain, range, and interval(s) of increase or decrease for the function.

19. $f(x) = 2^x$

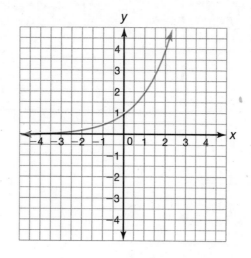

x	f(x)
−2	$\frac{1}{4}$
−1	$\frac{1}{2}$
0	1
1	2
2	4

x-intercept: none

y-intercept: (0, 1)

asymptote: $y = 0$

domain: all real numbers

range: $y > 0$

interval(s) of increase or decrease: increasing over the entire domain

20. $f(x) = 4^x$

x	f(x)
−2	
−1	
0	
1	
2	

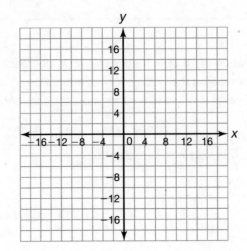

21. $f(x) = \left(\dfrac{1}{3}\right)^x$

x	f(x)
−2	
−1	
0	
1	
2	

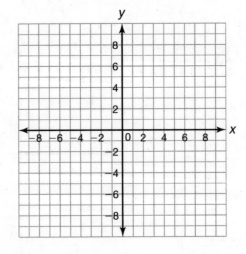

Name _____ Date _____

22. $f(x) = \left(\frac{1}{4}\right)^x$

x	f(x)
−2	
−1	
0	
1	
2	

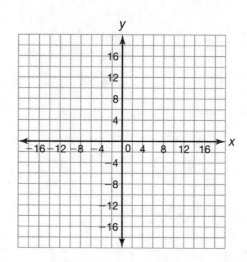

23. $f(x) = -2 \cdot 2^x$

x	f(x)
−2	
−1	
0	
1	
2	

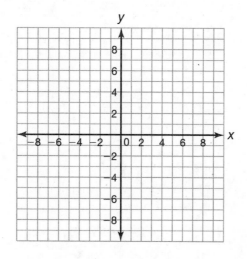

5

24. $f(x) = -2 \cdot \left(\frac{1}{2}\right)^x$

x	f(x)
−2	
−1	
0	
1	
2	

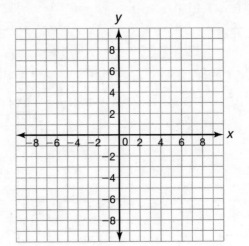

Name _____ Date _____

Let the Transformations Begin!
Translations of Linear and Exponential Functions

Vocabulary

Match each definition to its corresponding term.

1. the mapping, or movement, of all the points of a figure in a plane according to a common operation

   A basic function

2. a type of transformation that shifts the entire graph left or right

   B transformation

3. a function that can be described as the simplest function of its type

   C vertical translation

4. a type of transformation that shifts the entire graph up or down

   D coordinate notation

5. the variable on which a function operates

   E argument of a function

6. notation that uses ordered pairs to describe a transformation on a coordinate plane

   F horizontal translation

5

Problem Set

Rewrite each function $g(x)$ in terms of the basic function $f(x)$.

1. $f(x) = x$
   $g(x) = x + 4$
   $g(x) = f(x) + 4$

2. $f(x) = x$
   $g(x) = x - 7$

3. $f(x) = x$
   $g(x) = x - 8$

4. $f(x) = 3^x$
   $g(x) = 3^x + 1$

5. $f(x) = 3^x$
   $g(x) = 3^x + 2$

6. $f(x) = 4^x$
   $g(x) = 4^x - 6$

Represent each vertical translation, $g(x)$, using coordinate notation.

7. $f(x) = x$

$g(x) = x + 8$

$(x, y) \rightarrow (x, y + 8)$

8. $f(x) = x$

$g(x) = x + 9$

9. $f(x) = x$

$g(x) = x - 4$

10. $f(x) = 4^x$

$g(x) = 4^x - 1$

11. $f(x) = 4^x$

$g(x) = 4^x + 6$

12. $f(x) = 3^x$

$g(x) = 3^x - 5$

Rewrite each function $g(x)$ in terms of the basic function $f(x)$.

13. $f(x) = 3^x$

$g(x) = 3^{(x + 1)}$

$g(x) = 3^{(x + 1)} = f(x + 1)$

14. $f(x) = 3^x$

$g(x) = 3^{(x + 5)}$

15. $f(x) = 2^x$

$g(x) = 2^{(x - 1)}$

16. $f(x) = 2^x$

$g(x) = 2^{(x - 9)}$

17. $f(x) = 2x$

$g(x) = 2(x - 3)$

18. $f(x) = 2x$

$g(x) = 2(x + 4)$

Represent each horizontal translation, $g(x)$, using coordinate notation.

19. $f(x) = 3^x$

$g(x) = 3^{(x - 2)}$

$(x, y) \rightarrow (x + 2, y)$

20. $f(x) = 3^x$

$g(x) = 3^{(x + 2)}$

21. $f(x) = 4^x$

$g(x) = 4^{(x + 1)}$

22. $f(x) = 4^x$

$g(x) = 4^{(x - 3)}$

23. $f(x) = 3x$

$g(x) = 3(x - 1)$

24. $f(x) = 3x$

$g(x) = 3(x + 1)$

Name _____   Date _____

Describe each graph in relation to its basic function.

25. Compare $f(x) = (x) + b$ when $b < 0$ to the basic function $h(x) = x$.

The graph of $f(x)$ is b units below the graph of $h(x)$.

26. Compare $f(x) = b^{x-c}$ when $c > 0$ to the basic function $h(x) = b^x$.

27. Compare $f(x) = (x - b)$ when $b > 0$ to the basic function $h(x) = x$.

28. Compare $f(x) = b^{x-c}$ when $c < 0$ to the basic function $h(x) = b^x$.

29. Compare $f(x) = b^x + k$ when $k > 0$ to the basic function $h(x) = b^x$.

30. Compare $f(x) = (x - b)$ when $b < 0$ to the basic function $h(x) = x$.

Each coordinate plane shows the graph of $f(x)$. Sketch the graph of $g(x)$.

31. $g(x) = f(x) + 2$

32. $g(x) = f(x) + 4$

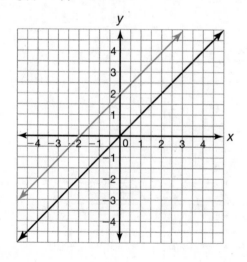

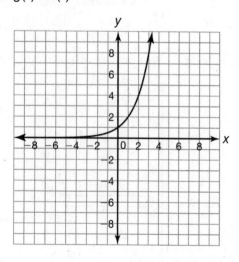

33. $g(x) = f(x) - 2$

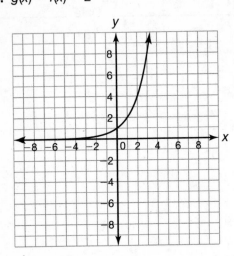

34. $g(x) = f(x - 3)$

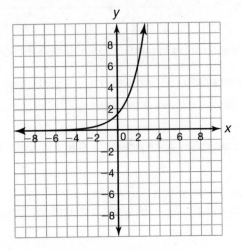

35. $g(x) = f(x + 3)$

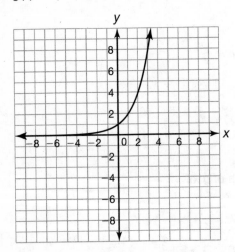

36. $g(x) = f(x - 4)$

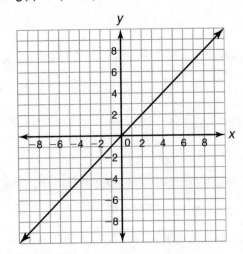

5

37. $g(x) = f(x) + 5$

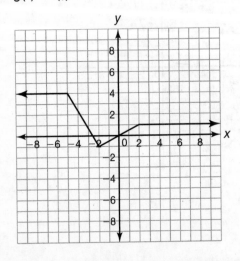

38. $g(x) = f(x + 5)$

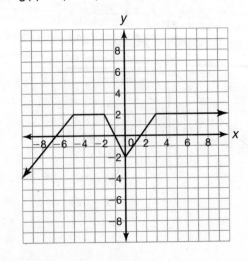

Name _____ Date _____

Write the equation of the function given each translation.

39. $f(x) = x$

Vertical translation up 2 units

$g(x) = x + 2$

40. $f(x) = x$

Vertical translation down 5 units

41. $f(x) = 3^x$

Horizontal translation right 4 units

42. $f(x) = 2^x$

Horizontal translation left 6 units

43. $f(x) = 3^x$

Vertical translation down 5 units

44. $f(x) = 4x$

Horizontal translation right 3 units

Each graph shows the function $g(x)$ as a translation of the function $f(x)$. Write the equation of $g(x)$.

45.

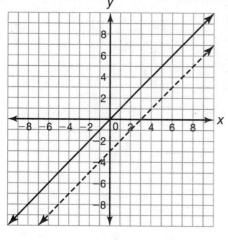

$g(x) = x - 3$

46.

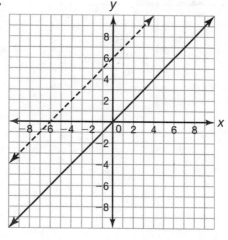

47.

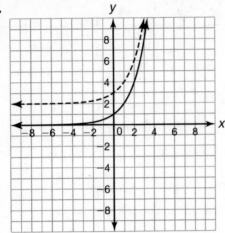

48.

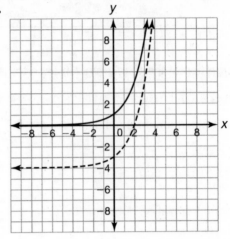

49.

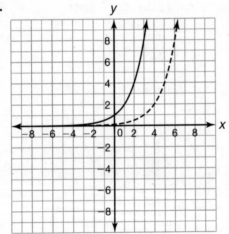

50.

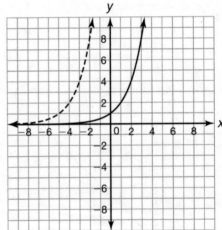

Name _____ Date _____

Take Some Time to Reflect
Reflections of Linear and Exponential Functions

Vocabulary

Define each term in your own words.

1. reflection

2. line of reflection

Problem Set

Rewrite each function $g(x)$ in terms of the basic function $f(x)$.

1. $f(x) = 3^x$

   $g(x) = -(3^x)$

   $g(x) = -f(x)$

2. $f(x) = 3^x$

   $g(x) = 3^{-x}$

3. $f(x) = 4^x$

   $g(x) = -(4^x)$

4. $f(x) = 4^x$

   $g(x) = 4^{-x}$

5. $f(x) = 2^x + 4$

   $g(x) = 2^{-x} + 4$

6. $f(x) = 2^x - 1$

   $g(x) = -(2^x - 1)$

5

Represent each reflection using coordinate notation. Identify whether $g(x)$ is a reflection about a horizontal line of reflection or a vertical line of reflection.

7. $f(x) = 2^x$

$g(x) = -(2^x)$

$(x, y) \rightarrow (x, -y)$

$g(x)$ is a reflection about the horizontal line $y = 0$.

8. $f(x) = 2^x$

$g(x) = 2^{-x}$

9. $f(x) = 5x$

$g(x) = -(5x)$

10. $f(x) = 5x$

$g(x) = 5(-x)$

11. $f(x) = 3^x + 7$

$g(x) = 3^{-x} + 7$

12. $f(x) = 4^x - 3$

$g(x) = -(4^x - 3)$

Each coordinate plane shows the graph of $f(x)$. Sketch the graph of $g(x)$.

13. $g(x) = -f(x)$

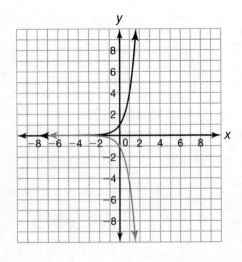

14. $g(x) = f(-x)$

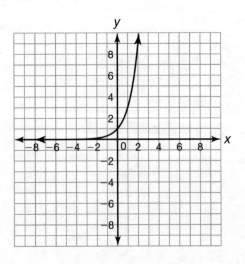

Name _____ Date _____

15. $g(x) = f(-x)$

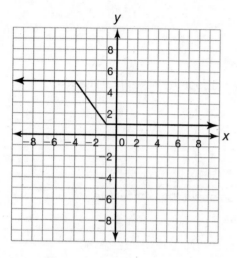

16. $g(x) = -f(x)$

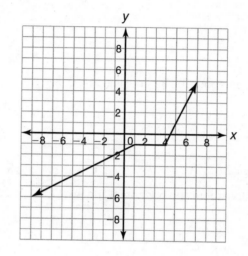

17. $g(x) = -f(x)$

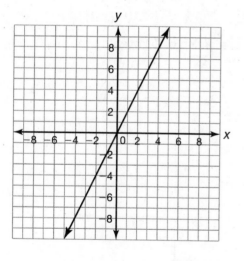

18. $g(x) = f(-x)$

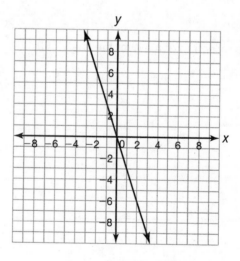

Write a function, $g(x)$, to describe each reflection of $f(x)$.

19. $f(x) = 3^x$

Reflection about the horizontal line $y = 0$.

$g(x) = -3^x$

20. $f(x) = 4^x$

Reflection about the vertical line $x = 0$.

21. $f(x) = -12x$

Reflection about the vertical line $x = 0$.

22. $f(x) = 7x$

Reflection about the horizontal line $y = 0$.

23. $f(x) = 2^x + 9$

Reflection about the horizontal line $y = 0$.

24. $f(x) = -8^x + 1$

Reflection about the vertical line $x = 0$.

Write an equation for $g(x)$ given each transformation. Sketch the graph of $g(x)$.

25. $f(x) = 5^x$

$g(x)$ is a reflection of $f(x)$ over the line $y = 0$.

$g(x) = -5^x$

26. $f(x) = 5^x$

$g(x)$ is a reflection of $f(x)$ over the line $x = 0$.

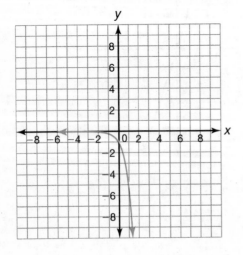

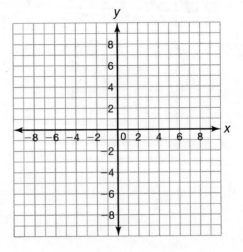

Name _____ Date _____

27. $f(x) = 3^x$

g(x) is a translation of f(x) up 2 units.

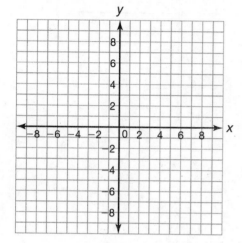

28. $f(x) = 4^x$

g(x) is a translation of f(x) right 3 units.

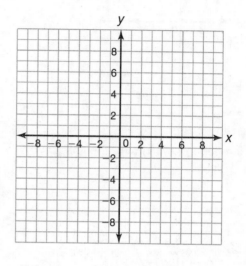

29. $f(x) = 4^x$

g(x) is a translation of f(x) down 4 units.

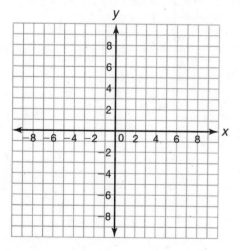

30. $f(x) = 3^x$

g(x) is a translation of f(x) left 5 units.

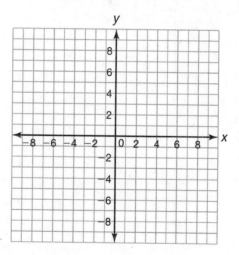

Identify the transformation required to transform *f*(*x*) to *g*(*x*) as shown in each graph.

31.

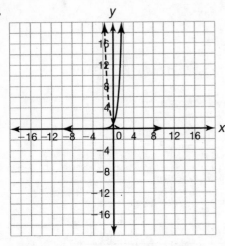

g(*x*) is a reflection of *f*(*x*) over the line *x* = 0.

32.

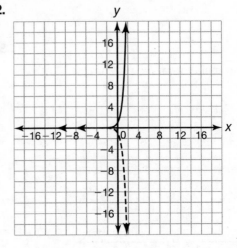

33.

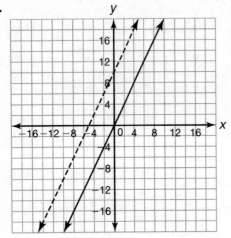

34.

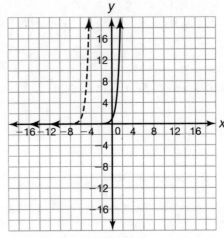

Name _____ Date _____

35.

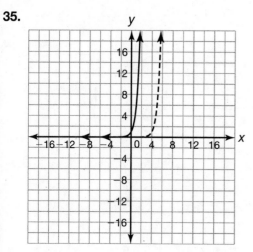

36.

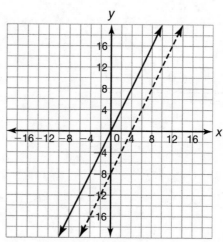

Identify the transformation required to transform each $f(x)$ to $g(x)$.

37. $f(x) = 8^x$

$g(x) = -(8^x)$

$g(x)$ is a reflection of $f(x)$ over the line $y = 0$.

38. $f(x) = 9^x$

$g(x) = 9^{-x}$

39. $f(x) = 8^x$

$g(x) = 8^x - 5$

40. $f(x) = 3^x$

$g(x) = 3^{x-1}$

41. $f(x) = 10x$

$g(x) = 10x + 2$

42. $f(x) = -12x$

$g(x) = -12(x + 1)$

5

5

Name _____ Date _____

Radical! Because It's Cliché!
Properties of Rational Exponents

Vocabulary

Match each definition to its corresponding term.

1. the number a in the expression $\sqrt[n]{a}$ **A** cube root

2. the number b when $b^3 = a$ **B** index

3. the exponent $\frac{1}{n}$ in the expression $a^{\frac{1}{n}}$ **C** nth root

4. the number n in the expression $\sqrt[n]{a}$ **D** radicand

5. the number b when $b^n = a$ **E** rational exponent

Problem Set

Write each expression as a single power.

1. $\dfrac{10^5}{10^8}$

     $\dfrac{10^5}{10^8} = 10^{5-8} = 10^{-3}$

2. $\dfrac{10^0}{10^4}$

3. $\dfrac{10^2}{10^5}$

4. $\dfrac{x^4}{x^9}$

5. $\dfrac{5^3}{5^{10}}$

6. $\dfrac{y^2}{y^8}$

Evaluate each expression.

7. $\sqrt[3]{216} =$

$\sqrt[3]{216} = 6$

8. $\sqrt[3]{64} =$

9. $\sqrt[3]{-125} =$

10. $\sqrt[3]{-343} =$

11. $\sqrt[3]{729} =$

12. $\sqrt[3]{-8} =$

Evaluate each expression.

13. $\sqrt[5]{32} =$

$\sqrt[5]{32} = 2$

14. $\sqrt[4]{625} =$

15. $\sqrt[6]{729} =$

16. $\sqrt[5]{-1024} =$

17. $\sqrt[7]{-128} =$

18. $\sqrt[5]{-243} =$

Write each radical as a power.

19. $\sqrt[4]{15}$

$\sqrt[4]{15} = 15^{\frac{1}{4}}$

20. $\sqrt[3]{5}$

21. $\sqrt[4]{31}$

22. $\sqrt[3]{x}$

23. $\sqrt[6]{y}$

24. $\sqrt{z}$

Name _____ Date _____

Write each power as a radical.

25. $12^{\frac{1}{3}}$

$12^{\frac{1}{3}} = \sqrt[3]{12}$

26. $7^{\frac{1}{5}}$

27. $18^{\frac{1}{4}}$

28. $a^{\frac{1}{2}}$

29. $d^{\frac{1}{5}}$

30. $c^{\frac{1}{6}}$

Write each expression in radical form.

31. $5^{\frac{2}{3}}$

$5^{\frac{2}{3}} = \sqrt[3]{5^2}$

32. $8^{\frac{2}{5}}$

33. $18^{\frac{3}{4}}$

34. $x^{\frac{3}{5}}$

35. $y^{\frac{4}{3}}$

36. $m^{\frac{5}{2}}$

Write each expression in rational exponent form.

37. $\sqrt[4]{6^3}$

$\sqrt[4]{6^3} = 6^{\frac{3}{4}}$

38. $\sqrt[5]{8^4}$

39. $\sqrt[3]{12^2}$

40. $\sqrt{n^5}$

41. $\sqrt[4]{p^7}$

42. $\sqrt[5]{m^3}$

5

Name _____ Date _____

Checkmate!
Solving Exponential Functions

Problem Set

Complete each table. Write a function that represents the data in the table and explain how you determined your expression.

1.

x	f(x)	Expression
0	1	3^0
1	3	3^1
2	9	3^2
3	27	3^3
4	81	3^4
5	243	3^5
x	3^x	-----

The exponents of the expressions in the third column equal x. So, $f(x) = 3x$.

2.

x	f(x)	Expression
0	6	$4^0 + 5$
1	9	
2	21	
3	69	
4	261	
5	1029	
x		-----

5

3.

x	f(x)	Expression
0	−1	-2^0
1	−2	
2	−4	
3		
4		
5		
x		-----

4.

x	f(x)	Expression
−2	$-\dfrac{1}{2}$	-2^{-1}
−1	−1	
0	−2	
1		
2		
3		
x		-----

5.

x	f(x)	Expression
0	$-\dfrac{1}{25}$	-5^{-2}
1	$-\dfrac{1}{5}$	
2	−1	
3		
4		
5		
x		-----

6.

x	f(x)	Expression
0	16	2^4
1	8	
2	4	
3		
4		
5		
x		-----

Name _____ Date _____

Graph each function.

7. $f(x) = 3^x$

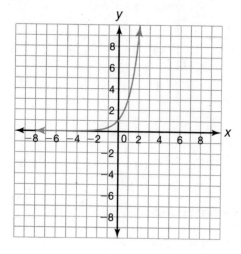

8. $f(x) = 8^{-x}$

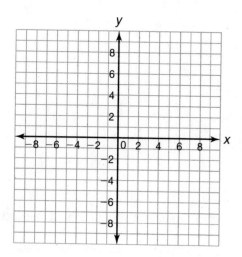

9. $f(x) = 5 \cdot 2^{-x}$

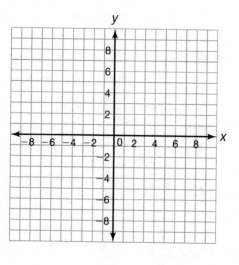

10. $f(x) = 2 \cdot 3^x$

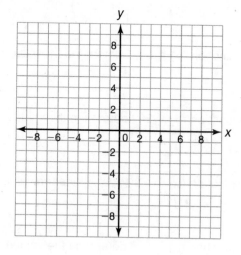

11. $f(x) = -4^x$ **12.** $f(x) = -3^{x+2}$

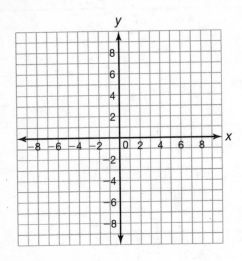   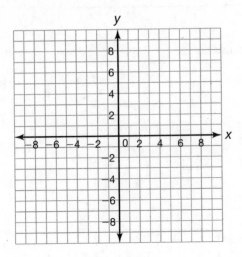

Use the intersection feature of your graphing calculator to answer each question.

13. For the function $f(x) = 6^{x-1}$ determine the value of x for which $f(x) = 7776$.

For the function $f(x) = 6^{x-1}$, $f(x) = 7776$ when $x = 6$.

14. For the function $f(x) = -4^{x+2}$ determine the value of x for which $f(x) = -4096$.

15. For the function $f(x) = 5^{-x+1}$ determine the value of x for which $f(x) = 625$.

16. For the function $f(x) = 2^{x+4}$ determine the values of x for which $f(x) < 128$.

17. For the function $f(x) = -3^{x+1}$ determine the values of x for which $f(x) > -9$.

18. For the function $f(x) = 5^{x+2}$ determine the values of x for which $f(x) = 15,625$.

Name _____ Date _____

Solve each exponential equation for x.

19. $4^x = 256$

$4^x = 256$

$4^4 = 256$

$x = 4$

20. $6^{3x} = 216$

21. $2^{5-x} = \dfrac{1}{16}$

22. $3^{-2x} = \dfrac{1}{729}$

23. $4^{x+3} = 4$

24. $\dfrac{1}{5^{x+4}} = 625$

25. $-6^{x-2} = \dfrac{1}{-1296}$

26. $\dfrac{1}{2^{x-6}} = \dfrac{1}{4}$

5

For each pair of expressions, determine whether the second expression is an equivalent form of the first expression.

27. 2^{s-1} $\frac{1}{2}(2)^s$

$\qquad$ $2^{-1} \cdot 2^s$

$\qquad$ 2^{s-1}

28. 3^{x+1} $\frac{1}{3}(3)^x$

29. 2^{2x+1} $2(4)^x$

30. 5^{2x-1} $\frac{1}{5}(25)^x$

31. $4(64)^x$ 4^{3x+1}

32. $\frac{1}{2}\left(\frac{1}{8}\right)^x$ 2^{-3x-1}

Write the exponential function represented by the table of values.

33.

x	y
0	2
1	1
2	$\frac{1}{2}$
3	$\frac{1}{4}$

$f(x) = a \cdot b^x$

$f(x) = 2 \cdot b^x$

$1 = 2 \cdot b^1$

$\frac{1}{2} = b$

$f(x) = 2\left(\frac{1}{2}\right)^x$

34.

x	y
0	1
2	25
4	625
6	15625

Name _____ Date _____

35.

x	y
0	1
1	$\frac{3}{4}$
2	$\frac{9}{16}$
3	$\frac{27}{64}$

36.

x	y
0	−1
2	−4
4	−16
6	−64

37.

x	y
0	3
3	$\frac{1}{9}$
6	$\frac{1}{243}$
9	$\frac{1}{6561}$

38.

x	y
0	−2
1	$-\frac{1}{2}$
2	$-\frac{1}{8}$
3	$-\frac{1}{32}$

5

5

Name _____ Date _____

Prepping for the Robot Challenge
Solving Linear Systems Graphically and Algebraically

Vocabulary

Match each term to its corresponding definition.

1. a process of solving a system of equations by substituting a variable in one equation with an equivalent expression

   a. system of linear equations

2. systems with no solutions

   b. break-even point

3. the point when the cost and the income are equal

   c. substitution method

4. systems with one or many solutions

   d. consistent systems

5. two or more linear equations that define a relationship between quantities

   e. inconsistent systems

6

Problem Set

Write a system of linear equations to represent each problem situation. Define each variable. Then, graph the system of equations and estimate the break-even point. Explain what the break-even point represents with respect to the given problem situation.

1. Eric sells model cars from a booth at a local flea market. He purchases each model car from a distributor for $12, and the flea market charges him a booth fee of $50. Eric sells each model car for $20.

   Eric's income can be modeled by the equation $y = 20x$, where y represents the income (in dollars) and x represents the number of model cars he sells.

   Eric's expenses can be modeled by the equation $y = 12x + 50$, where y represents the expenses (in dollars) and x represents the number of model cars he purchases from the distributor.

   $$\begin{cases} y = 20x \\ y = 12x + 50 \end{cases}$$

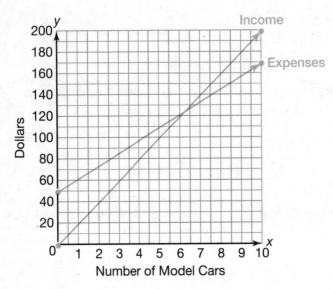

   The break-even point is between 6 and 7 model cars. Eric must sell more than 6 model cars to make a profit.

Name _____ Date _____

2. Ramona sets up a lemonade stand in front of her house. Each cup of lemonade costs Ramona $0.30 to make, and she spends $6 on the advertising signs she puts up around her neighborhood. She sells each cup of lemonade for $1.50.

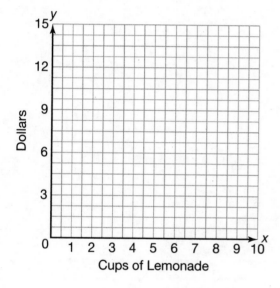

3. Chen starts his own lawn mowing business. He initially spends $180 on a new lawnmower. For each yard he mows, he receives $20 and spends $4 on gas.

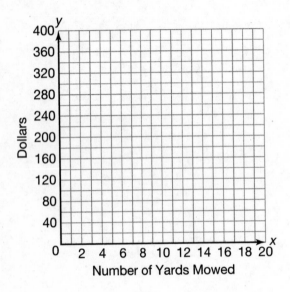

Name _____ Date _____

4. Olivia is building birdhouses to raise money for a trip to Hawaii. She spends a total of $30 on the tools needed to build the houses. The material to build each birdhouse costs $3.25. Olivia sells each birdhouse for $10.

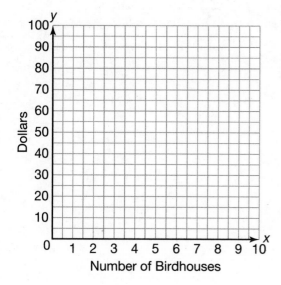

5. The Spanish Club is selling boxes of fruit as a fundraiser. The fruit company charges the Spanish Club $7.50 for each box of fruit and a shipping and handling fee of $100 for the entire order. The Spanish Club sells each box of fruit for $15.

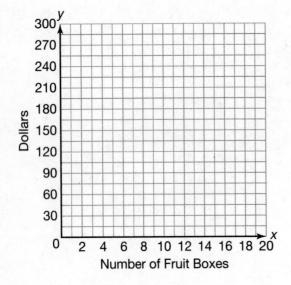

Name _____ Date _____

6. Jerome sells flowers for $12 per bouquet through his Internet flower site. Each bouquet costs him $5.70 to make. Jerome also paid a one-time fee of $150 for an Internet marketing firm to advertise his company.

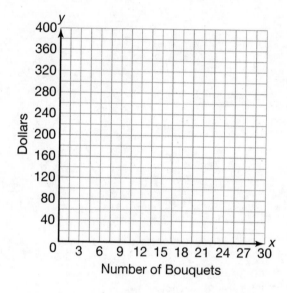

Transform both equations in each system of equations so that each coefficient is an integer.

7. $\begin{cases} \frac{1}{2}x + \frac{3}{2}y = 4 \\ \frac{2}{3}x - \frac{1}{3}y = 7 \end{cases}$

8. $\begin{cases} -\frac{1}{3}x + \frac{1}{2}y = 5 \\ \frac{3}{4}x - \frac{1}{4}y = 10 \end{cases}$

$\frac{1}{2}x + \frac{3}{2}y = 4 \qquad \frac{2}{3}x - \frac{1}{3}y = 7$

$2\left(\frac{1}{2}x + \frac{3}{2}y = 4\right) \qquad 3\left(\frac{2}{3}x - \frac{1}{3}y = 7\right)$

$x + 3y = 8 \qquad\quad 2x - y = 21$

9. $\begin{cases} \frac{5}{4}x - 3 = \frac{1}{6}y \\ \frac{2}{5}x + \frac{1}{5}y = \frac{9}{5} \end{cases}$

10. $\begin{cases} 0.5x + 1.2y = 2 \\ 3.3x - 0.7y = 3 \end{cases}$

11. $\begin{cases} 0.2x - 0.4y = 2 \\ -0.1x - 0.5y = 1.1 \end{cases}$

12. $\begin{cases} 0.3y = 2 - 0.8x \\ 1.1x = 3y - 0.4 \end{cases}$

Name _____ Date _____

Solve each system of equations by substitution. Determine whether the system is consistent or inconsistent.

13. $\begin{cases} y = 2x - 3 \\ x = 4 \end{cases}$

$y = 2(4) - 3$

$y = 8 - 3$

$y = 5$

The solution is (4, 5).

The system is consistent.

14. $\begin{cases} 2x + y = 9 \\ y = 5x + 2 \end{cases}$

15. $\begin{cases} y = 3x - 2 \\ y - 3x = 4 \end{cases}$

16. $\begin{cases} \frac{1}{2}x + \frac{3}{2}y = -7 \\ \frac{1}{3}y = 2x - 10 \end{cases}$

6

17. $\begin{cases} 0.8x - 0.2y = 1.5 \\ 0.1x + 1.2y = 0.8 \end{cases}$

18. $\begin{cases} 0.3y = 0.6x + 0.3 \\ 1.2x + 0.6 = 0.6y \end{cases}$

6

Name _____ Date _____

There's Another Way?
Using Linear Combinations to Solve a Linear System

Vocabulary

Define the term in your own words.

1. linear combinations method

Problem Set

Write a system of equations to represent each problem situation. Solve the system of equations using the linear combinations method.

1. The high school marching band is selling fruit baskets as a fundraiser. They sell a large basket containing 10 apples and 15 oranges for $20. They sell a small basket containing 5 apples and 6 oranges for $8.50. How much is the marching band charging for each apple and each orange?

Let x represent the amount charged for each apple. Let y represent the amount charged for each orange.

$\begin{cases} 10x + 15y = 20 \\ 5x + 6y = 8.50 \end{cases}$ $\begin{aligned} 10x + 15y &= 20 \\ -2(5x + 6y &= 8.50) \end{aligned}$

$$10x + 15y = 20$$
$$\underline{-10x - 12y = -17}$$
$$3y = 3$$
$$y = 1$$

$$10x + 15(1) = 20$$
$$10x + 15 = 20$$
$$10x = 5$$
$$x = 0.5$$

The solution is (0.5, 1). The band charges $0.50 for each apple and $1.00 for each orange.

2. Asna works on a shipping dock at a tire manufacturing plant. She loads a pallet with 4 Mudslinger tires and 6 Roadripper tires. The tires on the pallet weigh 212 pounds. She loads a second pallet with 7 Mudslinger tires and 2 Roadripper tires. The tires on the second pallet weigh 184 pounds. How much does each Mudslinger tire and each Roadripper tire weigh?

3. The Pizza Barn sells one customer 3 large pepperoni pizzas and 2 orders of breadsticks for $30. They sell another customer 4 large pepperoni pizzas and 3 orders of breadsticks for $41. How much does the Pizza Barn charge for each pepperoni pizza and each order of breadsticks?

Name _____ Date _____

4. Nancy and Warren are making large pots of chicken noodle soup. Nancy opens 4 large cans and 6 small cans of soup and pours them into her pot. Her pot contains 115 ounces of soup. Warren opens 3 large cans and 5 small cans of soup. His pot contains 91 ounces of soup. How many ounces of soup does each large can and each small can contain?

5. Taylor and Natsumi are making block towers out of large and small blocks. They are stacking the blocks on top of each other in a single column. Taylor uses 4 large blocks and 2 small blocks to make a tower 63.8 inches tall. Natsumi uses 9 large blocks and 4 small blocks to make a tower 139.8 inches tall. How tall is each large block and each small block?

6. Dave has 2 buckets that he uses to fill the water troughs on his horse farm. He wants to determine how many ounces each bucket holds. On Tuesday, he fills an empty 2000 ounce water trough with 7 large buckets and 5 small buckets of water. On Thursday, he fills the same empty water trough with 4 large buckets and 10 small buckets of water. How many ounces does each bucket hold?

Solve each system of equations using the linear combinations method.

7. $\begin{cases} 3x + 5y = 8 \\ 2x - 5y = 22 \end{cases}$

$3x + 5y = 8$

$\underline{2x - 5y = 22}$

$\phantom{3x +{}} 5x = 30$

$\phantom{3x + 5{}} x = 6$

$3(6) + 5y = 8$

$18 + 5y = 8$

$\phantom{18 + {}}5y = -10$

$\phantom{18 + 5{}}y = -2$

The solution is $(6, -2)$.

8. $\begin{cases} 4x - y = 2 \\ 2x + 2y = 26 \end{cases}$

Name _____ Date _____

9. $\begin{cases} 10x - 6y = -6 \\ 5x - 5y = 5 \end{cases}$

10. $\begin{cases} 2x - 4y = 4 \\ -3x + 10y = 14 \end{cases}$

11. $\begin{cases} 3x + 2y = 14 \\ 4x + 5y = 35 \end{cases}$

12. $\begin{cases} x + 6y = 11 \\ 2x - 12y = 10 \end{cases}$

13. $\begin{cases} 1.5x + 1.2y = 0.6 \\ 0.8x - 0.2y = 2 \end{cases}$

14. $\begin{cases} \dfrac{3}{4}x + \dfrac{1}{2}y = -\dfrac{3}{4} \\ \dfrac{2}{3}x + \dfrac{2}{3}y = \dfrac{2}{3} \end{cases}$

6

Name _____ Date _____

What's For Lunch?
Solving More Systems

Problem Set

Write a system of equations to represent each problem situation. Solve the system of equations using any method. Then, answer any associated questions.

1. Jason and Jerry are competing at a weightlifting competition. They are both lifting barbells containing 200 pounds of plates (weights). Jason's barbell has 4 large and 10 small plates on it. Jerry's barbell has 6 large and 5 small plates on it. How much does each large plate and each small plate weigh?

   Let x represent the weight (in pounds) of a large plate. Let y represent the weight (in pounds) of a small plate.

   $$\begin{cases} 4x + 10y = 200 \\ 6x + 5y = 200 \end{cases}$$

   One possible solution path:

   Linear Combinations Method:

   $$4x + 10y = 200$$
   $$-2(6x + 5y = 200)$$

   $$\begin{array}{r} 4x + 10y = 200 \\ \underline{-12x - 10y = -400} \\ -8x = -200 \\ x = 25 \end{array}$$

   $$4(25) + 10y = 200$$
   $$100 + 10y = 200$$
   $$10y = 100$$
   $$y = 10$$

   The solution is (25, 10). Each large plate weighs 25 pounds. Each small plate weighs 10 pounds.

6

2. Rachel needs to print some of her digital photos. She is trying to choose between Lightning Fast Foto and Snappy Shots. Lightning Fast Foto charges a base fee of $5 plus an additional $0.20 per photo. Snappy Shots charges a base fee of $7 plus an additional $0.10 per photo. Determine the number of photos for which both stores will charge the same amount. Explain which store Rachel should choose depending on the number of photos she needs to print.

Name _____ Date _____

3. Raja is trying to decide which ice cream shop is the better buy. Cold & Creamy Sundaes charges $2.50 per sundae plus an additional $0.25 for each topping. Colder & Creamier Sundaes charges $1.50 per sundae plus an additional $0.50 for each topping. Determine the number of toppings for which both vendors charge the same amount. Explain which vendor is the better buy depending on the number of toppings Raja chooses.

4. Marcus is selling t-shirts at the State Fair. He brings 200 shirts to sell. He has long-sleeve and short-sleeved T-shirts for sale. On the first day of the fair, he sells $\frac{1}{2}$ of his long-sleeved T-shirts and $\frac{1}{3}$ of his short-sleeved T-shirts for a total of 80 T-shirts sold. How many of each type of T-shirt did Marcus bring to the fair?

Name _____ Date _____

5. Alicia has a booth at the flea market where she sells purses and wallets. All of her purses are the same price and all of her wallets are the same price. The first hour of the day, she sells 10 purses and 6 wallets for a total of $193. The second hour, she sells 8 purses and 10 wallets for a total of $183. How much does Alicia charge for each purse and each wallet?

6. Weston wants to buy a one-year membership to a golf course. Rolling Hills Golf Course charges a base fee of $200 and an additional $15 per round of golf. Majestic View Golf Course charges a base fee of $350 and an additional $10 per round of golf. Determine the number of rounds of golf for which both golf courses charge the same amount. Explain which golf course Weston should become a member at depending on the number of rounds he intends to play.

6

Name _____ Date _____

Which Is the Best Method?
Using Graphing, Substitution, and Linear Combinations

Problem Set

Write a system of equations to represent each problem situation. Solve the system of equations using any method and answer any associated questions.

1. Jun received two different job offers to become a real estate sales agent. Dream Homes offered Jun a base salary of $20,000 per year plus a 2% commission on all real estate sold. Amazing Homes offered Jun a base salary of $25,000 per year plus a 1% commission on all real estate sold. Determine the amount of real estate sales in dollars for which both real estate companies will pay Jun the same amount. Explain which offer Jun should accept based on the amount of real estate sales he expects to have.

Let x represent the amount of Jun's real estate sales in dollars. Let y represent the yearly income when Jun has x dollars in real estate sales.

$$\begin{cases} y = 0.02x + 20{,}000 & \text{Dream Homes} \\ y = 0.01x + 25{,}000 & \text{Amazing Homes} \end{cases}$$

One possible solution path:

Substitution Method:

$0.02x + 20{,}000 = 0.01x + 25{,}000$ $y = 0.02(500{,}000) + 20{,}000$

$0.01x + 20{,}000 = 25{,}000$ $y = 10{,}000 + 20{,}000$

$\quad\quad 0.01x = 5000$ $y = 30{,}000$

$\quad\quad\quad x = 500{,}000$

The solution is (500,000, 30,000). Both real estate companies will pay Jun $30,000 per year for $500,000 in real estate sales. If Jun expects to sell less than $500,000 of real estate per year, then he should accept the offer from Amazing Homes. If Jun expects to sell more than $500,000 of real estate per year, then he should accept the offer from Dream Homes.

6

2. Stella is trying to choose between two rental car companies. Speedy Trip Rental Cars charges a base fee of $24 plus an additional fee of $0.05 per mile. Wheels Deals Rental Cars charges a base fee of $30 plus an additional fee of $0.03 per mile. Determine the amount of miles driven for which both rental car companies charge the same amount. Explain which company Stella should use based on the number of miles she expects to drive.

6

Name _____ Date _____

3. Renee has two job offers to be a door-to-door food processor salesperson. Pro Process Processors offers her a base salary of $15,000 per year plus an additional $25 for each processor she sells. Puree Processors offers her a base salary of $18,000 per year plus an additional $21 for each processor she sells. Determine the number of food processors Renee would have to sell for both companies to pay her the same amount. Explain which job offer Renee should accept based on the number of food processors she expects to sell.

4. Alex needs to rent a bulldozer. Smith's Equipment Rentals rents bulldozers for a delivery fee of $600 plus an additional $37.50 per day. Robinson's Equipment Rentals rents bulldozers for a delivery fee of $400 plus an additional $62.50 per day. Determine the number of rental days for which both rental companies charge the same amount. Explain which company Alex should choose based on the number of days he expects to rent a bulldozer.

Name _____ Date _____

5. Serena has job offers from two car dealerships. Classic Cars offers her a base salary of $22,000 per year plus an additional 1% commission on all sales she makes. Sweet Rides offers her a base salary of $13,000 per year plus an additional 2.5% commission on all sales she makes. Determine the amount of car sales in dollars for which both dealerships will pay Serena the same amount. Explain which offer Serena should accept based on the amount of car sales she expects to have.

6. Dominique is trying to choose a satellite Internet service provider. Reliable Satellite charges customers a monthly fee of $26 plus an additional $0.30 per hour of online time. Super Satellite charges customers a monthly fee of $18 plus an additional $0.50 per hour of online time. Determine the number of hours of online time for which both providers charge the same amount. Explain which provider Dominique should choose based on the number of hours she expects to spend online each month.

6

Name _____ Date _____

The Playoffs
Graphing Inequalities

Vocabulary

Define the term in your own words

1. half-plane

Problem Set

Write a linear inequality in two variables to represent each problem situation.

1. Tanya is baking zucchini muffins and pumpkin muffins for a school event. She needs at least 500 muffins for the event.

   $x + y \geq 500$

2. Hiro needs to buy new pens and pencils for school. Pencils cost $1 each and pens cost $2.50 each. He has $10 to spend.

3. Patti makes decorative flower pots. It costs her $20 to purchase the materials for each pot. She wants to charge more than $6 per hour of labor plus her materials cost for each pot.

4. Jose and Devon are working on a construction job together. Devon can put in 4 times as many hours per week as Jose. Together they must work at least 80 hours per week.

5. The Foxes are playing the Titans. The Titans have been scoring 28 or more points per game this season. Between 7-point touchdowns and 3-point field goals, the Foxes need to score more than the Titan's lowest score to have a hope of winning the game.

6. Jack made twice his fundraising goal, which was less than the total that Cameron raised. Cameron raised $14 more than 5 times her goal.

Tell whether the graph of each linear inequality will have a dashed line or a solid line. Explain your reasoning.

7. $x - 3y \leq 32$

The line will be solid because the symbol is $\leq$.

8. $8y + 7x > 15$

9. $y < 14x + 9$

10. $-5.2y - 8.3x \leq -28.6$

11. $\frac{2}{3}x + \frac{4}{9}y \geq 3$

12. $y - 17 > x + 8$

13. $185x + 274y \geq 65$

14. $36 < 9y - 2x$

For each inequality, use the test point (0, 0) to determine which half-plane should be shaded.

15. $5x + 7y > -13$

$5(0) + 7(0) > -13$

$0 > -13$

The half-plane that includes (0, 0) should be shaded because the inequality is true for that point.

16. $y - 30 \leq 9x$

17. $-8y > 6x + 12$

18. $46 \geq -5y + 10x$

Name _____ Date _____

19. $31.9x + 63.7y < -44.5$

20. $y - \dfrac{5}{6} > \dfrac{1}{2}x + \dfrac{1}{3}$

Graph each linear inequality.

21. $y < 4x + 2$

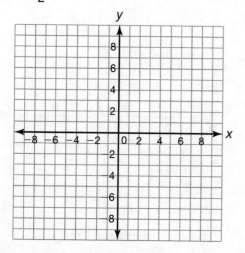

22. $y \geq 10 - x$

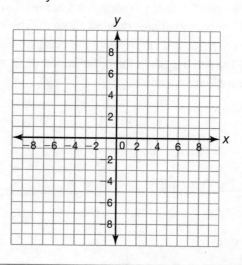

23. $y \geq \dfrac{1}{2}x - 3$

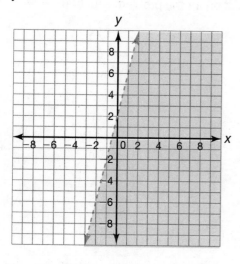

24. $-x + y > 1$

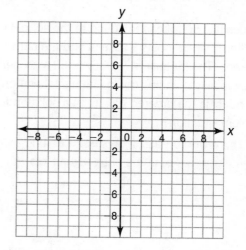

7

25. $3x - 4y \geq 8$

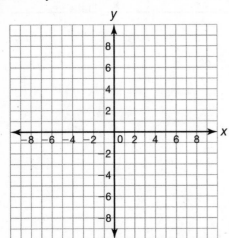

26. $\frac{3}{8}y - \frac{1}{4}x < \frac{3}{4}$

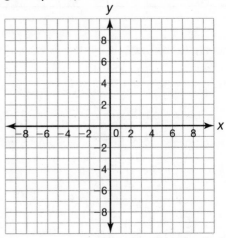

Graph each inequality and determine if the ordered pair is a solution for the problem situation.

27. Marcus has 50 tokens to spend at the school carnival. The Ferris wheel costs 7 tokens and the carousel costs 5 tokens. The inequality $7x + 5y \leq 50$ represents the possible ways Marcus could use his tokens on the two rides. Is the ordered pair (6, 3) a solution for the problem situation?

No. The ordered pair (6, 3) is not a solution to the inequality. It is not in the shaded half-plane.

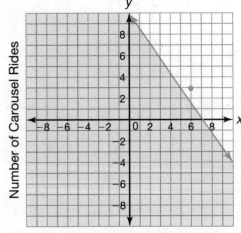

Number of Ferris Wheel Rides

28. Sophia has \$2 to buy oranges and apples. Oranges cost \$0.45 each and apples cost \$0.25 each. The inequality $0.45x + 0.25y \leq 2$ represents the possible ways Sophia could spend her \$2. Is the ordered pair (2, 3) a solution for the problem situation?

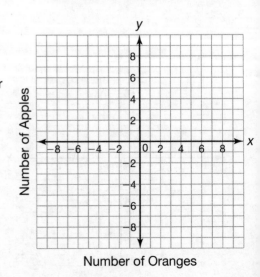

Number of Oranges

Name _____ Date _____

29. Noah plays football. His team's goal is to score at least 15 points per game. A touchdown is worth 6 points and a field goal is worth 3 points. Noah's league does not allow teams to try for the extra point after a touchdown. The inequality $6x + 3y \geq 15$ represents the possible ways Noah's team could score points to reach their goal. Is the ordered pair $(6, -1)$ a solution for the problem situation?

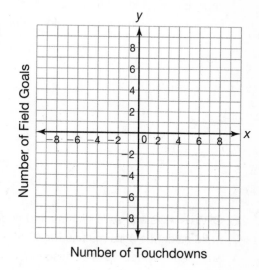

Number of Touchdowns

30. Lea has $5 to buy notebooks and pens. Notebooks cost $1.25 each and pens cost $0.75 each. The inequality $1.25x + 0.75y \leq 5$ represents the possible ways Lea could spend her $5. Is the ordered pair $(5, 2)$ a solution for the problem situation?

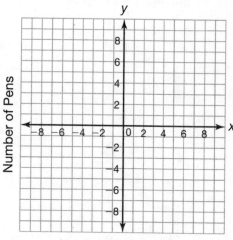

Number of Notebooks

31. Leon has $10 to buy squash and carrots. Squash cost $1.50 each and carrots cost $2.75 per bunch. The inequality $1.50x + 2.75y \leq 10$ represents the possible ways Leon could spend his $10. Is the ordered pair $(-2, 4)$ a solution for the problem situation?

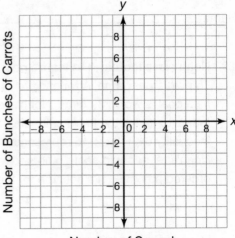

Number of Squash

32. Olivia makes and sells muffins and scones at a school bake sale. She sells muffins for $0.50 each and scones for $0.80 each. She hopes to raise at least $20. The inequality $0.50x + 0.80y \geq 20$ represents the possible ways Olivia could reach her goal. Is the ordered pair $(20, 32)$ a solution for the problem situation?

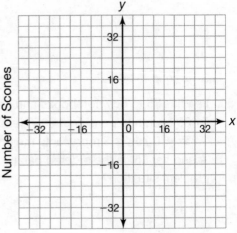

Number of Muffins

Name _____ Date _____

Working the System
Systems of Linear Inequalities

Vocabulary

Define each term in your own words.

1. constraints

2. solution of a system of linear inequalities

Problem Set

Write a system of linear inequalities that represents each problem situation. Remember to define your variables.

1. Jamal runs the bouncy house at a festival. The bouncy house can hold a maximum of 1200 pounds at one time. He estimates that adults weigh approximately 200 pounds and children under 16 weigh approximately 100 pounds. For 1 four-minute session of bounce time, Jamal charges adults $3 each and children $2 each. Jamal hopes to charge at least $24 for each session.

x = the number of adults

y = the number of children

$$\begin{cases} 3x + 2y \geq 24 \\ 200x + 100y \leq 1200 \end{cases}$$

2. Carlos works at a movie theater selling tickets. The theater has 300 seats and charges $7.50 for adults and $5.50 for children. The theater expects to make at least $2000 for each showing.

3. The maximum capacity for an average passenger elevator is 15 people and 3000 pounds. It is estimated that adults weigh approximately 200 pounds and children under 16 weigh approximately 100 pounds.

4. Pablo's pickup truck can carry a maximum of 1000 pounds. He is loading his truck with 20-pound bags of cement and 80-pound bags of cement. He hopes to load at least 10 bags of cement into his truck.

5. Eiko is drawing caricatures at a fair for 8 hours. She can complete a small drawing in 15 minutes and charges $10 for the drawing. She can complete a larger drawing in 45 minutes and charges $25 for the drawing. Eiko hopes to make at least $200 at the fair.

6. Sofia is making flower arrangements to sell in her shop. She can complete a small arrangement in 30 minutes that sells for $20. She can complete a larger arrangement in 1 hour that sells for $50. Sofia hopes to make at least $350 during her 8-hour workday.

7

Name _____ Date _____

Determine whether each given point is a solution to the system of linear inequalities.

7. $\begin{cases} 2x - y > 4 \\ -x + y \le 7 \end{cases}$

Point: $(-2, -10)$

$$2x - y > 4 \qquad\qquad\qquad\qquad -x + y \le 7$$
$$2(-2) - (-10) > 4 \qquad\qquad -(-2) + (-10) \le 4$$
$$-4 + 10 > 4 \qquad\qquad\qquad 2 - 10 \le 7$$
$$6 > 4 \ \checkmark \qquad\qquad\qquad -8 \le 7 \ \checkmark$$

Yes. The point $(-2, -10)$ is a solution to the system of inequalities.

8. $\begin{cases} x + 5y < -1 \\ 2y \ge -3x - 2 \end{cases}$

Point: $(0, -1)$

9. $\begin{cases} 4x + y < 21 \\ \frac{1}{2}x \le 36 - 5y \end{cases}$

Point: $(3, 7)$

10. $\begin{cases} 5x + 3y > 6 \\ -2x + 2y < 20 \end{cases}$

Point: (−2, 6)

11. $\begin{cases} 15x + 25y \geq 300 \\ 20x + 30y \leq 480 \end{cases}$

Point: (14, 8)

12. $\begin{cases} -2.1x + 7y \geq -49.5 \\ -y \leq -6.3x + 78 \end{cases}$

Point: (10, −8)

Graph each system of linear inequalities and identify two solutions.

13. $\begin{cases} y - 3x < 5 \\ y + x > 3 \end{cases}$

Answers will vary.

(2, 3) and (6, 0)

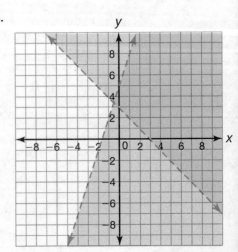

Name _____ Date _____

14. $\begin{cases} y > 2x + 3 \\ y < 2x - 5 \end{cases}$

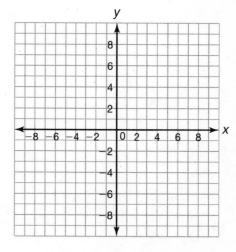

15. $\begin{cases} y \le -\dfrac{2}{3}x + 3 \\ y \ge 3x - 4 \end{cases}$

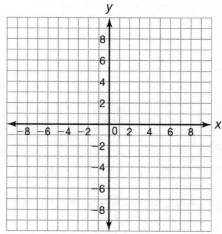

16. $\begin{cases} y < -\dfrac{1}{2}x + 6 \\ y < 2x + 1 \end{cases}$

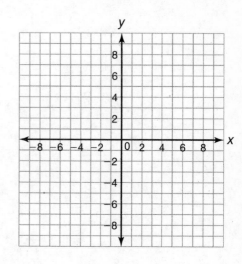

17. $\begin{cases} y \geq -\dfrac{1}{3}x + 4 \\ y \geq 2x + 5 \end{cases}$

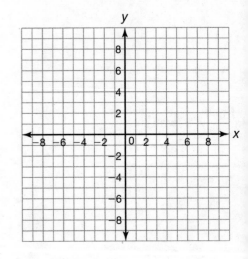

18. $\begin{cases} y > -4x + 8 \\ y < -4x - 2 \end{cases}$

Name _____ Date _____

Our Biggest Sale of the Season!
Systems with More Than Two Linear Inequalities

Problem Set

Write a system of linear inequalities that represents each problem situation. Remember to define your variables.

1. Ronna is shopping for a winter coat. The regular price of a winter coat is between $65 and $180. The store is running a special promotion where all coats are up to 35% off the regular price. Write a system of linear inequalities that represents the amount Ronna could spend.

   Let r represent the regular price.

   Let s represent the amount Ronna could spend.

   $$\begin{cases} r \geq 65 \\ r \leq 180 \\ s \geq 0.65r \\ s < r \end{cases}$$

2. Stephen is shopping for a snowboard. The regular price of a snowboard is between $120 and $425. The store is running a special promotion where all snowboards are between 25% and 75% off the regular price. Write a system of linear inequalities that represents the amount Stephen could spend.

3. Ling is shopping for a gold necklace. The regular price of a necklace is between $55 and $325. The store is running a special promotion where all necklaces are between 20% and 40% off the regular price. Write a system of linear inequalities that represents the amount Ling could spend.

4. Mario is shopping for a watch. The regular price of a watch is between $45 and $120. The store is running a special promotion where all watches are at least 25% off the regular price. Write a system of linear inequalities that represents the amount Mario could spend.

5. A company manufactures at most 20 mattresses each day. The company produces a twin size mattress and a queen size mattress. Its daily production goal is to produce at least 5 of each type of mattress. Write a system of linear inequalities that represents the number of each type of mattress that can be produced.

6. A company manufactures at most 200 tires each day. The company produces an all-weather tire and a snow tire. Its daily production goal is to produce at least 75 of each type of tire. Write a system of linear inequalities that represents the number of each type of tire that can be produced.

Name _____ Date _____

Graph the solution set for each system of linear inequalities. Label all points of intersection of the boundary lines. Then determine a point that satisfies all of the linear inequalities in the system.

7. $\begin{cases} y \leq 4 \\ 2x - y \leq 10 \\ y > -x - 4 \end{cases}$

8. $\begin{cases} y \geq -2 \\ y \leq 4 \\ x + 1 > y \\ x - 1 < y \end{cases}$

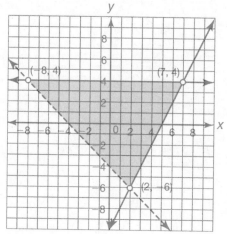

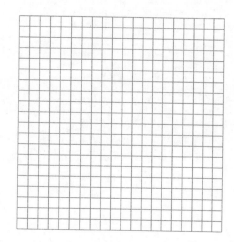

Answers will vary.

A solution to the system of inequalities would be (0, 0).

9. $\begin{cases} y \le 2 + x \\ y > x - 1 \\ 2x + y \ge -3 \\ -x + 1 > y \end{cases}$

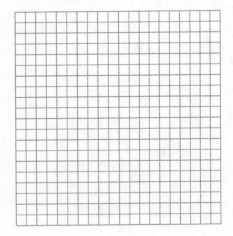

10. $\begin{cases} y > -2 \\ y \le x + 1 \\ -x \le y + 3 \\ y \le -x + 1 \\ y \le 0 \end{cases}$

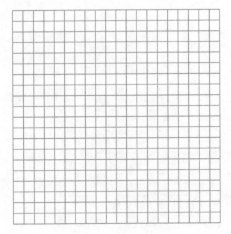

11. $\begin{cases} y > -2 \\ y \le 5 \\ x \ge -3 \\ x \le 1 \\ y > 3x + 1 \end{cases}$

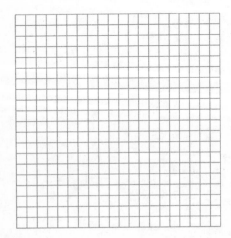

12. $\begin{cases} y \le 3x + 2 \\ y < 4 - x \\ -2x + 3y \le 2 \\ 3y \ge 2x - 8 \end{cases}$

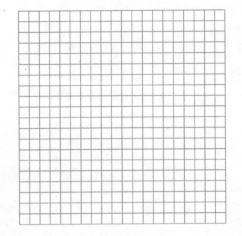

Name _____ Date _____

Analyze the solution set for the system of linear inequalities to answer each question.

Pedro is shopping for a surfboard. The regular price of a surfboard is between $200 and $400. The store is running a special promotion where all surfboards are between 20% and 60% off the regular price. The system of linear inequalities represents the amount Pedro can save.

Let r represent the regular price.

Let s represent the amount Pedro can save.

$$\begin{cases} r \geq 200 \\ r \leq 400 \\ s \leq 0.60r \\ s \geq 0.20r \end{cases}$$

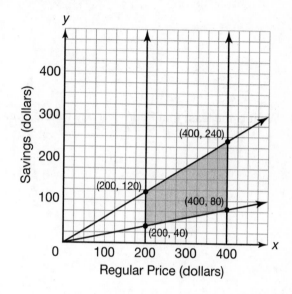

13. What is the most that Pedro can save?

The most Pedro can save is $240 represented by the point (400, 240).

14. What is the least that Pedro can save?

15. What is the most that Pedro will pay for the most expensive surfboard?

16. What is the most that Pedro will pay for the least expensive surfboard?

17. What is the least that Pedro will pay for the most expensive surfboard?

18. What is the least that Pedro will pay for the least expensive surfboard?

7

Name _____ Date _____

Take It to the Max . . . or Min
Linear Programming

Vocabulary

Define the term in your own words.

1. linear programming

Problem Set

Write a system of linear inequalities to represent each problem situation. Remember to define your variables.

1. A company is manufacturing two different models of lamps, a table lamp and a floor lamp. A table lamp takes 1 hour to make and a floor lamp takes 2 hours to make. The company has 9 employees working 8-hour days. The total manufacturing capacity is 40 lamps per day.

Let t represent the number of table lamps.

Let f represent the number of floor lamps.

9 employees $\times$ 8 hours per day = 72 work hours per day

$$\begin{cases} t \geq 0 \\ f \geq 0 \\ t + f \leq 40 \\ t + 2f \leq 72 \end{cases}$$

2. A company is manufacturing calculators. A financial calculator costs \$65 to make and a graphing calculator costs \$105 to make. The budget available for materials is \$2500 per day. The manufacturing capacity is 20 calculators per day.

3. A company is manufacturing computers. A tablet computer costs $300 to make and a laptop computer costs $600 to make. The budget available for materials is $20,000 per day. The manufacturing capacity is 50 computers per day.

4. A furniture company is manufacturing sofas and loveseats. A loveseat takes 5 hours and $650 to make. A sofa takes 8 hours and $950 to make. The company has 30 employees working 8-hour days. The daily operating budget is $25,000 per day for materials to make at most 40 pieces of furniture.

5. An electronics company is manufacturing headphones. In-ear headphones take 2 hours and $65 to make. Around-ear headphones take 3 hours and $85 to make. The company has 14 employees working 12-hour days. The daily operating budget is $5000 per day for materials to make at most 65 pairs of headphones.

6. A company is manufacturing golf clubs. A putter takes 2 hours and $80 to make. A driver takes 2 hours and $120 to make. The company has 6 employees working 12 hour days. The daily operating budget is $3000 per day for materials. The company wants to make at least 10 of each kind of club per day.

Name _____ Date _____

Graph the solution set for each system of linear inequalities. Label all points of intersection of the boundary lines.

7. $\begin{cases} y \geq 0 \\ x \geq 0 \\ 3x + y \leq 18 \\ x + 3y \leq 30 \end{cases}$

8. $\begin{cases} y \geq 0 \\ x \geq 0 \\ x + y \leq 20 \\ 4x + 9y \leq 135 \end{cases}$

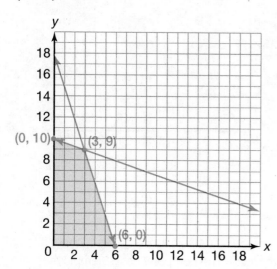

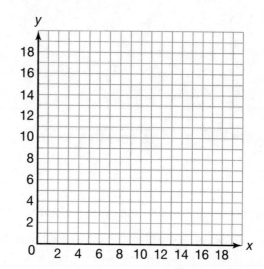

9. $\begin{cases} y \geq 15 \\ x \geq 10 \\ 3x + 2y \leq 90 \\ x + 2y \leq 70 \end{cases}$

10. $\begin{cases} y \geq 10 \\ x \geq 20 \\ x + y \leq 90 \\ x + 4y \leq 240 \end{cases}$

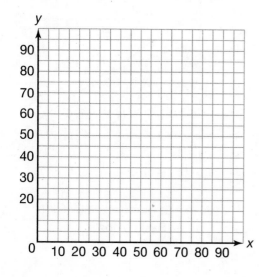

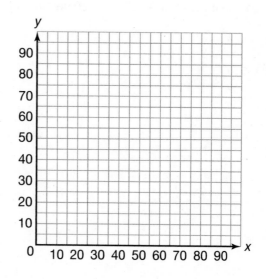

7

11. $\begin{cases} y \geq 0 \\ x \geq 0 \\ x + y \leq 26 \\ x + 4y \leq 80 \end{cases}$

12. $\begin{cases} y \geq 14 \\ x \geq 10 \\ x + 5y \leq 130 \\ 2x + 5y \leq 150 \end{cases}$

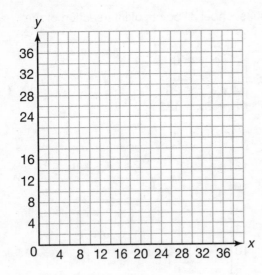

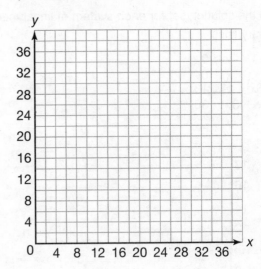

Analyze the solution set for the system of linear inequalities to answer each question.

An electronics company is manufacturing electronic book readers. A basic model takes 4 hours and $40 to make. A touch screen model takes 6 hours and $120 to make. The company has 10 employees working 12-hour days. The daily operating budget is $1920 per day for materials. The company would like at least 3 basic models and 8 touch screen models produced per day. The system of linear inequalities represents the problem situation. The graph shows the solution set for the system of linear inequalities.

Let *x* represent the number of basic models.

Let *y* represent the number of touch screen models.

$\begin{cases} y \geq 8 \\ x \geq 3 \\ 4x + 6y \leq 120 \\ 40x + 120y \leq 1920 \end{cases}$

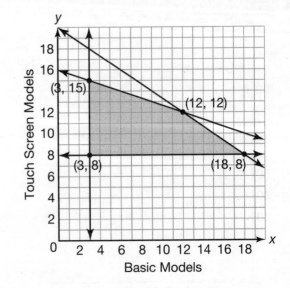

Name _____ Date _____

13. How many of each model should the company produce to minimize their daily cost?

$C(x, y) = 40x + 120y$

$C(3, 8) = 40(3) + 120(8) = 1080$

$C(18, 8) = 40(18) + 120(8) = 1680$

$C(3, 15) = 40(3) + 120(15) = 1920$

$C(12, 12) = 40(12) + 120(12) = 1920$

The minimum daily cost is $1080. To minimize their daily cost, the company should produce 3 basic models and 8 touch screen models.

14. How many of each model should the company produce to maximize the number of work hours utilized per day?

15. The company earns $30 for each basic model sold and $50 for each touch screen model sold. How many of each model should the company produce to maximize their profit?

16. How many of each model would have to be produced to maximize the company's daily cost?

17. How many of each model would have to be produced to minimize the number of work hours utilized per day?

18. During a special promotion, the company earns $20 for each basic model sold and $30 for each touch screen model sold. How many of each model should the company produce to maximize their profit?

Name _____ Date _____

Start Your Day the Right Way
Graphically Representing Data

Vocabulary

Choose the term that best completes each statement.

dot plot	five number summary	data distribution
symmetric	discrete data	skewed left
histogram	skewed right	frequency
box-and-whisker plot	bin	continuous

1. A(n) _____ is a graphical way to display quantitative data using vertical bars.

2. A data distribution is _____ if the peak of the data is to the left side of the graph with only a few data points to the right side of the graph.

3. _____ are data that have only a finite number of values or data that can be "counted."

4. A(n) _____ displays the data distribution based on a five number summary.

5. The overall shape of a graph which shows the way in which data are spread out or clustered together is called the _____.

6. _____ are data which can take any numerical value within a range.

7. A data distribution is _____ if the peak of the data is to the right side of the graph with only a few data points to the left side of the graph.

8. A(n) _____ is a graph that shows how discrete data are distributed using a number line.

9. For a set of data, the _____ consists of the minimum value, the first quartile, the median, the third quartile, and the maximum value.

10. A data distribution is _____ if the peak of the data is in the middle of the graph. The left and right sides of the graph are nearly mirror images of each other.

11. The number of data values included in a given bin of a data set is called _____.

12. The bar width in a histogram that represents an interval of data is often referred to as a _____.

Problem Set

Construct the graphical display for each given data set. Describe the distribution of the data.

1. Construct a dot plot to display the scores on a recent math quiz. The data are 12, 14, 8, 13, 12, 14, 5, 13, 14, 3, 15, 15, 10, 13, 12, 0, 14, 11, 14, 13, and 10.

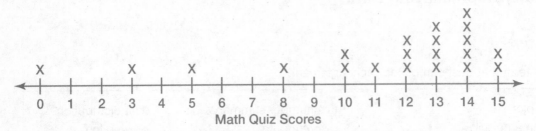

The data are skewed left.

2. Construct a dot plot to display the number of canned goods donated by each student during a charity event. The data are 15, 18, 18, 22, 13, 15, 19, 17, 18, 17, 16, 10, 17, 20, 19, 25, 17, 18, 19, and 16.

3. Construct a dot plot to display the number of items purchased by a number of randomly chosen customers at a toy store. The data are 2, 4, 3, 7, 12, 3, 1, 5, 6, 3, 4, 2, 4, 3, 7, 14, 10, 3, 5, and 9.

Name _____ Date _____

4. Construct a box-and-whisker plot to display the number of pets owned by a number of randomly chosen students. The data are 2, 0, 5, 1, 2, 1, 0, 8, 4, 3, 9, 1, 2, 3, and 1.

5. Construct a box-and-whisker plot to display the scores on a recent science test. The data are 90, 95, 100, 70, 85, 65, 90, 80, 65, 70, 75, 80, 85, 80, 60, 80, 75, and 85.

6. Construct a box-and-whisker plot to display the number of miles from school that a number of randomly chosen students live. The data are 5, 10, 15, 12, 1, 14, 9, 15, 3, 10, 12, 15, 8, 14, 13, and 2.

7. Construct a histogram to display the circumferences of the pumpkins in the Jeffiers' family pumpkin crop. The data are 22.1, 35.6, 15.8, 36.9, 40.0, 28.5, 38.4, 20.4, 25.8, 34.1, 39.9, 42.2, 24.3, 22.7, 19.8, 27.9, 22.2, 34.3, 40.4, 20.6, 38.2, and 18.1. Use $10 \leq x < 20$ as the first interval.

8. Construct a histogram to display the scores on a recent English quiz. The data are 18, 45, 20, 32, 9, 35, 49, 28, 25, 19, 5, 30, 22, 24, and 14. Use $0 \leq x < 10$ as the first interval.

Name _____ Date _____

Analyze the given dot plot which displays the number of home runs by each of the girls on the softball team this season. Use the dot plot to answer each question.

Softball Team Home Runs

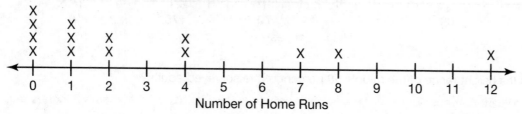

Number of Home Runs

9. Describe the distribution of the data in the dot plot and explain what it means in terms of the problem situation.

The data are skewed right, because a majority of the data values are on the left of the plot and only a few of the data values are on the right of the plot. This means that a majority of the players on the softball team hit a small number of home runs, while only a few players on the team hit a large number of home runs.

10. How many players are on the softball team?

11. How many players hit more than 2 home runs?

12. How many players hit at least 1 home run?

13. How many players hit more than 1 and fewer than 9 home runs?

14. How many players scored more than 12 home runs?

Analyze the given box-and-whisker plot which displays the heights of 40 randomly chosen adults. Use the box-and-whisker plot to answer each question.

Heights of 40 Randomly Chosen Adults

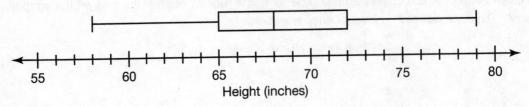

15. What is the height range of the middle 50 percent of the surveyed adults?

The middle 50 percent of the surveyed adults are at least 65 inches and at most 72 inches tall.

16. How many of the surveyed adults are exactly 68 inches tall?

17. What percent of the surveyed adults are 68 inches tall or shorter?

18. What is the height of the tallest adult surveyed?

19. How many of the surveyed adults are at least 58 inches tall?

20. Describe the distribution of the data in the box-and-whisker plot and explain what it means in terms of the problem situation.

Name _____ Date _____

Analyze the given histogram which displays the ACT composite score of several randomly chosen students. Use the histogram to answer each question.

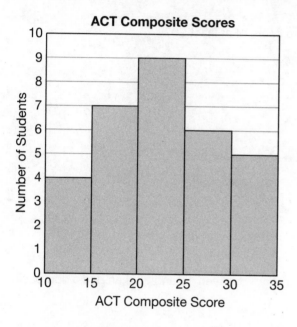

21. How many students are represented by the histogram?

There are a total of 31 students represented by the histogram.

22. Describe the distribution of the data in the histogram and explain what it means in terms of the problem situation.

23. How many of the students had an ACT composite score of exactly 25?

24. How many of the students had an ACT composite score of at least 20?

25. How many of the students had an ACT composite score less than 30?

26. How many more students had an ACT composite score between 15 and 20 than had a composite score between 30 and 35?

Name _____ Date _____

Which Measure Is Better?
Determining the Best Measure of Center for a Data Set

Vocabulary

Define each term in your own words.

1. statistics

2. measure of central tendency

Problem Set

Create a dot plot of each given data set. Calculate the mean and median. Determine which measure of center best describes each data set.

1. The data are 1, 3, 2, 0, 7, 2, 1, 10, 1, 12, 1, 2, 0, 3, and 4.

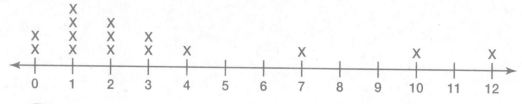

$$\bar{x} = \frac{\Sigma x}{n}$$

$$= \frac{0 + 0 + 1 + 1 + 1 + 1 + 2 + 2 + 2 + 3 + 3 + 4 + 7 + 10 + 12}{15}$$

$$\approx 3.27$$

The mean is approximately 3.27 and the median is 2. The median is the best measure of center because the data are skewed right.

2. The data are 7, 2, 9, 9, 10, 12, 17, 10, 6, 11, 9, 10, 8, 11, and 8.

3. The data are 4, 0, 13, 15, 14, 10, 13, 8, 13, 12, 11, 13, 14, 1, 15, 13, 14, 12, 10, and 7.

4. The data are 50, 50, 40, 70, 60, 50, 20, 50, 80, 40, 60, 40, and 50.

Name _____ Date _____

5. The data are 40, 45, 48, 49, 50, 49, 47, 50, 49, 42, 49, 50, 48, 50, and 47.

6. The data are 13, 12, 12, 11, 17, 10, 11, 12, 14, 20, 15, 12, 18, 13, 12, 17, 14, and 11.

Determine which measure of center best describes the data in each given data display. Then determine the mean and median, if possible. If it is not possible, explain why not.

7.

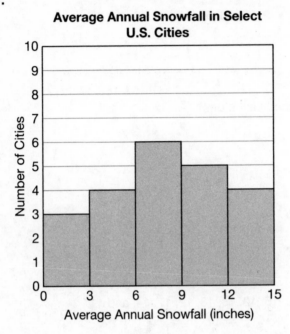

Average Annual Snowfall in Select U.S. Cities

The mean is the best measure of center to describe the data because the data are symmetric. The mean and median cannot be determined because the data values are not given.

8.

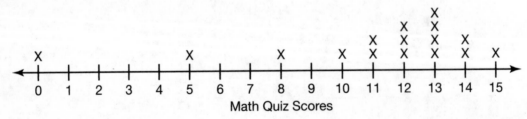

Math Quiz Scores

Name _____ Date _____

9.

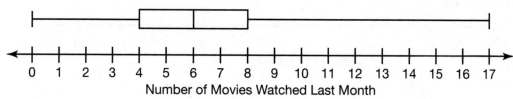

Number of Movies Watched Last Month

10.

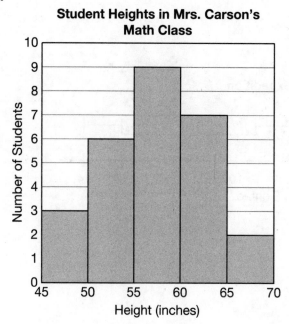

11.

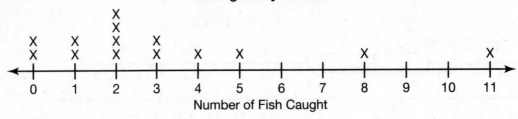

Fishing Derby Results

Number of Fish Caught

12.

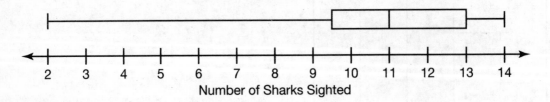

Results of Diving Expedition

Number of Sharks Sighted

Name _____ Date _____

You Are Too Far Away!
Calculating IQR and Identifying Outliers

Vocabulary

Match each definition to its corresponding term.

1. interquartile range (IQR)

    a. A value calculated using the formula Q1 − (IQR · 1.5).

2. outlier

    b. A value calculated by subtracting Q1 from Q3.

3. lower fence

    c. A value calculated using the formula Q3 + (IQR · 1.5).

4. upper fence

    d. A data value that is significantly greater than or less than the other values in a data set.

Problem Set

Calculate the IQR of each given data set. Determine whether there are any outliers in each set and list them.

1. The data are 4, 4, 5, 5, 8, 9, 10, 10, 12, 12, 16, 20, and 30.

   Q1 = 5, Q3 = 14

   IQR = Q3 − Q1

         = 14 − 5

         = 9

   Lower Fence: Upper Fence:

   Q1 − (IQR · 1.5) = 5 − (9 · 1.5)   Q3 + (IQR · 1.5) = 14 + (9 · 1.5)

                    = 5 − 13.5   = 14 + 13.5

                    = − 8.5   = 27.5

   The value 30 is an outlier because it is greater than the upper fence.

2. The data are 0, 3, 10, 16, 16, 18, 20, 21, 22, 24, 25, 25, 27, 30, 35, and 41.

Name _____ Date _____

3. The data are 9, 15, 26, 30, 32, 32, 35, 36, 38, 40, 40, 45, and 59.

4. The data are 18, 25, 30, 32, 33, 33, 35, 38, 39, 40, 42, 43, 44, 48, and 55.

5. The data are 22, 19, 20, 20, 21, 25, 10, 8, 18, 28, 32, 24, and 25.

6. The data are 60, 55, 70, 80, 20, 60, 105, 65, 75, 100, 55, 15, 115, 65, 70, 45, and 60.

Name _____ Date _____

Calculate the IQR of the data set represented in each box-and-whisker plot and determine whether there are any outliers in each data set.

7.

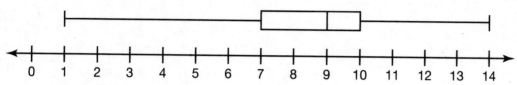

Q1 = 7, Q3 = 10

IQR = Q3 − Q1

   = 10 − 7

   = 3

Lower Fence:

Q1 − (IQR · 1.5) = 7 − (3 · 1.5)

            = 7 − 4.5

            = 2.5

Upper Fence:

Q3 + (IQR · 1.5) = 10 + (3 · 1.5)

            = 10 + 4.5

            = 14.5

There is at least 1 outlier less than the lower fence because the minimum value of the data set is 1.

8.

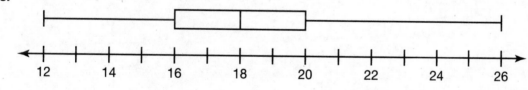

9.

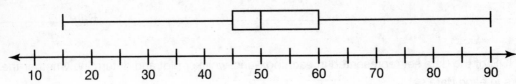

10.

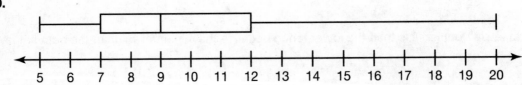

Name _____ Date _____

11.

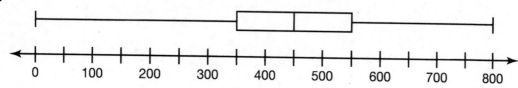

12.

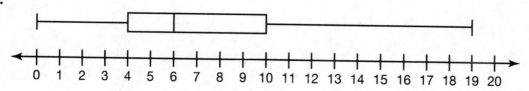

Name _____ Date _____

Whose Scores Are Better?
Calculating and Interpreting Standard Deviation

Vocabulary

Define each term in your own words.

1. standard deviation

2. normal distribution

Problem Set

Calculate the mean and the standard deviation of each data set without the use of a calculator.

1. The data are 0, 3, 6, 7, and 9.

$$\bar{x} = \frac{0 + 3 + 6 + 7 + 9}{5}$$

$$= \frac{25}{5}$$

$$= 5$$

$$\sigma = \sqrt{\frac{25 + 4 + 1 + 4 + 16}{5}}$$

$$= \sqrt{\frac{50}{5}}$$

$$= \sqrt{10}$$

$$\approx 3.16$$

$(x_1 - \bar{x})^2 = (0 - 5)^2 = 25$
$(x_2 - \bar{x})^2 = (3 - 5)^2 = 4$
$(x_3 - \bar{x})^2 = (6 - 5)^2 = 1$
$(x_4 - \bar{x})^2 = (7 - 5)^2 = 4$
$(x_5 - \bar{x})^2 = (9 - 5)^2 = 16$

The mean is 5. The standard deviation is approximately 3.16.

2. The data are 6, 8, 9, 10, 10, and 11.

3. The data are 1, 5, 10, 15, 16, 20, and 24.

Name _____ Date _____

4. The data are 13, 14, 15, 15, 16, 16, 17, and 18.

5. The data are represented by a dot plot.

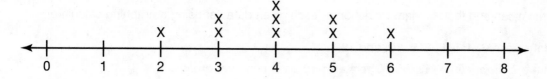

6. The data are represented by a dot plot.

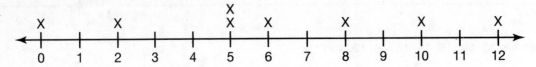

Calculate the mean and the standard deviation of each given data set using a graphing calculator.

7. The data are 1, 3, 4, 6, 6, 8, 9, 10, and 12.

The mean is approximately 6.56. The standard deviation is approximately 3.34.

8. The data are 18, 20, 24, 25, 26, 26, 28, 30, 32, and 35.

9. The data are 102, 103, 103, 104, 104, 104, 105, 105, 106, 106, and 107.

10. The data are 3.5, 4, 5.5, 6, 6, 7, 7.5, 8, 9.5, and 10.5.

Name _____ Date _____

11. The data are represented by a dot plot.

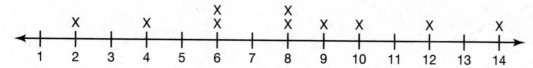

12. The data are represented by a dot plot.

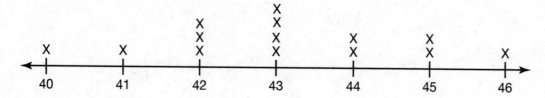

Name _____ Date _____

Putting the Pieces Together
Analyzing and Interpreting Data

Vocabulary

For each problem situation, identify whether a stem-and-leaf plot or a side-by-side stem-and-leaf plot would be appropriate. Explain your choice for each.

1. For a history project, Roberto is comparing the ages of the U.S. Presidents at inauguration and at death.

2. During the Summer Olympic Games, Karen keeps track of the number of gold medals won by the various countries participating.

Problem Set

Construct a box-and-whisker plot of each given data set and include any outliers. Calculate the most appropriate measure of center and spread for each data set based on the data distribution.

1. The data are 0, 2, 3, 4, 4, 5, 5, 5, 6, 6, 8, and 9.

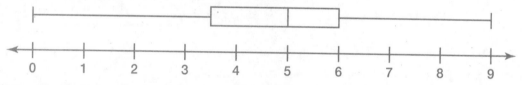

The most appropriate measure of center is the mean, and the most appropriate measure of spread is the standard deviation because the data are symmetric.
The mean is 4.75 and the standard deviation is approximately 2.35.

2. The data are 1, 6, 9, 12, 14, 15, 17, 17, 17, 18, 18, 18, 19, and 20.

3. The data are 50, 53, 57, 58, 58, 59, 59, 60, 60, 60, 61, 61, 62, 63, and 67.

4. The data are 20, 20, 20, 21, 21, 21, 22, 22, 23, 24, 25, 28, and 30.

5. The data are 80, 85, 90, 30, 70, 90, 95, 10, 100, 70, 80, 55, 50, 95, 65, and 90.

6. The data are 7, 11, 10, 13, 0, 3, 10, 9, 17, 11, 10, 20, 9, 8, and 12.

Name _____ Date _____

Two data sets are given in a side-by-side stem-and-leaf plot. Calculate the most appropriate measure of center and spread for each set based on the data distribution.

7.

Data Set 1		Data Set 2
8 7 5 3	0	3 4 6 9
8 4	1	1 4 5
2	2	5
0	3	2

Key: 2|5 = 25

For each data set, the most appropriate measure of center is the median and the most appropriate measure of spread is the IQR, because the data are skewed right.
For Data Set 1, the median is 11 and the IQR is 14.
For Data Set 2, the median is 11 and the IQR is 15.

8.

Data Set 1		Data Set 2
9 8 7	1	8 9
8 7 5 5 3	2	0 2 4 4 6 9
2 1 0	3	1 3

Key: 2|0 = 20

9.

Data Set 1		Data Set 2
9 9	5	9
7 5 1	6	5 8
8 6 2	7	0 4
2 0	8	1 1 5 7

Key: 6|5 = 65

10.

Data Set 1		Data Set 2
	0	9
9	1	4
8 3	2	2 5
9 5 1	3	3 6
5 5 4 3 2 0	4	0 0 1 1 1 2

Key: 1|4 = 14

Name _____ Date _____

11.

Data Set 1		Data Set 2
9 9 9 8 8 8	3	7 9
8 6 5 2	4	0 3 4 5 8
5 1	5	2 5 5 6 6
0	6	1 2

Key: 4|0 = 40

12.

Data Set 1		Data Set 2
7 5 3 3 2 1	10	1 1 3 5 8 8 9
8 5 2	11	1 3 5
9 4	12	5
2	13	3
0	14	

Key: 12|5 = 125

Name _____ Date _____

Like a Glove
Least Squares Regression

Vocabulary

Write a definition for each term.

1. least squares regression line

2. interpolation

3. extrapolation

Problem Set

Determine the least squares regression line for each set of points. Round your answer to the nearest hundredth.

1. (3, 4), (7, 6) and (−2, −4)

$n = 3$

$\Sigma x = 3 + 7 + (-2)$
$= 8$

$\Sigma y = 4 + 6 + (-4)$
$= 6$

$\Sigma x^2 = 3^2 + 7^2 + (-2)^2$
$= 9 + 49 + 4$
$= 62$

$\Sigma xy = (3 \cdot 4) + (7 \cdot 6) + (-2 \cdot -4)$
$= 12 + 42 + 8$
$= 62$

$(\Sigma x)^2 = 8^2$
$= 64$

$a = \dfrac{n\Sigma xy - (\Sigma x)(\Sigma y)}{n\Sigma x^2 - (\Sigma x)^2}$

$= \dfrac{(3)(62) - (8)(6)}{(3)(62) - (64)}$

$= \dfrac{186 - 48}{186 - 64} = \dfrac{138}{122}$

$a \approx 1.13$

$b = \dfrac{(\Sigma y)(\Sigma x^2) - (\Sigma x)(\Sigma xy)}{n\Sigma x^2 - (\Sigma x)^2}$

$= \dfrac{(6)(62) - (8)(62)}{(3)(62) - (64)}$

$= \dfrac{372 - 496}{186 - 64} = \dfrac{-124}{122}$

$b \approx -1.02$

The least squares regression line for the points is $y = 1.13x - 1.02$.

2. (−7, 1), (3, 8) and (9, 7)

Name _____ Date _____

3. (−3, 6), (−2, −1) and (6, −4)

4. (−8, 7), (−5, 3), (3, 6) and (9, 0)

9

5. (−7, −1), (−5, −9), (3, 3) and (6, 9)

6. (−8, 6), (−8, −2), (−6, −9) and (−5, −4)

Name _____ Date _____

While in high school, Clayton started his own T-shirt printing business. The table shows the number of T-shirts Clayton has sold each year since starting his business in 2006.

Year	2006	2007	2008	2009	2010	2011	2012
Number of T-shirts	50	75	175	125	250	350	375

The linear regression equation representing the data shown in the table is $y = 57.14x + 28.57$, where x represents the number of years since 2006 and y represents the number of T-shirts sold. Use the regression equation to predict the number of T-shirts Clayton sold during each given year. Then compare the prediction to the actual number of T-shirts or determine if the prediction is reasonable based on the problem situation.

7. 2008

For 2008, $x = 2$.

$y = 57.14x + 28.57$

$y = 57.14(2) + 28.57$

$y = 114.28 + 28.57$

$y = 142.85$

The total number of T-shirts sold in 2008 should be about 143. The actual number of T-shirts sold was 175, so the predicted value is fairly close to the actual value.

8. 2010

9. 2012

10. 2014

11. 2020

12. 2000

Name _____ Date _____

Gotta Keep It Correlatin'
Correlation

Problem Set

Determine whether the points in each scatter plot have a positive correlation, a negative correlation, or no correlation. Then determine which *r*-value is most accurate.

1.

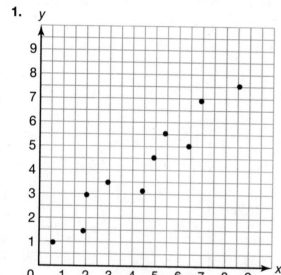

A $r = 0.8$

B $r = -0.8$

C $r = 0.08$

D $r = -0.08$

These data have a positive correlation. Because of this the *r*-value must be positive. Also, the data are fairly close to forming a straight line, so $r = 0.8$ (A) would be the most accurate.

2.

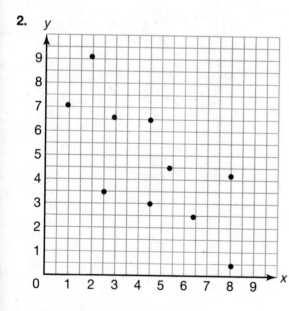

A $r = 0.9$

B $r = -0.6$

C $r = 0.02$

D $r = -0.006$

3.

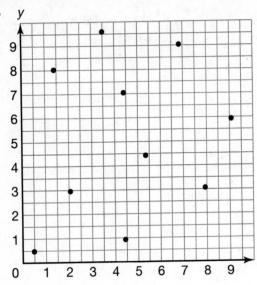

A $r = 0.01$

B $r = 0.8$

C $r = -0.5$

D $r = 0.5$

4.

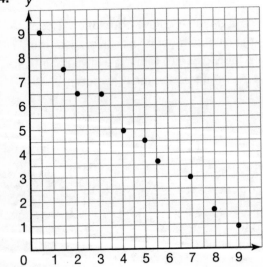

A $r = -0.009$

B $r = 0.8$

C $r = -0.9$

D $r = 0.2$

Name _____ Date _____

5.

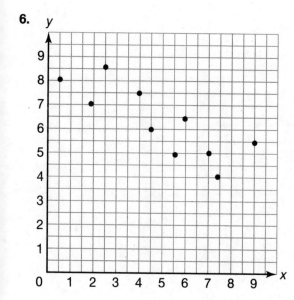

A $r = -0.003$

B $r = -0.6$

C $r = 0.004$

D $r = 0.7$

6.

A $r = 0.01$

B $r = -0.8$

C $r = -0.01$

D $r = 0.9$

Determine the correlation coefficient of each data set. Round your answer to the nearest ten thousandth.

7. (3, 2), (5, 7) and (10, 9)

$$\bar{x} = \frac{3 + 5 + 10}{3}$$

$$= 6$$

$$\bar{y} = \frac{2 + 7 + 9}{3}$$

$$= 6$$

$$\sum_{i=1}^{n}(x_i - \bar{x})^2$$

$$\begin{array}{c} (-3)^2 = 9 \\ (-1)^2 = 1 \\ (4)^2 = 16 \end{array} \right\} 9 + 1 + 16 = 26$$

$(x_i - \bar{x})$

$3 - 6 = -3$

$5 - 6 = -1$

$10 - 6 = 4$

$(y_i - \bar{y})$

$2 - 6 = -4$

$7 - 6 = 1$

$9 - 6 = 3$

$$\sum_{i=1}^{n}(y_i - \bar{y})^2$$

$$\begin{array}{c} (-4)^2 = 16 \\ (1)^2 = 1 \\ (3)^2 = 9 \end{array} \right\} 16 + 1 + 9 = 26$$

$$\sum_{i=1}^{n}(x_i - \bar{x})(y_i - \bar{y})$$

$$\begin{array}{c} -3 \cdot -4 = 12 \\ -1 \cdot 1 = -1 \\ 4 \cdot 3 = 12 \end{array} \right\} 12 + (-1) + (12) = 23$$

$$\sqrt{\sum_{i=1}^{n}(x_i - \bar{x})^2} \sqrt{\sum_{i=1}^{n}(y_i - \bar{y})^2} = \sqrt{26} \cdot \sqrt{26}$$

$$= 26$$

$$r = \frac{\sum_{i=1}^{n}(x_i - \bar{x})(y_i - \bar{y})}{\sqrt{\sum_{i=1}^{n}(x_i - \bar{x})^2} \sqrt{\sum_{i=1}^{n}(y_i - \bar{y})^2}}$$

$$= \frac{23}{26}$$

$$\approx 0.8846$$

The correlation coefficient of this data set is 0.8846.

Name _____ Date _____

8. (2, 10), (3, 3) and (10, 5)

9. (2, 2), (5, 3) and (7, 6)

Name _____ Date _____

10. (5, 6), (7, 4) and (8, 2)

9

11. (2, 8), (3, 5) and (6, 6)

Name _____ Date _____

12. (4, 8), (6, 11) and (8, 15)

Determine the linear regression equation and correlation coefficient for each data set. State if the linear regression equation is appropriate for the data set. Round your answer to the nearest ten thousandth.

13.

Year	2007	2008	2009	2010	2011	2012
Profit (dollars)	50,000	75,000	150,000	125,000	195,000	225,000

x = years since 2007

$y = 34{,}571.4286x + 50{,}238.0952$

$r = 0.9571$

Because the r-value is close to 1, the linear regression equation is appropriate for the data set.

14.

Year	2007	2008	2009	2010	2011	2012
Profit (dollars)	100,000	85,000	91,000	82,000	79,500	74,000

15.

Time (seconds)	0	1	2	3	4	5
Height (feet)	5	21	34	31	18	3

Name _____ Date _____

16.

Time (seconds)	0	1	2	3	4	5
Height (feet)	63	56	42	36	28	12

17.

Year	2007	2008	2009	2010	2011	2012
Units Sold	1480	14,105	8925	18,750	5250	2650

18.

Year	2007	2008	2009	2010	2011	2012
Units Sold	5245	7840	7075	9130	10,620	12,635

9

Name _____ Date _____

The Residual Effect
Creating Residual Plots

9

Vocabulary

Write a definition for each term.

1. residual

2. residual plot

Problem Set

Complete each table. Round your answers to the nearest tenth. Construct a residual plot.

1. Linear regression equation: $y = 0.5x$

x	y	Predicted Value	Residual Value
5	3	2.5	0.5
10	4	5	−1
15	9	7.5	1.5
20	7	10	−3
25	13	12.5	0.5
30	15	15	0

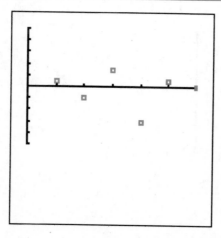

2. Linear regression equation: $y = -0.4x + 16.3$

x	y	Predicted Value	Residual Value
2	5		
4	15		
6	26		
8	23		
10	11		
12	3		

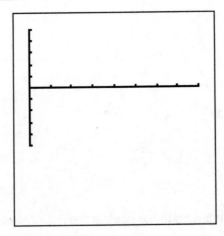

3. Linear regression equation: $y = 3x - 2.1$

x	y	Predicted Value	Residual Value
1	1.5		
3	6.5		
5	12.5		
7	19.5		
9	24.5		
11	31.5		

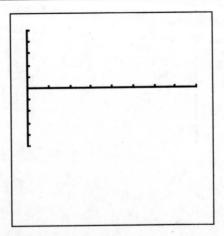

Name _____ Date _____

4. Linear regression equation: $y = -9.6x + 641.7$

x	y	Predicted Value	Residual Value
10	600		
20	450		
30	300		
40	200		
50	150		
60	125		

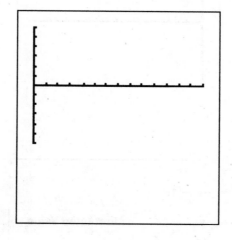

5. Linear regression equation: $y = 4.9x + 16.4$

x	y	Predicted Value	Residual Value
100	505		
90	460		
80	415		
70	360		
60	305		
50	265		

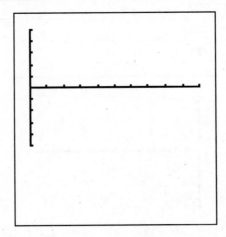

6. Linear regression equation: $y = -x + 19.7$

x	y	Predicted Value	Residual Value
2	17		
4	16		
6	15		
8	12		
10	9		
12	8		

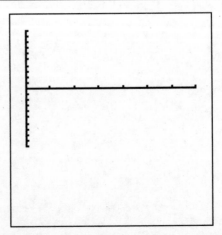

Name _____ Date _____

Consider the scatter plot, its line of best fit, and the corresponding residual plot of each data set. State if a linear model is appropriate for the data.

7. Linear regression equation: $y = 2.96x + 5.30$, $r = 0.9964$

x	2	4	6	8	10	12
y	12	16	22.5	29.5	36	40

Scatter Plot & Line of Best Fit

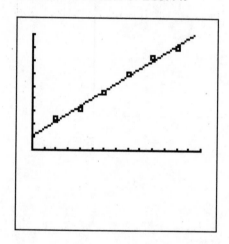

Residual Plot

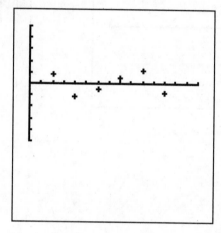

Based on the shape of the scatter plot and the correlation coefficient, a linear model appears to be appropriate for the data. Based on the residual plot, a linear model appears to be appropriate for the data.

8. Linear regression equation: $y = 0.24x + 9.04$, $r = 0.1570$

x	1	3	5	7	9	11
y	4	8	17	18	10	6

Scatter Plot & Line of Best Fit

Residual Plot

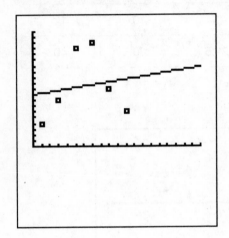
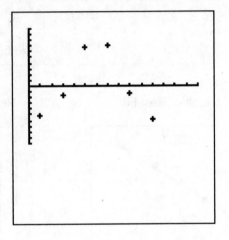

Name _____ Date _____

9. Linear regression equation: $y = 14.08x - 163.13$, $r = 0.9746$

x	10	20	30	40	50	60
y	49	103	207	346	511	762

Scatter Plot & Line of Best Fit

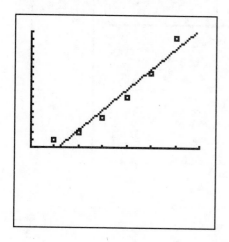

Residual Plot

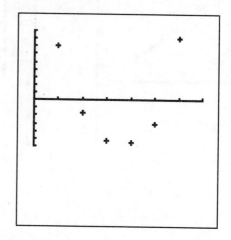

10. Linear regression equation: $y = -1.91x + 59$, $r = -0.9968$

x	5	10	15	20	25	30
y	48	41	32	19	12	1

Scatter Plot & Line of Best Fit

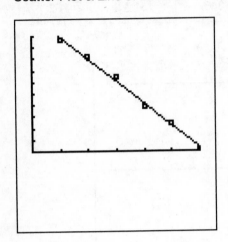

Residual Plot

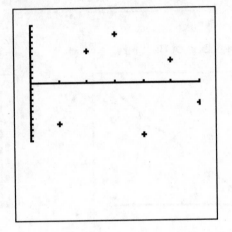

Name _____ Date _____

11. Linear regression equation: $y = 4.01x + 1.43$, $r = 0.9997$

x	1	2	3	4	5	6
y	5.5	9.25	13.5	17.75	21.25	25.5

Scatter Plot & Line of Best Fit

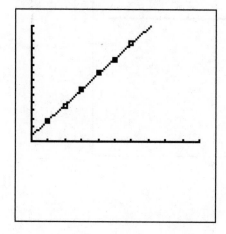

Residual Plot

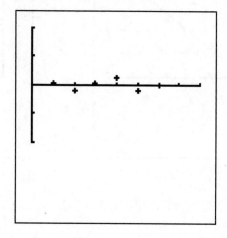

12. Linear regression equation: $y = 3.93x - 11.33$, $r = 0.8241$

x	2	4	6	8	10	12
y	9	2	1	12	25	48

Scatter Plot & Line of Best Fit

Residual Plot

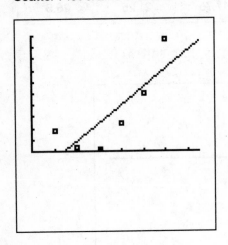
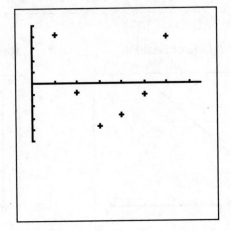

Name _____ Date _____

To Fit or Not To Fit? That Is The Question!
Using Residual Plots

Problem Set

For each data set, determine the linear regression equation. Then, construct a scatter plot and a corresponding residual plot. State if a linear model is appropriate for the data. Round your answers to the nearest hundredth. Round the correlation coefficient to the nearest ten thousandth.

1.

x	10	20	30	40	50	60	70	80
y	351	601	849	1099	1351	1601	1849	2099
Prediction	350.66	600.46	850.26	1100.06	1349.86	1599.66	1849.46	2099.26
Residual	0.34	0.54	−1.26	−1.06	1.14	1.34	−0.46	−0.26

Linear regression equation: $y = 24.98x + 100.86$, $r = 1.0000$

Scatter Plot & Line of Best Fit

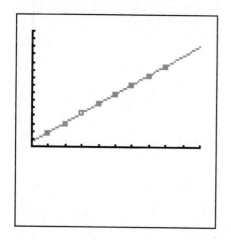

Residual Plot

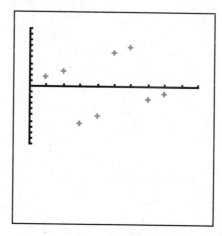

Based on the shape of the scatter plot and the correlation coefficient, a linear model appears to be appropriate for the data. Based on the residual plot, a linear model appears to be appropriate for the data.

2.

x	2	4	6	8	10	12	14	16
y	8	14	20	26	32	38	44	50
Prediction								
Residual								

Linear regression equation:

Scatter Plot & Line of Best Fit

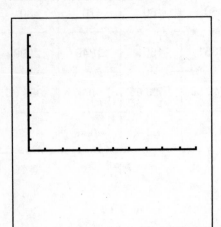

Residual Plot

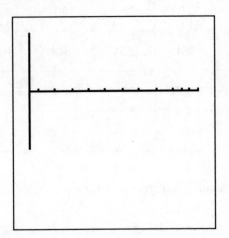

Name _____ Date _____

3.

x	1	3	5	7	9	11	13	15
y	2	10	26	50	82	122	170	226
Prediction								
Residual								

Linear regression equation:

Scatter Plot & Line of Best Fit

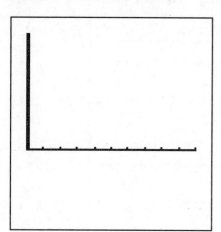

Residual Plot

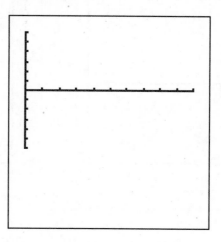

4.

x	2	4	6	8	10	12	14	16
y	2	5	11	25	57	129	291	656
Prediction								
Residual								

Linear regression equation:

Scatter Plot & Line of Best Fit

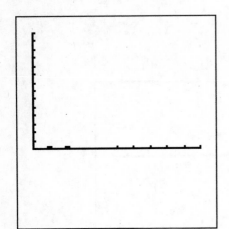

Residual Plot

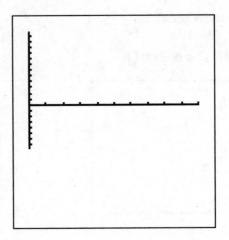

Name _____ Date _____

5.

x	1	2	3	4	5	6	7	8
y	37.5	35.5	32.5	30	27.5	25.5	22.5	20
Prediction								
Residual								

Linear regression equation:

Scatter Plot & Line of Best Fit

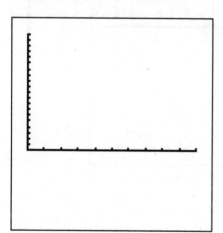

Residual Plot

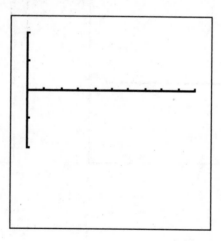

6.

x	2	4	6	8	10	12	14	16
y	50	48	46	44	40	36	30	24
Prediction								
Residual								

Linear regression equation:

Scatter Plot & Line of Best Fit

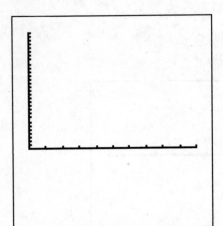

Residual Plot

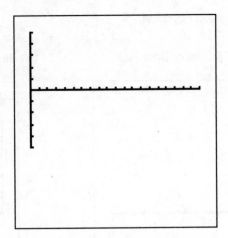

Name _____ Date _____

Who Are You? Who? Who?
Causation vs. Correlation

Vocabulary

Choose the word from the box that best completes each sentence.

causation	necessary condition	confounding variable
common response	sufficient condition	

1. A correlation is a _____ for causation, but a correlation is not a _____ for causation.

2. A _____ is when some other reason may cause the same result.

3. _____ is when one event causes a second event.

4. A _____ is when there are other variables that are unknown or unobserved.

Problem Set

Determine whether each correlation implies causation. List reasons why or why not.

1. The amount of ice cream a grocery store sells is negatively correlated to the amount of soup that the grocery store sells.

   The correlation does not imply causation. There may be a correlation between ice cream sales and soup sales. For instance, ice cream sales may increase as soup sales decrease because ice cream sales typically increase in warmer weather and soup sales typically decrease in warmer weather. However, this trend does not mean that an increase in ice cream sales causes the soup sales to decrease.

2. The number of new entry-level jobs in a city is positively correlated to the number of new home sales.

3. There is a positive correlation between the total number of dollars paid toward an education and a person's annual salary.

4. There is a negative correlation between the number of times a person washes their hands during the day and the number of times that person catches a cold.

5. There is a negative correlation between the number of hours a student plays video games per day and the grades a student receives in school.

6. There is a positive correlation between the number of hours a student spends studying and the grades a student receives in school.

Name _____ Date _____

Read each statement. Then answer the questions. Explain your reasoning.

7. A study claims that eating a healthy breakfast improves school performance.

   a. Do you think that eating breakfast every morning is a necessary condition for a student to perform well at school?

   Yes. It is very difficult for a student to perform well in school without a healthy breakfast.

   b. Do you think that eating breakfast every morning is a sufficient condition for a student to perform well at school?

   No. Not every student who eats breakfast every morning performs well at school.

8. A teacher said that students who read a book slowly will understand the story.

   a. Do you think that reading a book slowly is a necessary condition for understanding the story?

   b. Do you think that reading a book slowly is a sufficient condition for a student to understand the story?

9. A reporter claims that when there are a large number of paramedics at a disaster site, there are a large number of fatalities.

   a. Do you think that a large number of paramedics at a disaster site is a necessary condition for a large number of fatalities?

   b. Do you think that a large number of paramedics at a disaster site is a sufficient condition for a large number of fatalities?

10. An adult claims that if you play with fire, you are going to have bad dreams.

    a. Do you think that playing with fire is a necessary condition for a person to have bad dreams?

    b. Do you think that playing with fire is a sufficient condition for a person to have bad dreams?

11. A dietician says that if people reduce their caloric intake they will lose weight.

    a. Do you think that reducing caloric intake is a necessary condition for a person to lose weight?

    b. Do you think that reducing caloric intake is a sufficient condition for a person to lose weight?

12. A cosmetic company claims that if you use sunscreen you will not get skin cancer.

    a. Do you think that using sunscreen is a necessary condition for a person to not get skin cancer?

    b. Do you think that using sunscreen is a sufficient condition for a person to not get skin cancer?

Name _____ Date _____

Could You Participate in Our Survey?
Interpreting Frequency Distributions

Vocabulary

Match each definition to its corresponding term.

1. displays the total of the frequencies of the rows or columns of a frequency distribution

   a. categorical data

2. displays the frequencies for categorical data in a two-way table

   b. two-way frequency table

3. non-numerical data that can be grouped into categories

   c. frequency distribution

4. displays categorical data by representing the number of occurrences that fall into each group for two variables

   d. joint frequency

5. any frequency you record within the body of a two-way frequency table

   e. frequency marginal distribution

Problem Set

Organize each data set into a two-way frequency table. Then complete the frequency marginal distribution for the data set.

1.

Class	Favorite Color
A	Red
A	Blue
B	Red
B	Purple
B	Blue
A	Red
B	Green
B	Green
A	Blue
B	Purple

Class	Favorite Color
B	Blue
A	Blue
A	Green
A	Red
B	Blue
B	Blue
A	Purple
B	Green
A	Red
B	Purple

Two-way frequency table:

Favorite Color of Students

		Red	Blue	Purple	Green
Class	Class A	////	///	/	/
	Class B	/	////	///	///

Frequency marginal distribution:

Favorite Color of Students

		Red	Blue	Purple	Green	Total
Class	Class A	4	3	1	1	9
	Class B	1	4	3	3	11
	Total	5	7	4	4	20

Name _____ Date _____

2.

Class	Favorite Sport to Watch on TV
11th Grade	Football
11th Grade	Baseball
12th Grade	Football
12th Grade	Football
11th Grade	Basketball
12th Grade	Football
11th Grade	Baseball
11th Grade	Football
12th Grade	Basketball
11th Grade	Baseball

Class	Favorite Sport to Watch on TV
12th Grade	Football
11th Grade	Basketball
11th Grade	Basketball
12th Grade	Football
12th Grade	Baseball
11th Grade	Football
12th Grade	Basketball
12th Grade	Baseball
11th Grade	Basketball
12th Grade	Football

Two-way frequency table:

Favorite Sport to Watch on TV

Class			

Frequency marginal distribution:

Favorite Sport to Watch on TV

Class				

3.

Class	Favorite Fruit
5th Grade	Apple
6th Grade	Banana
5th Grade	Apple
5th Grade	Apple
5th Grade	Banana
6th Grade	Grapes
6th Grade	Orange
6th Grade	Apple
5th Grade	Orange
5th Grade	Banana

Class	Favorite Fruit
5th Grade	Banana
6th Grade	Apple
6th Grade	Orange
6th Grade	Apple
6th Grade	Banana
5th Grade	Grapes
5th Grade	Banana
5th Grade	Apple
6th Grade	Orange
5th Grade	Grapes

Two-way frequency table:

Favorite Fruit of Students

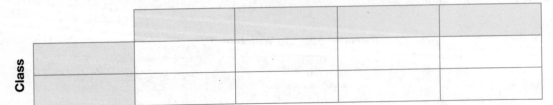

Frequency marginal distribution:

Favorite Fruit of Students

Name _____ Date _____

4.

Class	Favorite Sports Boys Play
A	Soccer
A	Baseball
C	Basketball
B	Soccer
B	Soccer
C	Basketball
B	Football
C	Baseball
A	Baseball
C	Basketball

Class	Favorite Sports Boys Play
C	Soccer
A	Basketball
A	Baseball
B	Soccer
B	Football
B	Football
C	Baseball
A	Football
A	Soccer
C	Basketball

Two-way frequency table:

Favorite Sports Boys Play

Class				

Frequency marginal distribution:

Favorite Sports Boys Play

Class					

5.

Class	Favorite Sports Girls Play
A	Basketball
B	Soccer
B	Swimming
C	Basketball
C	Softball
A	Soccer
B	Soccer
A	Softball
C	Basketball
C	Swimming

Class	Favorite Sports Girls Play
A	Basketball
A	Basketball
B	Soccer
C	Basketball
B	Softball
B	Swimming
A	Swimming
A	Softball
C	Soccer
A	Softball

Two-way frequency table:

Favorite Sports Girls Play

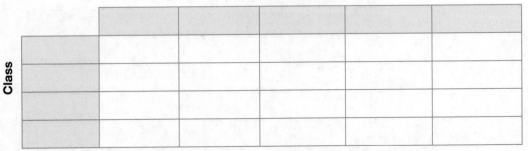

Class				

Frequency marginal distribution:

Favorite Sports Girls Play

Class				

Name _____ Date _____

6.

Class	Favorite Subject
A	Algebra
A	English
B	History
B	History
B	Algebra
A	Algebra
A	English
B	English
A	English
B	History

Class	Favorite Subject
B	History
B	Algebra
A	English
B	Algebra
A	English
A	History
B	Algebra
B	Algebra
A	History
A	English

Two-way frequency table:

Favorite Subject of Students

Class			

Frequency marginal distribution:

Favorite Subject of Students

Class				

Construct a bar graph to represent each data set shown in the frequency marginal distribution table.

7.

Favorite Color of Students

		Red	Blue	Purple	Green	Total
Class	**Class A**	5	7	3	1	16
	Class B	6	5	5	2	18
	Total	11	12	8	3	34

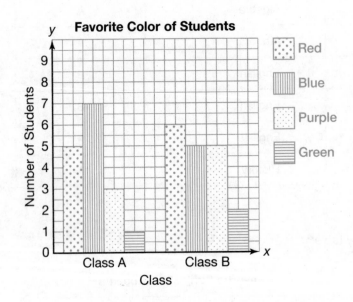

Name _____ Date _____

8.

Favorite Color of Students

		Red	Blue	Purple	Green	Total
Class	**Class A**	5	7	3	1	16
	Class B	6	5	5	2	18
	Total	11	12	8	3	34

10

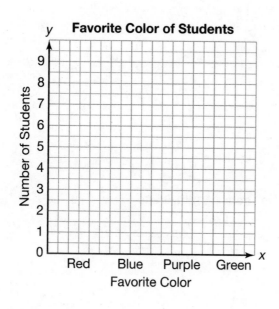

Favorite Color of Students

9.

Favorite Sport to Watch on TV

Class	Football	Baseball	Basketball	Total
11th Grade	16	7	12	35
12th Grade	13	5	18	36
Total	29	12	30	71

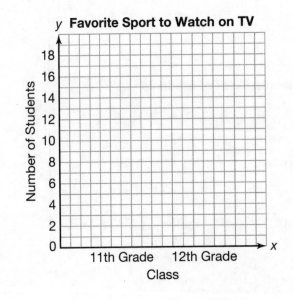

Name _____ Date _____

10.

Favorite Sport to Watch on TV

Class	Football	Baseball	Basketball	Total
11th Grade	16	7	12	35
12th Grade	13	5	18	36
Total	29	12	30	71

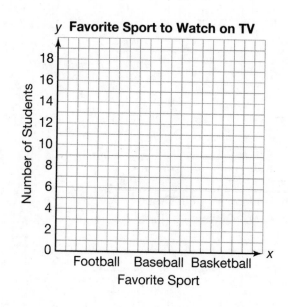

Favorite Sport to Watch on TV

11.

Favorite Fruit of Students

Class		Apple	Banana	Grapes	Orange	Total
	5th Grade	17	15	8	6	46
	6th Grade	12	11	3	9	35
	Total	29	26	11	15	81

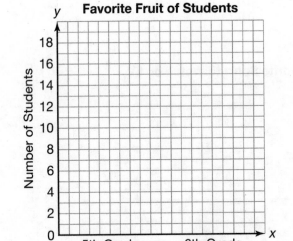

Favorite Fruit of Students

Name _____ Date _____

12.

Favorite Fruit of Students

		Apple	Banana	Grapes	Orange	Total
Class	5th Grade	17	15	8	6	46
	6th Grade	12	11	3	9	35
	Total	29	26	11	15	81

Favorite Fruit of Students

10

Name _____ Date _____

It's So Hot Outside!
Relative Frequency Distribution

Vocabulary

Write a brief explanation of the difference between a relative frequency distribution and a relative frequency marginal distribution.

Problem Set

Complete the relative frequency distribution and relative frequency marginal distribution for each frequency marginal distribution.

1.

Favorite Music of Students

	Pop	Rap	Country	Rock	Total
Class A	15	10	4	7	36
Class B	12	17	6	5	40
Total	27	27	10	12	76

Favorite Music of Students

	Pop	Rap	Country	Rock	Total
Class A	$\frac{15}{76} \approx 0.197$	$\frac{10}{76} \approx 0.132$	$\frac{4}{76} \approx 0.053$	$\frac{7}{76} \approx 0.092$	$\frac{36}{76} \approx 0.474$
Class B	$\frac{12}{76} \approx 0.158$	$\frac{17}{76} \approx 0.224$	$\frac{6}{76} \approx 0.079$	$\frac{5}{76} \approx 0.066$	$\frac{40}{76} \approx 0.526$
Total	$\frac{27}{76} \approx 0.355$	$\frac{27}{76} \approx 0.355$	$\frac{10}{76} \approx 0.132$	$\frac{12}{76} \approx 0.158$	$\frac{76}{76} = 1$

2.

Favorite Books of Students

Class		Biography	Mystery	Romance	Historical	Total
	Class A	7	12	5	9	33
	Class B	11	3	9	12	35
	Class C	12	14	6	8	40
	Total	30	29	20	29	108

Favorite Books of Students

Class		Biography	Mystery	Romance	Historical	Total
	Class A					
	Class B					
	Class C					
	Total					

3.

Favorite Movies of Students

Class		Comedy	Drama	Horror	Total
	Class A	20	8	3	31
	Class B	18	6	9	33
	Total	38	14	12	64

Favorite Books of Students

Class		Comedy	Drama	Horror	Total
	Class A				
	Class B				
	Total				

Name _____ Date _____

4.

Favorite Subject of Students

	Biology	History	Geometry	Total
Class A	13	8	9	30
Class B	8	15	5	28
Class C	4	11	14	29
Total	25	34	28	87

Favorite Subject of Students

	Biology	History	Geometry	Total
Class A				
Class B				
Class C				
Total				

5.

Favorite Vegetable of Students

	Green Beans	Broccoli	Carrots	Corn	Total
Class A	9	4	12	8	33
Class B	10	7	6	11	34
Total	19	11	18	19	67

Favorite Vegetable of Students

	Green Beans	Broccoli	Carrots	Corn	Total
Class A					
Class B					
Total					

6.

Favorite Winter Sport of Students

	Skiing	Tubing	Sledding	Skating	Total
Class A	13	7	9	4	33
Class B	11	5	14	9	39
Total	24	12	23	13	72

Favorite Winter Sport of Students

	Skiing	Tubing	Sledding	Skating	Total
Class A					
Class B					
Total					

Name _____ Date _____

Construct a stacked bar graph of each relative frequency distribution.

7.

Favorite Winter Sport of Students

Class		Skiing	Tubing	Sledding	Skating	Total
	11th Grade	$\frac{20}{163} \approx 0.123$	$\frac{16}{163} \approx 0.098$	$\frac{32}{163} \approx 0.196$	$\frac{11}{163} \approx 0.067$	$\frac{79}{163} \approx 0.485$
	12th Grade	$\frac{24}{163} \approx 0.147$	$\frac{18}{163} \approx 0.110$	$\frac{27}{163} \approx 0.166$	$\frac{15}{163} \approx 0.092$	$\frac{84}{163} \approx 0.515$
	Total	$\frac{44}{163} \approx 0.270$	$\frac{34}{163} \approx 0.209$	$\frac{59}{163} \approx 0.362$	$\frac{26}{163} \approx 0.160$	$\frac{163}{163} = 1$

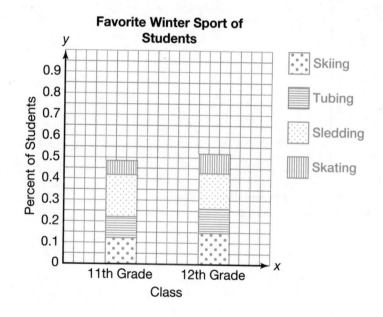

Favorite Winter Sport of Students

8.

Favorite Winter Sport of Students

		Skiing	Tubing	Sledding	Skating	Total
Class	**11th Grade**	$\frac{20}{163} \approx 0.123$	$\frac{16}{163} \approx 0.098$	$\frac{32}{163} \approx 0.196$	$\frac{11}{163} \approx 0.067$	$\frac{79}{163} \approx 0.485$
	12th Grade	$\frac{24}{163} \approx 0.147$	$\frac{18}{163} \approx 0.110$	$\frac{27}{163} \approx 0.166$	$\frac{15}{163} \approx 0.092$	$\frac{84}{163} \approx 0.515$
	Total	$\frac{44}{163} \approx 0.270$	$\frac{34}{163} \approx 0.209$	$\frac{59}{163} \approx 0.362$	$\frac{26}{163} \approx 0.160$	$\frac{163}{163} = 1$

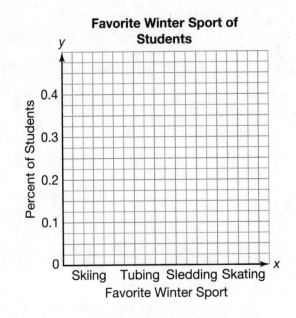

Favorite Winter Sport of Students

Name _____ Date _____

9.

Favorite Movies of Students

Class	Comedy	Drama	Horror	Total
11th Grade	$\frac{42}{164} \approx 0.256$	$\frac{15}{164} \approx 0.091$	$\frac{27}{164} \approx 0.165$	$\frac{84}{164} \approx 0.512$
12th Grade	$\frac{40}{164} \approx 0.244$	$\frac{22}{164} \approx 0.134$	$\frac{18}{164} \approx 0.110$	$\frac{80}{164} \approx 0.488$
Total	$\frac{82}{164} = 0.5$	$\frac{37}{164} \approx 0.226$	$\frac{45}{164} \approx 0.274$	$\frac{164}{164} = 1$

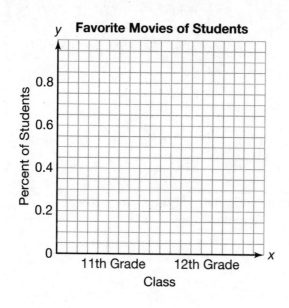

Favorite Movies of Students

10.

Favorite Movies of Students

		Comedy	Drama	Horror	Total
Class	**11th Grade**	$\frac{42}{164} \approx 0.256$	$\frac{15}{164} \approx 0.091$	$\frac{27}{164} \approx 0.165$	$\frac{84}{164} \approx 0.512$
	12th Grade	$\frac{40}{164} \approx 0.244$	$\frac{22}{164} \approx 0.134$	$\frac{18}{164} \approx 0.110$	$\frac{80}{164} \approx 0.488$
	Total	$\frac{82}{164} = 0.5$	$\frac{37}{164} \approx 0.226$	$\frac{45}{164} \approx 0.274$	$\frac{164}{164} = 1$

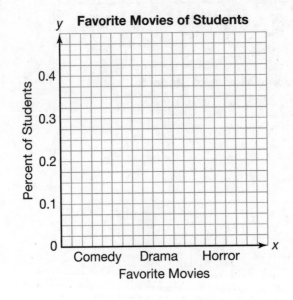

Name _____ Date _____

11.

Favorite Subject of Students

	Chemistry	English	Algebra	Total
Class A	$\frac{10}{108} \approx 0.093$	$\frac{17}{108} \approx 0.157$	$\frac{8}{108} \approx 0.074$	$\frac{35}{108} \approx 0.324$
Class B	$\frac{13}{108} \approx 0.120$	$\frac{9}{108} \approx 0.083$	$\frac{15}{108} \approx 0.139$	$\frac{37}{108} \approx 0.343$
Class C	$\frac{8}{108} \approx 0.074$	$\frac{12}{108} \approx 0.111$	$\frac{16}{108} \approx 0.148$	$\frac{36}{108} \approx 0.333$
Total	$\frac{31}{108} \approx 0.287$	$\frac{38}{108} \approx 0.352$	$\frac{39}{108} \approx 0.361$	$\frac{108}{108} = 1$

Class (left axis label)

10

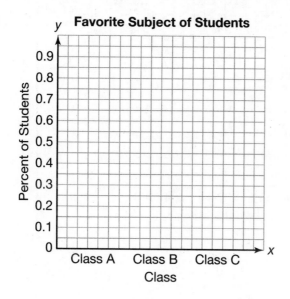

Favorite Subject of Students

12.

Favorite Subject of Students

	Chemistry	English	Algebra	Total
Class A	$\frac{10}{108} \approx 0.093$	$\frac{17}{108} \approx 0.157$	$\frac{8}{108} \approx 0.074$	$\frac{35}{108} \approx 0.324$
Class B	$\frac{13}{108} \approx 0.120$	$\frac{9}{108} \approx 0.083$	$\frac{15}{108} \approx 0.139$	$\frac{37}{108} \approx 0.343$
Class C	$\frac{8}{108} \approx 0.074$	$\frac{12}{108} \approx 0.111$	$\frac{16}{108} \approx 0.148$	$\frac{36}{108} \approx 0.333$
Total	$\frac{31}{108} \approx 0.287$	$\frac{38}{108} \approx 0.351$	$\frac{39}{108} \approx 0.361$	$\frac{108}{108} = 1$

(Class)

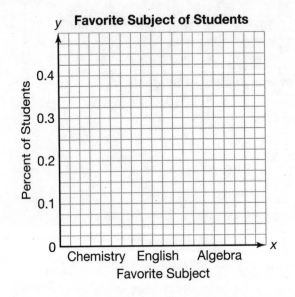

Name _____ Date _____

She Blinded Me with Science!
Relative Frequency Conditional Distribution

Vocabulary

Define the term in your own words.

1. relative frequency conditional distribution

Problem Set

Complete the relative frequency conditional distribution for each two-way table.

1.

		Grades of Students				
		A	**B**	**C**	**D**	**F**
Class	**Algebra**	6	4	8	1	1
	Geometry	6	11	9	2	2
	Trigonometry	3	7	12	5	3

		Grades of Students					
		A	**B**	**C**	**D**	**F**	**Total**
Class	**Algebra**	$\frac{6}{20} = 30\%$	$\frac{4}{20} = 20\%$	$\frac{8}{20} = 40\%$	$\frac{1}{20} = 5\%$	$\frac{1}{20} = 5\%$	$\frac{20}{20} = 100\%$
	Geometry	$\frac{6}{30} = 20\%$	$\frac{11}{30} \approx 36.7\%$	$\frac{9}{30} = 30\%$	$\frac{2}{30} \approx 6.7\%$	$\frac{2}{30} \approx 6.7\%$	$\frac{30}{30} = 100\%$
	Trigonometry	$\frac{3}{30} = 10\%$	$\frac{7}{30} \approx 23.3\%$	$\frac{12}{30} = 40\%$	$\frac{5}{30} \approx 16.7\%$	$\frac{3}{30} = 10\%$	$\frac{30}{30} = 100\%$

2.

Grades of Students

Class	A	B	C	D	F
Computer Programming	7	13	12	1	2
Journalism	8	11	4	1	0
Cinematography	15	9	8	1	0

Grades of Students

Class	A	B	C	D	F	Total
Computer Programming						
Journalism						
Cinematography						

3.

Student's Choice of Shakespeare Play to Study

Class	Hamlet	Macbeth	King Lear	Othello
Class A	9	10	13	5
Class B	14	8	7	8

Student's Choice of Shakespeare Play to Study

Class	Hamlet	Macbeth	King Lear	Othello
Class A				
Class B				
Total				

Name _____ Date _____

4.

Student's Choice of Musical to Perform

	Carousel	South Pacific	The King and I	The Sound of Music
Class A	8	5	14	9
Class B	11	8	12	4

Class

Student's Choice of Musical to Perform

	Carousel	South Pacific	The King and I	The Sound of Music
Class A				
Class B				
Total				

Class

5.

Favorite Lunch Item of Students

	Pizza	Salad	Chicken	Burger
Class A	12	3	10	8
Class B	9	8	13	5
Class C	7	9	7	12

Class

Favorite Lunch Item of Students

	Pizza	Salad	Chicken	Burger	Total
Class A					
Class B					
Class C					

Class

6.

Favorite Gym Activity of Students

		Volleyball	Basketball	Softball	Flag Football
Class	Class A	9	10	4	12
	Class B	12	5	7	6
	Class C	9	3	14	6

Favorite Gym Activity of Students

		Volleyball	Basketball	Softball	Flag Football	Total
Class	Class A					
	Class B					
	Class C					

Name _____ Date _____

The relative frequency conditional distribution shows the sports that female and male students choose to participate in. Use the relative frequency conditional distribution to answer each question.

Favorite Sports of Students

Class	Basketball	Soccer	Track & Field	Swimming	Total
Female Students	$\frac{18}{85} \approx 21.2\%$	$\frac{14}{85} \approx 16.5\%$	$\frac{22}{85} \approx 25.9\%$	$\frac{31}{85} \approx 36.5\%$	$\frac{85}{85} = 100\%$
Male Students	$\frac{24}{97} \approx 24.7\%$	$\frac{19}{97} \approx 19.6\%$	$\frac{20}{97} \approx 20.6\%$	$\frac{34}{97} \approx 35.1\%$	$\frac{97}{97} = 100\%$

7. What percent of female students participate in track & field?

Of the female students, 25.9% participate in track & field.

8. What percent of male students participate in basketball?

9. Which sport is the most popular among female students?

10. Which sport is the least popular among male students?

11. Which sport is the least popular among female students?

12. Which sport is the most popular among male students?

Name _____ Date _____

Oh! Switch the Station!
Drawing Conclusions from Data

Problem Set

A student committee at South Park High School must decide on a location for this year's senior picnic. They take a survey of three senior classes to help make their decision. The data from the survey is shown in the table. For each question, create a distribution to support your answer.

Class	Location
Class A	Beach
Class A	Beach
Class A	Water Park
Class B	Water Park
Class B	Beach
Class B	Beach
Class B	Amusement Park
Class C	Amusement Park
Class C	Amusement Park
Class A	Beach
Class A	Beach
Class A	Beach
Class C	Amusement Park
Class C	Amusement Park
Class B	Water Park
Class B	Amusement Park
Class A	Amusement Park
Class B	Water Park
Class C	Water Park
Class B	Water Park
Class C	Amusement Park

Class	Location
Class C	Amusement Park
Class B	Water Park
Class B	Water Park
Class C	Amusement Park
Class A	Beach
Class A	Water Park
Class B	Water Park
Class B	Water Park
Class B	Beach
Class C	Beach
Class A	Beach
Class A	Beach
Class C	Beach
Class B	Water Park
Class C	Water Park
Class B	Beach
Class C	Beach
Class B	Water Park
Class C	Water Park
Class A	Amusement Park
Class A	Beach

1. Which location is most popular among all three classes?

   Frequency marginal distribution table:

   Favorite Senior Picnic Location of Students

	Beach	Amusement Park	Water Park	Total
Class A	### //// 9	/// 2	// 2	13
Class B	//// 4	// 2	### ### 10	16
Class C	/// 3	### // 7	/// 3	13
Total	16	11	15	42

   The beach is the most popular location among all three classes.

2. Which location is least popular among all three classes?

Name _____ Date _____

3. Which location is most preferred by Class B?

4. Which location is least preferred in Class A?

5. Which class had the highest percentage of students prefer the water park as the location for the senior picnic?

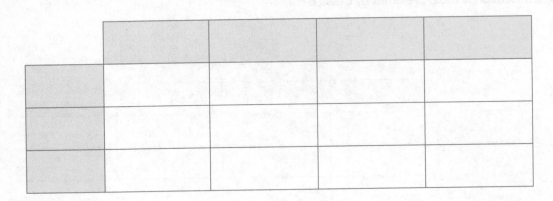

6. Which class least preferred the amusement park as the location for the senior picnic?

Name _____ Date _____

7. Which class had the most students in agreement as to their preferred location within the class?

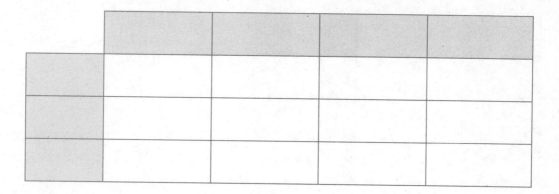

8. Which class made up the smallest percentage of the students who supported the most popular overall location, the beach?

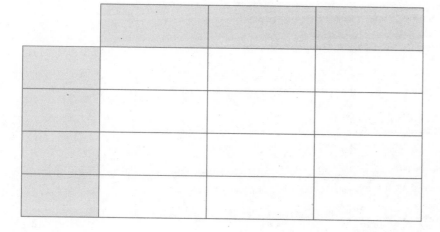

9. Which class made up the highest percentage of the students who supported the least popular overall location, the amusement park?

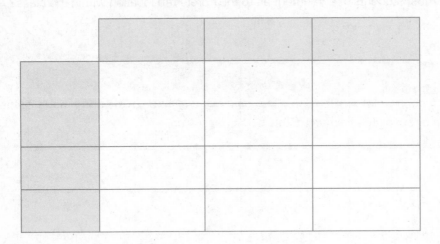

10. Which class made up the highest percentage of the students who supported the water park as their favorite senior picnic location?

Name _____ Date _____

Up and Down or Down and Up
Exploring Quadratic Functions

Vocabulary

Write the given quadratic function in standard form. Then describe the shape of the graph and whether it has an absolute maximum or absolute minimum. Explain your reasoning.

$f(x) = -4 + 2x^2 - x$

Problem Set

Write each quadratic function in standard form.

1. $f(x) = x(x + 3)$

$f(x) = x(x + 3)$

$f(x) = x \cdot x + x \cdot 3$

$f(x) = x^2 + 3x$

2. $f(x) = 3x(x - 8) + 5$

3. $g(s) = (s + 4)s - 2$

4. $d(t) = (20 + 3t)t$

5. $f(n) = \dfrac{2n(3n - 6)}{3}$

6. $m(s) = \dfrac{s(s + 3)}{4}$

Write a quadratic function in standard form that represents each area as a function of the width. Remember to define your variables.

7. A builder is designing a rectangular parking lot. She has 300 feet of fencing to enclose the parking lot around three sides.

   Let x = the width of the parking lot

   The length of the parking lot = $300 - 2x$

   Let A = the area of the parking lot

   Area of a rectangle = width $\times$ length

   $A = w \cdot l$

   $A(x) = x \cdot (300 - 2x)$

   $\quad\quad = x \cdot 300 - x \cdot 2x$

   $\quad\quad = 300x - 2x^2$

   $\quad\quad = -2x^2 + 300x$

8. Aiko is enclosing a new rectangular flower garden with a rabbit garden fence. She has 40 feet of fencing.

9. Pedro is building a rectangular sandbox for the community park. The materials available limit the perimeter of the sandbox to at most 100 feet.

Name _____ Date _____

10. Lea is designing a rectangular quilt. She has 16 feet of piping to finish the quilt around three sides.

11. Kiana is making a rectangular vegetable garden alongside her home. She has 24 feet of fencing to enclose the garden around the three open sides.

12. Nelson is building a rectangular ice rink for the community park. The materials available limit the perimeter of the ice rink to at most 250 feet.

Use your graphing calculator to determine the absolute maximum of each function. Describe what the x- and y-coordinates of this point represent in terms of the problem situation.

13. A builder is designing a rectangular parking lot. He has 400 feet of fencing to enclose the parking lot around three sides. Let x = the width of the parking lot. Let A = the area of the parking lot. The function $A(x) = -2x^2 + 400x$ represents the area of the parking lot as a function of the width.

The absolute maximum of the function is at (100, 20,000).

The x-coordinate of 100 represents the width in feet that produces the maximum area.

The y-coordinate of 20,000 represents the maximum area in square feet of the parking lot.

14. Joelle is enclosing a portion of her yard to make a pen for her ferrets. She has 20 feet of fencing. Let x = the width of the pen. Let A = the area of the pen. The function $A(x) = -x^2 + 10x$ represents the area of the pen as a function of the width.

15. A baseball is thrown upward from a height of 5 feet with an initial velocity of 42 feet per second. Let t = the time in seconds after the baseball is thrown. Let h = the height of the baseball. The quadratic function $h(t) = -16t^2 + 42t + 5$ represents the height of the baseball as a function of time.

16. Hector is standing on top of a playground set at a park. He throws a water balloon upward from a height of 12 feet with an initial velocity of 25 feet per second. Let t = the time in seconds after the balloon is thrown. Let h = the height of the balloon. The quadratic function $h(t) = -16t^2 + 25t + 12$ represents the height of the balloon as a function of time.

17. Franco is building a rectangular roller-skating rink at the community park. The materials available limit the perimeter of the skating rink to at most 180 feet. Let x = the width of the skating rink. Let A = the area of the skating rink. The function $A(x) = -x^2 + 90x$ represents the area of the skating rink as a function of the width.

18. A football is thrown upward from a height of 6 feet with an initial velocity of 65 feet per second. Let t = the time in seconds after the football is thrown. Let h = the height of the football. The quadratic function $h(t) = -16t^2 + 65t + 6$ represents the height of the football as a function of time.

Name _____ Date _____

Just U and I
Comparing Linear and Quadratic Functions

Vocabulary

Write a definition for each term in your own words.

1. leading coefficient

2. second differences

Problem Set

Graph each table of values. Describe the type of function represented by the graph.

1.

x	y
−4	7
−2	6
0	5
2	4
4	3

The function represented by the graph is a linear function.

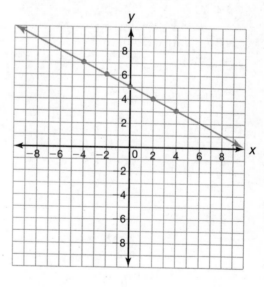

11

2.

x	y
−3	−2
−2	0
−1	2
0	4
1	6

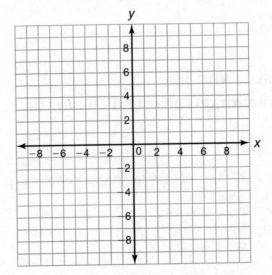

3.

x	y
−2	−8
0	0
2	4
4	4
6	0

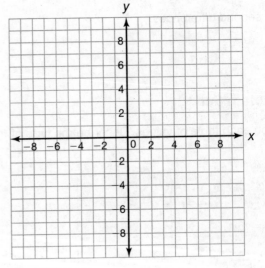

4.

x	y
−6	6
−4	0
−2	−2
0	0
2	6

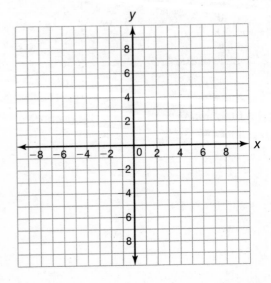

Name _____ Date _____

5.

x	y
1	6
2	3
3	0
4	−3
5	−6

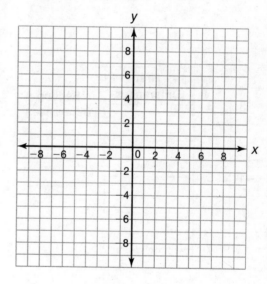

6.

x	y
−3	−9
0	0
3	3
6	0
9	−9

11

Calculate the first and second differences for each table of values. Describe the type of function represented by the table.

7.

x	y	First Differences		Second Differences
−2	−6			
		3		0
−1	−3			
		3		0
0	0			
		3		0
1	3			
		3		
2	6			

The function represented by the table is a linear function.

8.

x	y	First Differences	Second Differences
−2	12		
−1	3		
0	0		
1	3		
2	12		

9.

x	y	First Differences	Second Differences
−3	3		
−2	4		
−1	5		
0	6		
1	7		

10.

x	y	First Differences	Second Differences
−1	1		
0	0		
1	3		
2	10		
3	21		

Name _____ Date _____

11.

x	y	First Differences		Second Differences
−4	−48			
−3	−27			
−2	−12			
−1	−3			
0	0			

12.

x	y	First Differences		Second Differences
−1	10			
0	8			
1	6			
2	4			
3	2			

Name _____ Date _____

Walking the ... Curve?
Domain, Range, Zeros, and Intercepts

Vocabulary

Choose the term that best completes each sentence.

zeros	vertical motion model	interval	open interval
closed interval	half-closed interval	half-open interval	

1. An _____ is defined as the set of real numbers between two given numbers.

2. The x-intercepts of a graph of a quadratic function are also called the _____ of the quadratic function.

3. An _____ (a, b) describes the set of all numbers between a and b, but not including a or b.

4. A _____ or _____ $(a, b]$ describes the set of all numbers between a and b, including b but not including a. Or, $[a, b)$ describes the set of all numbers between a and b, including a but not including b.

5. A quadratic equation that models the height of an object at a given time is a _____.

6. A _____ $[a, b]$ describes the set of all numbers between a and b, including a and b.

Problem Set

Graph the function that represents each problem situation. Identify the absolute maximum, zeros, and the domain and range of the function in terms of both the graph and problem situation. Round your answers to the nearest hundredth, if necessary.

1. A model rocket is launched from the ground with an initial velocity of 120 feet per second. The function $g(t) = -16t^2 + 120t$ represents the height of the rocket, $g(t)$, t seconds after it was launched.

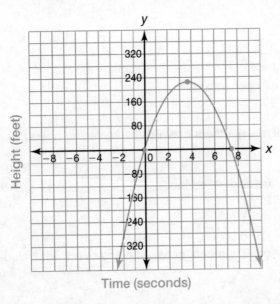

Absolute maximum: (3.75, 225)

Zeros: (0, 0), (7.5, 0)

Domain of graph: The domain is all real numbers from negative infinity to positive infinity.

Domain of the problem: The domain is all real numbers greater than or equal to 0 and less than or equal to 7.5.

Range of graph: The range is all real numbers less than or equal to 225.

Range of the problem: The range is all real numbers less than or equal to 225 and greater than or equal to 0.

2. A model rocket is launched from the ground with an initial velocity of 60 feet per second. The function $g(t) = -16t^2 + 60t$ represents the height of the rocket, $g(t)$, t seconds after it was launched.

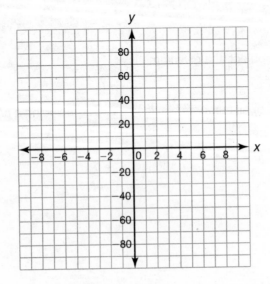

Name _____ Date _____

3. A baseball is thrown into the air from a height of 5 feet with an initial vertical velocity of 15 feet per second. The function $g(t) = -16t^2 + 15t + 5$ represents the height of the baseball, $g(t)$, t seconds after it was thrown.

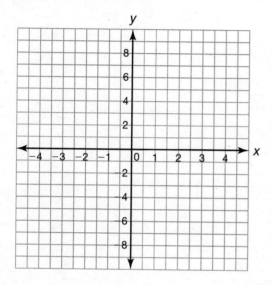

4. A football is thrown into the air from a height of 6 feet with an initial vertical velocity of 50 feet per second. The function $g(t) = -16t^2 + 50t + 6$ represents the height of the football, $g(t)$, t seconds after it was thrown.

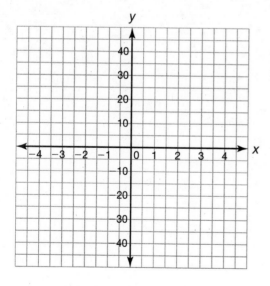

5. A tennis ball is dropped from a height of 25 feet. The initial velocity of an object that is dropped is 0 feet per second. The function $g(t) = -16t^2 + 25$ represents the height of the tennis ball, $g(t)$, t seconds after it was dropped.

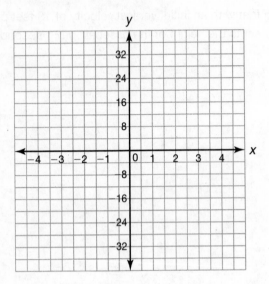

11

6. A tennis ball is dropped from a height of 150 feet. The initial velocity of an object that is dropped is 0 feet per second. The function $g(t) = -16t^2 + 150$ represents the height of the tennis ball, $g(t)$, t seconds after it was dropped.

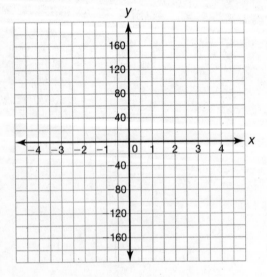

Name _____ Date _____

Use interval notation to represent each interval described.

7. All real numbers greater than or equal to −3 but less than 5.

$[-3, 5)$

8. All real numbers greater than or equal to −100.

9. All real numbers greater than −36 and less than or equal to 14.

10. All real numbers less than or equal to b.

11. All real numbers greater than or equal to c and less than or equal to d.

12. All real numbers greater than or equal to n.

Identify the intervals of increase and decrease for each function.

13. $f(x) = x^2 + 6x$

14. $f(x) = 3x^2 - 6x$

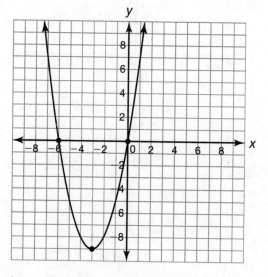

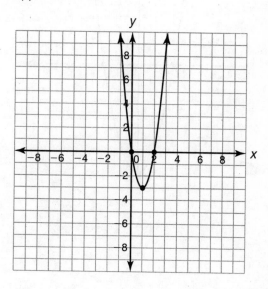

Interval of increase: $(-3, \infty)$

Interval of decrease: $(-\infty, -3)$

15. $f(x) = -x^2 + 2x + 8$

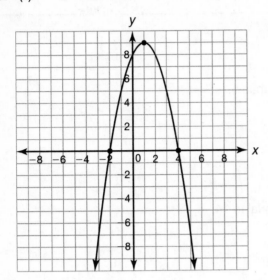

16. $f(x) = -6x^2 + 24x$

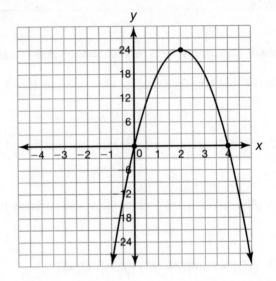

17. $f(x) = x^2 - 9$

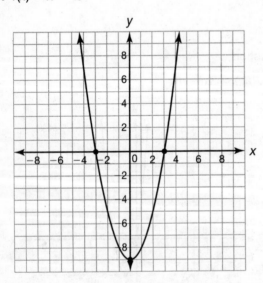

18. $f(x) = x^2 - 4x + 6$

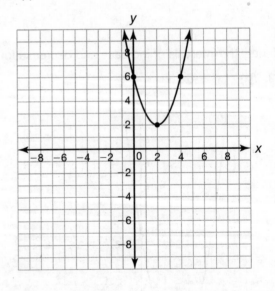

Name _____ Date _____

Are You Afraid of Ghosts?
Factored Form of a Quadratic Function

Vocabulary

Write a definition for each term in your own words.

1. factor an expression

2. factored form

Problem Set

Factor each expression.

1. $6x - 24$

$6x - 24 = 6(x) - 6(4)$

$\qquad = 6(x - 4)$

2. $3x + 36$

3. $10x + 15$

4. $42x - 35$

5. $-x - 9$

6. $-2x + 14$

Determine the *x*-intercepts of each quadratic function in factored form.

7. $f(x) = (x - 2)(x - 8)$

The *x*-intercepts are (2, 0) and (8, 0).

8. $f(x) = (x + 1)(x - 6)$

9. $f(x) = 3(x + 4)(x - 2)$

10. $f(x) = 0.25(x - 1)(x - 12)$

11. $f(x) = 0.5(x + 15)(x + 5)$

12. $f(x) = 4(x - 1)(x - 9)$

Write a quadratic function in factored form with each set of given characteristics.

13. Write a quadratic function that represents a parabola that opens downward and has *x*-intercepts (−2, 0) and (5, 0).

Answers will vary but functions should be in the form:

$f(x) = a(x + 2)(x - 5)$ for $a < 0$

14. Write a quadratic function that represents a parabola that opens downward and has *x*-intercepts (2, 0) and (14, 0).

15. Write a quadratic function that represents a parabola that opens upward and has *x*-intercepts (−8, 0) and (−1, 0).

16. Write a quadratic function that represents a parabola that opens upward and has *x*-intercepts (3, 0) and (7, 0).

Name _____ Date _____

17. Write a quadratic function that represents a parabola that opens downward and has x-intercepts $(-5, 0)$ and $(2, 0)$.

18. Write a quadratic function that represents a parabola that opens upward and has x-intercepts $(-12, 0)$ and $(-4, 0)$.

Determine the x-intercepts for each function using your graphing calculator. Write the function in factored form.

19. $f(x) = x^2 - 8x + 7$

x-intercepts: $(1, 0)$ and $(7, 0)$

factored form: $f(x) = (x - 1)(x - 7)$

20. $f(x) = 2x^2 - 10x - 48$

21. $f(x) = -x^2 - 20x - 75$

22. $f(x) = x^2 + 8x + 12$

23. $f(x) = -3x^2 - 9x + 12$

24. $f(x) = x^2 - 6x$

Determine the *x*-intercepts for each function. If necessary, rewrite the function in factored form.

25. $f(x) = (3x + 18)(x - 2)$

factored form: $f(x) = 3(x + 6)(x - 2)$

x-intercepts: $(-6, 0)$ and $(2, 0)$

26. $f(x) = (x + 8)(3 - x)$

27. $f(x) = (-2x + 8)(x - 14)$

28. $f(x) = (x + 16)(2x + 16)$

29. $f(x) = x(x + 7)$

30. $f(x) = (-3x + 9)(x + 3)$

11

Name _____ Date _____

Just Watch That Pumpkin Fly!
Investigating the Vertex of a Quadratic Function

Vocabulary

Graph the quadratic function. Plot and label the vertex. Then draw and label the axis of symmetry. Explain how you determine each location.

$h(t) = t^2 + 2t - 3$

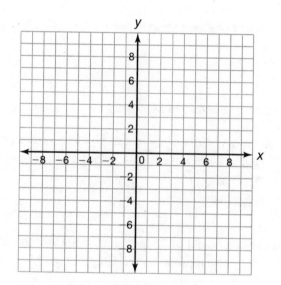

Problem Set

Write a function that represents the vertical motion described in each problem situation.

1. A catapult hurls a watermelon from a height of 36 feet at an initial velocity of 82 feet per second.

   $h(t) = -16t^2 + v_0 t + h_0$
   $h(t) = -16t^2 + 82t + 36$

2. A catapult hurls a cantaloupe from a height of 12 feet at an initial velocity of 47 feet per second.

3. A catapult hurls a pineapple from a height of 49 feet at an initial velocity of 110 feet per second.

4. A basketball is thrown from a height of 7 feet at an initial velocity of 58 feet per second.

5. A soccer ball is thrown from a height of 25 feet at an initial velocity of 46 feet per second.

6. A football is thrown from a height of 6 feet at an initial velocity of 74 feet per second.

Identify the vertex and the equation of the axis of symmetry for each vertical motion model.

7. A catapult hurls a grapefruit from a height of 24 feet at an initial velocity of 80 feet per second.
The function $h(t) = -16t^2 + 80t + 24$ represents the height of the grapefruit $h(t)$ in terms of time t.
The vertex of the graph is (2.5, 124).
The axis of symmetry is $x = 2.5$.

8. A catapult hurls a pumpkin from a height of 32 feet at an initial velocity of 96 feet per second.
The function $h(t) = -16t^2 + 96t + 32$ represents the height of the pumpkin $h(t)$ in terms of time t.

9. A catapult hurls a watermelon from a height of 40 feet at an initial velocity of 64 feet per second.
The function $h(t) = -16t^2 + 64t + 40$ represents the height of the watermelon $h(t)$ in terms of time t.

10. A baseball is thrown from a height of 6 feet at an initial velocity of 32 feet per second. The function $h(t) = -16t^2 + 32t + 6$ represents the height of the baseball $h(t)$ in terms of time t.

Name _____ Date _____

11. A softball is thrown from a height of 20 feet at an initial velocity of 48 feet per second. The function $h(t) = -16t^2 + 48t + 20$ represents the height of the softball $h(t)$ in terms of time t.

12. A rocket is launched from the ground at an initial velocity of 112 feet per second. The function $h(t) = -16t^2 + 112t$ represents the height of the rocket $h(t)$ in terms of time t.

Determine the axis of symmetry of each parabola.

13. The x-intercepts of a parabola are (3, 0) and (9, 0).

$$\frac{3+9}{2} = \frac{12}{2} = 6$$

The axis of symmetry is $x = 6$.

14. The x-intercepts of a parabola are (−3, 0) and (1, 0).

15. The x-intercepts of a parabola are (−12, 0) and (−2, 0).

16. Two symmetric points on a parabola are (−1, 4) and (5, 4).

17. Two symmetric points on a parabola are (−4, 8) and (2, 8).

18. Two symmetric points on a parabola are (3, 1) and (15, 1).

Determine the vertex of each parabola.

19. $f(x) = x^2 + 2x - 15$

axis of symmetry: $x = -1$

The axis of symmetry is $x = -1$.

The x-coordinate of the vertex is -1.

The y-coordinate when $x = -1$ is:

$f(-1) = (-1)^2 + 2(-1) - 15$

$\quad\quad = 1 - 2 - 15$

$\quad\quad = -16$

The vertex is $(-1, -16)$.

20. $f(x) = x^2 - 8x + 7$

axis of symmetry: $x = 4$

21. $f(x) = x^2 + 4x - 12$

x-intercepts: (2, 0) and (−6, 0)

22. $f(x) = -x^2 - 14x - 45$

x-intercepts: (−9, 0) and (−5, 0)

23. $f(x) = -x^2 + 8x + 20$

two symmetric points on the parabola:
(−1, 11) and (9, 11)

24. $f(x) = -x^2 + 16$

two symmetric points on the parabola:
(−3, 7) and (3, 7)

Name _____ Date _____

Determine another point on each parabola.

25. The axis of symmetry is $x = 3$.

A point on the parabola is (1, 4).

Another point on the parabola is a symmetric point that has the same y-coordinate as (1, 4). The x-coordinate is:

$\dfrac{1 + a}{2} = 3$

$1 + a = 6$

$a = 5$

Another point on the parabola is (5, 4).

26. The axis of symmetry is $x = -4$.

A point on the parabola is (0, 6).

27. The axis of symmetry is $x = 1$.

A point on the parabola is (−3, 2).

28. The vertex is (5, 2).

A point on the parabola is (3, −1).

29. The vertex is (−1, 6).

A point on the parabola is (2, 3).

30. The vertex is (3, −1).

A point on the parabola is (4, 1).

11

Name _____ Date _____

The Form Is "Key"
Vertex Form of a Quadratic Function

Vocabulary

Write a definition for the term in your own words.

1. vertex form

Problem Set

Determine the vertex of each quadratic function given in vertex form.

1. $f(x) = (x - 3)^2 + 8$

The vertex is (3, 8).

2. $f(x) = (x + 4)^2 + 2$

3. $f(x) = -2(x - 1)^2 - 8$

4. $f(x) = \frac{1}{2}(x - 2)^2 + 6$

5. $f(x) = -(x + 9)^2 - 1$

6. $f(x) = (x - 5)^2$

Determine the vertex of each quadratic function given in standard form. Use your graphing calculator. Rewrite the function in vertex form.

7. $f(x) = x^2 - 6x - 27$

The vertex is (3, −36).

The function in vertex form is
$f(x) = (x - 3)^2 - 36$.

8. $f(x) = -x^2 - 2x + 15$

9. $f(x) = 2x^2 - 4x - 6$

10. $f(x) = x^2 - 10x + 24$

11. $f(x) = -x^2 + 15x - 54$

12. $f(x) = -2x^2 - 14x - 12$

Determine the *x*-intercepts of each quadratic function given in standard form. Use your graphing calculator. Rewrite the function in factored form.

13. $f(x) = x^2 + 2x - 8$

The *x*-intercepts are (2, 0) and (−4, 0).

The function in factored form is

$f(x) = (x - 2)(x + 4)$.

14. $f(x) = -x^2 - x + 12$

15. $f(x) = -4x^2 + 12x - 8$

16. $f(x) = 2x^2 + 18x + 16$

17. $f(x) = \frac{1}{2}x^2 - \frac{1}{2}x - 3$

18. $f(x) = \frac{1}{3}x^2 - 2x$

Identify the form of each quadratic function as either standard form, factored form, or vertex form. Then state all you know about the quadratic function's key characteristics, based only on the given equation of the function.

19. $f(x) = 5(x - 3)^2 + 12$

The function is in vertex form.

The parabola opens up and the vertex

is (3, 12).

20. $f(x) = -(x - 8)(x - 4)$

21. $f(x) = -3x^2 + 5x$

22. $f(x) = \frac{2}{3}(x + 6)(x - 1)$

23. $f(x) = -(x + 2)^2 - 7$

24. $f(x) = 2x^2 - 1$

Name _____ Date _____

Write an equation for a quadratic function with each set of given characteristics.

25. The vertex is $(-1, 4)$ and the parabola opens down.

Answers will vary but functions should be in the form:

$f(x) = a(x - h)^2 + k$

$f(x) = a(x + 1)^2 + 4$, for $a < 0$

26. The x-intercepts are -3 and 4 and the parabola opens down.

27. The vertex is $(3, -2)$ and the parabola opens up.

28. The vertex is $(0, 8)$ and the parabola opens up.

29. The x-intercepts are 5 and 12 and the parabola opens up.

30. The x-intercepts are 0 and 7 and the parabola opens down.

Name _____ Date _____

More Than Meets the Eye
Transformations of Quadratic Functions

Vocabulary

Write a definition for each term in your own words.

1. vertical dilation

2. dilation factor

Problem Set

Describe the transformation performed on each function $g(x)$ to result in $d(x)$.

1. $g(x) = x^2$

$d(x) = x^2 - 5$

The graph of $g(x)$ is translated down 5 units.

2. $g(x) = x^2$

$d(x) = x^2 + 2$

3. $g(x) = 3x^2$

$d(x) = 3x^2 + 6$

4. $g(x) = \frac{1}{2}x^2$

$d(x) = \frac{1}{2}x^2 - 1$

5. $g(x) = (x + 2)^2$

$d(x) = (x + 2)^2 - 3$

6. $g(x) = -(x - 2)^2$

$d(x) = -(x - 2)^2 + 5$

Describe the transformation performed on each function $g(x)$ to result in $m(x)$.

7. $g(x) = x^2$

    $m(x) = (x + 4)^2$

    The graph of $g(x)$ is translated left 4 units.

8. $g(x) = x^2$

    $m(x) = (x - 8)^2$

9. $g(x) = x^2$

    $m(x) = (x + 1)^2$

10. $g(x) = x^2 - 7$

    $m(x) = (x + 2)^2 - 7$

11. $g(x) = x^2 + 8$

    $m(x) = (x + 3)^2 + 8$

12. $g(x) = x^2 - 6$

    $m(x) = (x - 5)^2 - 6$

Describe the transformation performed on each function $g(x)$ to result in $p(x)$.

13. $g(x) = x^2$

    $p(x) = -x^2$

    The graph of $p(x)$ is a horizontal reflection of the graph of $g(x)$.

14. $g(x) = x^2$

    $p(x) = (-x)^2$

15. $g(x) = x^2 + 2$

    $p(x) = -(x^2 + 2)$

16. $g(x) = x^2 - 5$

    $p(x) = (-x)^2 - 5$

17. $g(x) = \frac{2}{3}x^2 + 4$

    $p(x) = \frac{2}{3}(-x)^2 + 4$

18. $g(x) = 5x^2 - 7$

    $p(x) = -(5x^2 - 7)$

Represent each function $n(x)$ as a vertical dilation of $g(x)$ using coordinate notation.

19. $g(x) = x^2$

    $n(x) = 4x^2$

    $(x, y) \rightarrow (x, 4y)$

20. $g(x) = x^2$

    $n(x) = \frac{1}{2}x^2$

Name _____ Date _____

21. $g(x) = -x^2$

$n(x) = -5x^2$

22. $g(x) = -x^2$

$n(x) = -\dfrac{3}{4}x^2$

23. $g(x) = (x + 1)^2$

$n(x) = 2(x + 1)^2$

24. $g(x) = (x - 3)^2$

$n(x) = \dfrac{1}{2}(x - 3)^2$

Write an equation in vertex form for a function $g(x)$ with the given characteristics. Sketch a graph of each function $g(x)$.

25. The function $g(x)$ is quadratic.

The function $g(x)$ is continuous.

The graph of $g(x)$ is a horizontal reflection of the graph of $f(x) = x^2$.

The function $g(x)$ is translated 3 units up from $f(x) = -x^2$.

$g(x) = -(x - 0)^2 + 3$

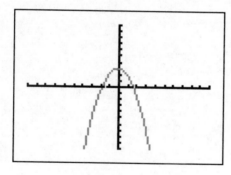

26. The function $g(x)$ is quadratic.

The function $g(x)$ is continuous.

The graph of $g(x)$ is a horizontal reflection of the graph of $f(x) = x^2$.

The function $g(x)$ is translated 2 units down and 5 units left from $f(x) = -x^2$.

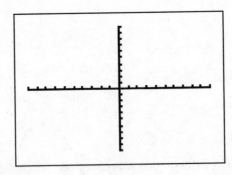

27. The function $g(x)$ is quadratic.

The function $g(x)$ is continuous.

The function $g(x)$ is vertically dilated with a dilation factor of 6.

The function $g(x)$ is translated 1 unit up and 4 units right from $f(x) = 6x^2$.

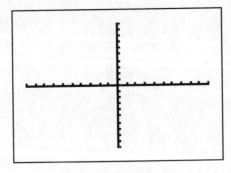

Name _____ Date _____

28. The function $g(x)$ is quadratic.

The function $g(x)$ is continuous.

The function $g(x)$ is vertically dilated with a dilation factor of $\frac{1}{2}$.

The function $g(x)$ is translated 2 units down and 6 units left from $f(x) = \frac{1}{2}x^2$.

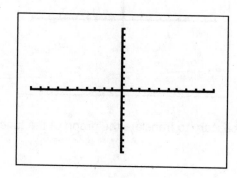

29. The function $g(x)$ is quadratic.

The function $g(x)$ is continuous.

The graph of $g(x)$ is a horizontal reflection of the graph of $f(x) = x^2$.

The function $g(x)$ is vertically dilated with a dilation factor of 3.

The function $g(x)$ is translated 2 units down and 4 units right from $f(x) = -3x^2$.

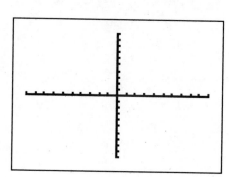

30. The function $g(x)$ is quadratic.

The function $g(x)$ is continuous.

The function $g(x)$ is vertically dilated with a dilation factor of $\frac{1}{4}$.

The function $g(x)$ is translated 3 units up and 2 units left from $f(x) = \frac{1}{4}x^2$.

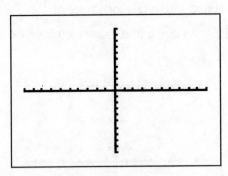

Describe the transformation(s) necessary to translate the graph of the function $f(x) = x^2$ into the graph of each function $g(x)$.

31. $g(x) = x^2 + 7$

The function $g(x)$ is translated 7 units up from $f(x) = x^2$.

32. $g(x) = -x^2 - 4$

33. $g(x) = (x - 2)^2 + 8$

34. $g(x) = 4x^2 + 1$

35. $g(x) = \frac{2}{3}(x + 4)^2 - 9$

36. $g(x) = -(x - 6)^2 + 3$

Name _____ Date _____

Controlling the Population
Adding and Subtracting Polynomials

Vocabulary

Match each definition with its corresponding term.

1. polynomial

    a. a polynomial with only 1 term

2. term

    b. the degree of the term with the greatest exponent

3. coefficient

    c. a mathematical expression involving the sum of powers in one or more variables multiplied by coefficients

4. monomial

    d. a polynomial with exactly 3 terms

5. binomial

    e. any number being multiplied by a power within a polynomial expression

6. trinomial

    f. each product in a polynomial expression

7. degree of a term

    g. a polynomial with exactly 2 terms

8. degree of a polynomial

    h. the exponent of a term in a polynomial

12

Problem Set

Identify the terms and coefficients in each expression.

1. $5x + 8$

The terms are $5x$ and 8. The coefficients are 5 and 8.

2. $2m^3$

3. $x^2 - 4x$

4. $-3w^4 + w^2 - 9$

5. -18

6. $10 - 3x^3 - 6x$

Determine whether each expression is a polynomial. If the expression is not a polynomial, explain why it is not.

7. $9 + 12x$

The expression is a polynomial.

8. $6m^{\frac{1}{2}}$

9. $\dfrac{3}{x} - 8x$

10. $-2w^3 + w^2 - 5$

11. $-2.5m$

12. $\dfrac{x}{7} + 10$

13. $\sqrt[3]{x} + 12$

14. $\dfrac{4}{5}m - \dfrac{1}{5}$

Name _____ Date _____

Determine whether each polynomial is a monomial, binomial, or trinomial. State the degree of the polynomial.

15. $8x + 3$

    The polynomial is a binomial with a degree of 1.

16. $5m^2$

17. $x^2 - 7x$

18. $-9n^4 + 6n^2 - 1$

19. -12

20. $4 - 10x^3 + 8x$

Write each polynomial in standard form. Classify the polynomial by its number of terms and by its degree.

21. $2x + 6x^2$

    $6x^2 + 2x$

    The polynomial is a binomial with a degree of 2.

22. $-9m^2 + 4m^3$

23. $10 - 5x$

24. $7x - 3 + 12x^2$

25. $15 + 4w - w^3$

26. $5x^2 - 15 + 20x$

27. $-1 - p^4$

28. $-6t^2 + 4t + 3t^3$

12

29. $-18a^3 + 54a - 22a^2$

30. $x^3 - x^2 - x^5$

Simplify each expression.

31. $(5x - 8) + (7x + 10)$
$5x - 8 + 7x + 10$
$(5x + 7x) + (-8 + 10)$
$12x + 2$

32. $(4m^2 + 9m) - (2m^2 + 6)$

33. $(-x^2 + 5x - 12) + (2x^2 - 6)$

34. $(10t^2 - 3t + 9) - (6t^2 - 7t)$

35. $(-5w^2 + 3w - 8) + (15w^2 - 4w + 11)$

36. $(3x^3 + 10x - 1) - (5x^2 + 10x - 9)$

37. $(-a^2 + 2a - 8) + (2a^2 - 9a + 15)$

38. $(14p^4 + 7p^2) + (8p^3 + 7p^2 - p)$

39. $(3x^4 + 3x^2 - 3) - (6x^5 - 9x^3 + 2)$

40. $(-7m^3 - m^2 - m) - (-10m^3 - m - 1)$

Name _____ Date _____

The graphs of the functions $f(x) = 2x + 1$, $g(x) = x^2 + x - 3$, and $h(x) = f(x) + g(x)$ are shown. Evaluate the function $h(x)$ for each given value of x. Use the graph of $h(x)$ to verify your answer.

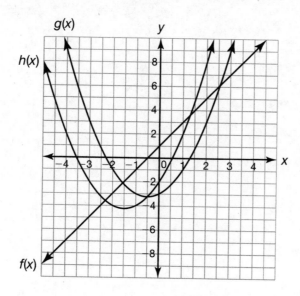

41. Evaluate $h(x)$ at $x = 2$.

$h(x) = f(x) + g(x)$

$\quad = 2x + 1 + x^2 + x - 3$

$\quad = x^2 + 3x - 2$

$h(2) = (2)^2 + 3(2) - 2$

$\quad = 4 + 6 - 2$

$\quad = 8$

42. Evaluate $h(x)$ at $x = -4$.

43. Evaluate $h(x)$ at $x = 0$.

44. Evaluate $h(x)$ at $x = 1$.

12

45. Evaluate $h(x)$ at $x = -2$.

46. Evaluate $h(x)$ at $x = -1.5$.

12

Name _____ Date _____

They're Multiplying—Like Polynomials!
Multiplying Polynomials

Problem Set

Determine the product of the binomials using algebra tiles.

1. $x + 1$ and $x + 1$

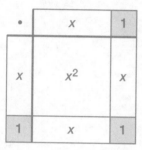

$(x + 1)(x + 1) = x^2 + 2x + 1$

2. $x + 1$ and $x + 4$

3. $x + 2$ and $x + 2$

4. $x + 3$ and $x + 3$

5. $2x + 1$ and $x + 3$

6. $2x + 3$ and $x + 2$

Determine the product of the binomials using multiplication tables.

7. $3x + 4$ and $2x + 2$

.	$2x$	2
$3x$	$6x^2$	$6x$
4	$8x$	8

$(3x + 4)(2x + 2) = 6x^2 + 6x + 8x + 8$
$= 6x^2 + 14x + 8$

8. $5m + 3$ and $4m + 6$

9. $6t + 5$ and $7t - 5$

10. $4x + 2$ and $4x - 2$

Name _____ Date _____

11. $10w - 1$ and $9w + 8$

12. $y + 12$ and $5y + 15$

Determine the product of the polynomials using the Distributive Property.

13. $2x(x + 6)$

$2x(x + 6) = 2x(x) + 2x(6)$
$= 2x^2 + 12x$

14. $4x^2(x + 2)$

15. $7x(x - 5)$

16. $(2x + 1)(x + 8)$

17. $(x + 3)(x^2 - 1)$

18. $(4x + 4)(5x - 5)$

19. $3x(x^2 + 5x - 1)$

20. $9x(3x^2 - 4x + 2)$

21. $(x + 2)(x^2 + 6x - 1)$

22. $(x - 4)(x^2 + 2x - 3)$

Name _____ Date _____

What *Factored* Into It?
Factoring Polynomials

Vocabulary

State the given property.

1. Symmetric Property of Equality

Problem Set

Factor out the greatest common factor of each polynomial, if possible.

1. $x^2 + 9x$

$x(x + 9)$

2. $m^2 - 4m$

3. $5x^2 + 20x - 15$

4. $24w^2 - 16$

5. $y^3 - 7y$

6. $2x^3 + 10x^2$

7. $3w + 10$

8. $20x^3 + 16x^2 + 8x$

9. $7m^3 - 21$

10. $15x^3 + 4$

Factor each trinomial using an area model.

11. $x^2 + 4x + 3$

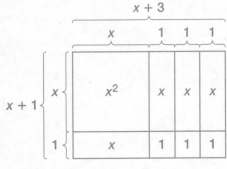

$x^2 + 4x + 3 = (x + 1)(x + 3)$

12. $x^2 + 5x + 6$

13. $x^2 - x - 6$

Name _____ Date _____

14. $x^2 - x - 12$

15. $x^2 + 7x + 10$

16. $x^2 + 3x - 4$

Factor each trinomial completely using multiplication tables. If possible, factor out the greatest common factor first.

17. $x^2 - 2x - 8$

$\cdot$	x	2
x	x^2	$2x$
-4	$-4x$	-8

$x^2 - 2x - 8 = (x - 4)(x + 2)$

18. $y^2 + 13y + 42$

19. $m^2 + 6m - 7$

20. $x^2 - 9x + 18$

21. $4w^2 + 12w - 40$

22. $2t^3 - 14t^2 + 24t$

23. $3m^3 + 36m^2 + 60m$

24. $2x^2 - 8x - 42$

Name _____ Date _____

Factor each polynomial using the trial and error method. If possible, factor out the greatest common factor first.

25. $x^2 + 11x + 10$

The factors of the constant term, 10, are:

-1, -10   1, 10

-2, -5   2, 5

$x^2 + 11x + 10 = (x + 1)(x + 10)$

26. $w^2 + 6w - 16$

27. $m^2 + 2m - 35$

28. $x^2 + 4x - 12$

29. $3n^2 - 27n + 60$

30. $2x^2 + 22x + 60$

Factor each polynomial.

31. $x^2 + 11x + 28 = \underline{\ (x + 4)(x + 7)\ }$

$x^2 - 11x + 28 = \underline{\ (x - 4)(x - 7)\ }$

$x^2 + 3x - 28 = \underline{\ (x - 4)(x + 7)\ }$

$x^2 - 3x + 28 = \underline{\ (x + 4)(x - 7)\ }$

32. $x^2 + 10x + 9 = $ _____

$x^2 - 10x + 9 = $ _____

$x^2 + 8x - 9 = $ _____

$x^2 - 8x - 9 = $ _____

33. $x^2 + 12x + 27 = $ _____

$x^2 - 12x + 27 = $ _____

$x^2 + 6x - 27 = $ _____

$x^2 - 6x - 27 = $ _____

34. $x^2 + 13x + 40 = $ _____

$x^2 - 13x + 40 = $ _____

$x^2 + 3x - 40 = $ _____

$x^2 - 3x - 40 = $ _____

35. $x^2 + 12x + 11 =$ _____

    $x^2 - 12x + 11 =$ _____

    $x^2 + 10x - 11 =$ _____

    $x^2 - 10x - 11 =$ _____

36. $x^2 + 13x + 36 =$ _____

    $x^2 - 13x + 36 =$ _____

    $x^2 + 5x - 36 =$ _____

    $x^2 - 5x - 36 =$ _____

Factor each polynomial completely. If possible, factor out the greatest common factor first.

37. $x^2 + 4x + 4$

·	x	2
x	x^2	$2x$
2	$2x$	4

$x^2 + 4x + 4 = (x + 2)(x + 2)$

38. $x^2 - 10x + 25$

39. $-32 - 12m - m^2$

40. $45 + 4w - w^2$

41. $5x^2 + 10x - 15$

42. $4x^2 + 32x + 64$

Name _____ Date _____

Zeroing In
Solving Quadratics by Factoring

Vocabulary

Complete the definition of the Zero Product Property.

1. The Zero Product Property states that if the product of two or more factors is equal to
_____ , then at least one factor must be equal to _____ .

If $ab = 0$, then _____ or _____ .
This property is also known as the _____ .

Define the term in your own words.

2. roots

Problem Set

Factor and solve each quadratic equation. Check your answer.

1. $x^2 + 5x + 6 = 0$

$x^2 + 5x + 6 = 0$ Check:

$(x + 3)(x + 2) = 0$ $(-3)^2 + 5(-3) + 6 = 0$ $(-2)^2 + 5(-2) + 6 = 0$

$x + 3 = 0$ or $x + 2 = 0$ $9 - 15 + 6 = 0$ $4 - 10 + 6 = 0$

$x = -3$ or $x = -2$ $0 = 0$ $0 = 0$

The roots are -3 and -2.

2. $x^2 - 3x - 4 = 0$

3. $m^2 + 2m - 35 = 0$

4. $-x^2 - 4x + 12 = 0$

5. $x^2 + 8x = 0$

6. $w^2 + 50 = -15w$

12

7. $-t^2 + 12t = 32$

Name _____ Date _____

8. $x^2 + 2x + 2 = 0$

9. $2t^2 + t - 3 = 0$

10. $w^2 + 5w - 32 = 2w - 4$

Determine the zeros of each quadratic function, if possible. Check your answer.

11. $f(x) = x^2 - 5x$

$f(x) = x^2 - 5x$ Check:

$0 = x^2 - 5x$ $(0)^2 - 5(0) \stackrel{?}{=} 0$ $(5)^2 - 5(5) \stackrel{?}{=} 0$

$0 = x(x - 5)$ $0 - 0 \stackrel{?}{=} 0$ $25 - 25 \stackrel{?}{=} 0$

$x = 0$ or $x - 5 = 0$ $0 = 0$ $0 = 0$

$x = 0$ or $x = 5$

The zeros are 0 and 5.

12. $f(x) = 3x^2 + 6x$

13. $f(x) = x^2 + 11x + 30$

14. $f(x) = x^2 - 9x - 36$

Name _____ Date _____

15. $f(x) = 2x^2 + 9x + 10$

16. $f(x) = x^2 + 5x + 14$

17. $f(x) = 3x^2 + 3x - 6$

18. $f(x) = \frac{1}{2}x^2 - \frac{3}{4}x$

Name _____ Date _____

What Makes You So Special?
Special Products

Vocabulary

Give an example of each term. Then, factor the expression.

1. perfect square trinomial

2. difference of two squares

3. sum of two cubes

4. difference of two cubes

12

Problem Set

Factor each binomial completely.

1. $x^2 - 25$

  $x^2 - 25 = (x + 5)(x - 5)$

2. $x^3 - 64$

3. $x^3 + 27$

4. $m^2 - 100$

5. $5x^3 + 40$

6. $t^3 - 125$

7. $8a^3 - 27$

8. $x^8 - y^8$

Factor the trinomial completely.

9. $x^2 + 16x + 64$
$x^2 + 16x + 64 = (x + 8)(x + 8)$

10. $k^2 - 20k + 100$

11. $2x^2 - 28x + 98$

12. $5x^2 + 10x + 5$

13. $z^3 + 18z^2 + 81z$

14. $3x^3 - 30x^2 + 75x$

Determine the root(s) of each quadratic equation. Check your answer(s).

15. $x^2 - 100 = 0$

$$x^2 - 100 = 0$$
$$(x + 10)(x - 10) = 0$$
$$x + 10 = 0 \quad \text{or} \quad x - 10 = 0$$
$$x = -10 \quad \text{or} \quad x = 10$$
The roots are -10 and 10.

Check:
$(-10)^2 - 100 \stackrel{?}{=} 0$
$100 - 100 \stackrel{?}{=} 0$
$0 = 0$

$(10)^2 - 100 \stackrel{?}{=} 0$
$100 - 100 \stackrel{?}{=} 0$
$0 = 0$

16. $m^2 - 16m + 64 = 0$

Name _____ Date _____

17. $6x^2 + 24x + 24 = 0$

18. $4x^2 - 9 = 0$

19. $t^2 + 22t + 121 = 0$

20. $12w^2 - 48w + 48 = 0$

Determine the zero(s) of each quadratic function. Check your answer(s).

21. $f(x) = x^2 - 225$

$$f(x) = x^2 - 225$$
$$0 = x^2 - 225$$
$$0 = (x + 15)(x - 15)$$
$$x + 15 = 0 \quad \text{or} \quad x - 15 = 0$$
$$x = -15 \quad \text{or} \qquad x = 15$$

The zeros are −15 and 15.

Check:

$$(-15)^2 - 225 \stackrel{?}{=} 0$$
$$225 - 225 \stackrel{?}{=} 0$$
$$0 = 0$$

$$(15)^2 - 225 \stackrel{?}{=} 0$$
$$225 - 225 \stackrel{?}{=} 0$$
$$0 = 0$$

22. $f(x) = x^2 + x + \dfrac{1}{4}$

23. $f(x) = 9x^2 - 1$

12

Name _____ Date _____

24. $f(x) = 8x^2 - 48x + 72$

25. $f(x) = 8x^2 - 50$

26. $f(x) = 2x^2 + 52x + 338$

Name _____ Date _____

Could It Be Groovy to Be a Square?
Approximating and Rewriting Radicals

Vocabulary

Choose the word that best completes each statement.

square root	positive (principal) square root	radicand
negative square root	extract the square root	radical expression

1. When solving certain quadratic equations, it is necessary to _____ from both sides of the equation.

2. Every positive number has both a(n) _____ and a(n) _____.

3. The _____ is the expression enclosed within a radical symbol.

4. A number b is a(n) _____ of a if $b^2 = a$.

5. An expression involving a radical symbol is called a(n) _____.

Problem Set

Rewrite each radical by extracting all perfect squares.

1. $\sqrt{25}$
   $\sqrt{25} = \pm 5$

2. $\sqrt{144}$

3. $\sqrt{400}$

4. $\sqrt{12}$

5. $\sqrt{32}$

6. $\sqrt{45}$

7. $\sqrt{300}$

8. $5\sqrt{54}$

Determine the approximate value of each radical expression to the nearest tenth.

9. $\sqrt{7}$

$2.6^2 = 6.76$

$2.7^2 = 7.29$

$\sqrt{7} \approx 2.6$

10. $\sqrt{37}$

11. $\sqrt{96}$

12. $\sqrt{27}$

13. $\sqrt{109}$

14. $\sqrt{405}$

Solve each quadratic equation. Approximate the roots to the nearest tenth.

15. $x^2 = 40$

$x^2 = 40$

$\sqrt{x^2} = \pm\sqrt{40}$

$x = \pm\sqrt{40}$

$6.3^2 = 39.69$

$6.4^2 = 40.96$

$\sqrt{40} \approx \pm6.3$

$x \approx \pm6.3$

The roots are approximately 6.3 and -6.3.

16. $m^2 = 68$

Name _____ Date _____

17. $t^2 = 15$ **18.** $x^2 = 83$

19. $(x - 5)^2 = 22$ **20.** $(x + 8)^2 = 29$

Solve each quadratic equation. Rewrite the roots in radical form.

21. $x^2 = 48$ **22.** $x^2 = 52$

$\qquad x^2 = 48$

$\qquad \sqrt{x^2} = \pm\sqrt{48}$

$\qquad x = \pm\sqrt{48}$

$\qquad x = \pm\sqrt{16 \cdot 3}$

$\qquad x = \pm\sqrt{16} \cdot \sqrt{3}$

$\qquad x = \pm 4\sqrt{3}$

The roots are $4\sqrt{3}$ and $-4\sqrt{3}$.

23. $x^2 = 27$

24. $x^2 = 175$

25. $(12 - x)^2 = 8$

26. $(x + 20)^2 = 80$

12

Name _____ Date _____

Another Method
Completing the Square

Vocabulary

Define the term in your own words.

1. completing the square

Problem Set

Use a geometric figure to complete the square for each expression. Factor the resulting trinomial.

1. $x^2 + 2x$

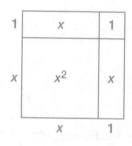

$x^2 + 2x + 1 = (x + 1)^2$

2. $x^2 + 4x$

3. $x^2 + 12x$

4. $x^2 + 9x$

5. $x^2 + 11x$

6. $x^2 + 28x$

Determine the unknown value that would make each trinomial a perfect square.

7. $x^2 - 10x + \underline{25}$

8. $x^2 + 14x + \underline{\hspace{1cm}}$

9. $x^2 + \underline{\hspace{0.5cm}}x + 9$

10. $x^2 - \underline{\hspace{0.8cm}}x + 81$

11. $x^2 + 7x + \underline{\hspace{1cm}}$

12. $x^2 - 15x + \underline{\hspace{1cm}}$

13. $x^2 - \underline{\hspace{1cm}}x + 169$

14. $x^2 + \underline{\hspace{0.5cm}}x + \dfrac{9}{4}$

Determine the roots of each quadratic equation by completing the square. Round your answer to the nearest hundredth. Check your answer.

15. $x^2 + 4x - 6 = 0$

$$x^2 + 4x - 6 = 0$$
$$x^2 + 4x = 6$$
$$x^2 + 4x + 4 = 6 + 4$$
$$(x + 2)^2 = 10$$
$$\sqrt{(x + 2)^2} = \pm\sqrt{10}$$
$$x + 2 = \pm\sqrt{10}$$
$$x = -2 \pm \sqrt{10}$$

$x \approx 1.16$ or $x \approx -5.16$

The roots are approximately 1.16 and −5.16.

Check:

$(1.16)^2 + 4(1.16) - 6 \overset{?}{=} 0$

$1.3456 + 4.64 - 6 \overset{?}{=} 0$

$-0.0144 \approx 0$

$(-5.16)^2 - 4(-5.16) - 6 \overset{?}{=} 0$

$26.6256 - 20.64 - 6 \overset{?}{=} 0$

$-0.0144 \approx 0$

Name _____ Date _____

16. $x^2 - 2x - 4 = 0$

17. $x^2 + 10x + 2 = 0$

18. $x^2 - 12x + 25 = 0$

19. $x^2 + 3x - 1 = 0$

20. $x^2 + x - 10 = 0$

Name _____ Date _____

Ladies and Gentlemen: Please Welcome the Quadratic Formula!
The Quadratic Formula

Vocabulary

Complete the Quadratic Formula. Then, identify the discriminant and explain what it indicates about the function.

The quadratic equation of the form $ax^2 + bx + c = 0$, can be written as the Quadratic Formula.

$$x =$$

Problem Set

Determine the approximate zeros or roots of each function or equation. Round your answers to the nearest thousandth, if necessary.

1. $f(x) = x^2 + 3x - 5$

$a = 1, b = 3, c = -5$

$x = \dfrac{-b \pm \sqrt{b^2 - 4ac}}{2a}$

$x = \dfrac{-(3) \pm \sqrt{(3)^2 - 4(1)(-5)}}{2(1)}$

$x = \dfrac{-3 \pm \sqrt{9 + 20}}{2}$

$x = \dfrac{-3 \pm \sqrt{29}}{2}$

$x = \dfrac{-3 + 5.385}{2}$ or $x = \dfrac{-3 - 5.385}{2}$

$x \approx 1.193$ or $x \approx -4.193$

2. $f(x) = -3x^2 - x + 7$

3. $2x^2 + 6x - 7 = 2$

4. $4x^2 - x - 1 = 5$

5. $f(x) = -8x^2 + 2x + 1$

6. $3x^2 + x + 3 = 5$

13

Name _____ Date _____

Determine the exact zeros or roots of each function or equation.

7. $f(x) = -2x^2 - 8x + 1$

$a = -2, b = -8, c = 1$

$x = \dfrac{-b \pm \sqrt{b^2 - 4ac}}{2a}$

$x = \dfrac{-(-8) \pm \sqrt{(-8)^2 - 4(-2)(1)}}{2(-2)}$

$x = \dfrac{8 \pm \sqrt{64 + 8}}{-4}$

$x = \dfrac{8 \pm \sqrt{72}}{-4}$

$x = \dfrac{8 \pm \sqrt{36 \cdot 2}}{-4}$

$x = \dfrac{8 \pm 6\sqrt{2}}{-4}$

$x = \dfrac{8 + 6\sqrt{2}}{-4}$ or $x = \dfrac{8 - 6\sqrt{2}}{-4}$

$x = -2 - \dfrac{3}{2}\sqrt{2}$ or $x = -2 + \dfrac{3}{2}\sqrt{2}$

8. $5x^2 + 8x - 3 = 1$

13

9. $-3x^2 + 6x + 2 = -5$

10. $f(x) = x^2 + 6x + 5$

11. $f(x) = -2x^2 + 5x - 1$

12. $-3x^2 + 8x - 2 = -6$

13

Name _____ Date _____

Use the discriminant to determine the number of zeros or roots each function or equation has. Then solve for the zeros or roots.

13. $f(x) = -x^2 + 6x + 7$

$a = -1, b = 6, c = 7$

$b^2 - 4ac = (6)^2 - 4(-1)(7)$

$\qquad = 36 + 28$

$\qquad = 64$

Because $b^2 - 4ac > 0$ the function has two zeros.

$x = \dfrac{-b \pm \sqrt{b^2 - 4ac}}{2a}$

$x = \dfrac{-(6) \pm \sqrt{64}}{2(-1)}$

$x = \dfrac{-6 \pm 8}{-2}$

$x = \dfrac{-6 + 8}{-2} \quad$ or $\quad x = \dfrac{-6 - 8}{-2}$

$x = \dfrac{2}{-2} \quad\quad$ or $\quad x = \dfrac{-14}{-2}$

$x = -1 \quad\quad\;$ or $\quad x = 7$

14. $2x^2 + 8x + 3 = -5$

15. $f(x) = 9x^2 + 5x + 1$

16. $6x^2 + 3x - 5 = 2$

17. $f(x) = 5x^2 + 10x + 5$

18. $f(x) = 7x^2 + 9x + 5$

13

Name _____ Date _____

It's Watching and Tracking!
Using a Calculator-Based Ranger to Model Quadratic Motion

Vocabulary

Define each term in your own words.

1. quadratic regression

2. coefficient of determination

Problem Set

Use your graphing calculator to determine the quadratic regression equation and coefficient of determination for the line of best fit of each given data set. Determine if the equation is a good fit for the data. Round your answers to the nearest hundredth.

1.

x	y
0	0
1	4.05
2	5.50
3	6.25
4	3.50
5	0

$y = -0.97x^2 + 4.84x + 0.03$

$r^2 \approx 0.99$

Because the r^2 value is close to 1, the quadratic regression equation is a good fit for the data.

2.

x	y
0	2.1
0.5	3.4
1	4.1
1.5	4.3
2	3.9
2.5	2.3

3.

x	y
−5	−0.5
−4	5
−1	7
0	3
0.5	−1
1	3

Name _____ Date _____

4.

x	y
−4	3.05
−3	−1.50
−2	−4.80
−1	−5.18
0	−3.75
1	−1.79

5.

x	y
0	6.2
1	4.5
2	1.5
3	−0.5
4	2.4
5	3.9

13

6.

x	y
−5	7.21
−4	1.80
−3	−2.40
−2	−5.92
−1	−1.40
0	2.73

Name _____ Date _____

They're A Lot More than Just Sparklers!
Solving Quadratic Inequalities

Problem Set

Determine the roots of each quadratic inequality. Use the interval method to determine the solution set of the inequality. Round your answer to the nearest thousandth if necessary.

1. $x^2 - 7x + 16 \geq 10$

$x^2 - 7x + 16 \geq 10$

$x^2 - 7x + 6 \geq 0$

$x^2 - 7x + 6 = 0$

$(x - 6)(x - 1) = 0$

$x - 6 = 0$ or $x - 1 = 0$

     $x = 6$ or $x = 1$

Test 0, 2, and 7.

$x^2 - 7x + 16 \geq 10$

$(0)^2 - 7(0) + 16 \geq 10$

$16 \geq 10$ ✔

$x^2 - 7x + 16 \geq 10$

$(2)^2 - 7(2) + 16 \geq 10$

$4 - 14 + 16 \geq 10$

$6 \geq 10$ ✗

$x^2 - 7x + 16 \geq 10$

$(7)^2 - 7(7) + 16 \geq 10$

$49 - 49 + 16 \geq 10$

$16 \geq 10$ ✔

Solution: $x \in (-\infty, 1]$ or $x \in [6, \infty)$

2. $x^2 + 7x - 2 < -12$

3. $x^2 + x - 15 < 4$

Name _____ Date _____

4. $-x^2 + 11x - 21 \leq 2$

5. $-x^2 + 4x - 5 \leq -2$

6. $-x^2 - 3x + 14 > -3$

A water balloon is thrown upward from a height of 5 feet with an initial velocity of 35 feet per second. The quadratic function $h(t) = -16t^2 + 35t + 5$ represents the height of the balloon, h, in feet t seconds after it is thrown. Use this information to answer each question.

7. How long does it take for the balloon to reach the ground? Round your answer to the nearest thousandth.

$0 = -16t^2 + 35t + 5$

$a = -16, b = 35, c = 5$

$t = \dfrac{-b \pm \sqrt{b^2 - 4ac}}{2a}$

$t = \dfrac{-(35) \pm \sqrt{(35)^2 - 4(-16)(5)}}{2(-16)}$

$t = \dfrac{-35 \pm \sqrt{1225 + 320}}{-32}$

$t = \dfrac{-35 \pm \sqrt{1545}}{-32}$

$t = \dfrac{-35 + 39.306}{-32}$ or $t = \dfrac{-35 - 39.306}{-32}$

$t \approx -0.1346$ or $t \approx 2.322$

It will take just over 2.3 seconds for the balloon to reach the ground.

Name _____ Date _____

8. Determine when the balloon is less than 10 feet above the ground. Round your answer to the nearest thousandth.

9. Determine when the balloon is more than 10 feet above the ground. Round your answer to the nearest thousandth.

13

10. Determine when the balloon is less than 20 feet above the ground. Round your answer to the nearest thousandth.

11. Determine when the balloon is more than 20 feet above the ground. Round your answer to the nearest thousandth.

13

Name _____ Date _____

12. Determine when the balloon is less than 30 feet above the ground. Round your answer to the nearest thousandth.

13

Name _____ Date _____

You Must Have a System
Systems of Quadratic Equations

Problem Set

Solve each system of equations algebraically. Then verify each solution graphically.

1. $\begin{cases} y = x^2 - 6x + 7 \\ y = 2x \end{cases}$

2. $\begin{cases} y = x^2 - 3x + 1 \\ y = x - 3 \end{cases}$

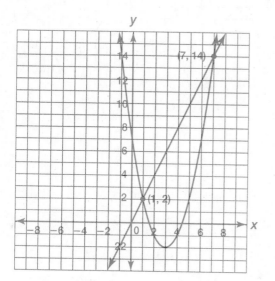

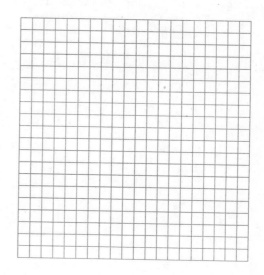

$$2x = x^2 - 6x + 7$$
$$0 = x^2 - 8x + 7$$
$$0 = (x - 7)(x - 1)$$

$x - 7 = 0$ or $x - 1 = 0$

$\quad x = 7 \qquad\qquad x = 1$

$\quad y = 2(7) \qquad\quad y = 2(1)$

$\quad y = 14 \qquad\qquad y = 2$

The system has two solutions:
(7, 14) and (1, 2).

3. $\begin{cases} y = 2x^2 + 16x + 24 \\ y = -x - 2 \end{cases}$

4. $\begin{cases} y = -x^2 + 6x - 6 \\ y = 3x + 1 \end{cases}$

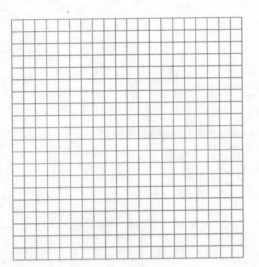
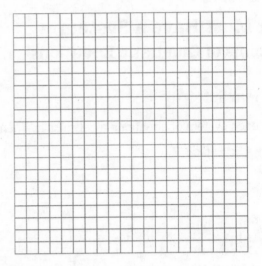

13

Name _____ Date _____

5. $\begin{cases} y = 4x^2 + 6x + 3 \\ y = -6x - 6 \end{cases}$

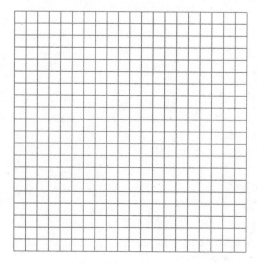

6. $\begin{cases} y = 3x^2 + 24x + 50 \\ y = 4x + 1 \end{cases}$

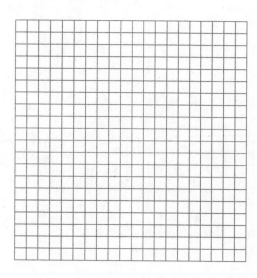

Solve each system of equations algebraically. Then verify each solution graphically.

7. $\begin{cases} y = x^2 - 2x + 1 \\ y = -x^2 + 3x + 4 \end{cases}$

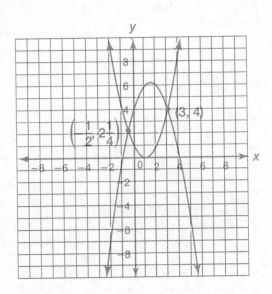

$$-x^2 + 3x + 4 = x^2 - 2x + 1$$
$$0 = 2x^2 - 5x - 3$$
$$0 = (2x + 1)(x - 3)$$

$2x + 1 = 0$ or

$$2x = -1$$
$$x = -\frac{1}{2}$$

$y = \left(-\frac{1}{2}\right)^2 - 2\left(-\frac{1}{2}\right) + 1$ $x - 3 = 0$

$y = \frac{1}{4} + 1 + 1$ $x = 3$

$y = \frac{9}{4} = 2\frac{1}{4}$ $y = (3)^2 - 2(3) + 1$

                           $y = 9 - 6 + 1$

                           $y = 4$

The system has two solutions: $\left(-\frac{1}{2}, 2\frac{1}{4}\right)$ and $(3, 4)$.

8. $\begin{cases} y = 2x^2 - x + 3 \\ y = x^2 + 5x - 6 \end{cases}$

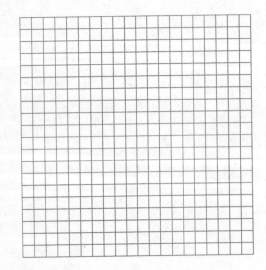

Name _____ Date _____

9. $\begin{cases} y = x^2 - 4x + 7 \\ y = -x^2 - 6x - 11 \end{cases}$

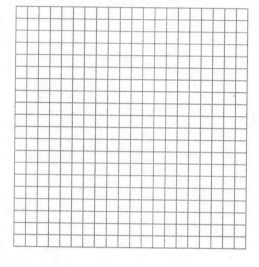

10. $\begin{cases} y = 2x^2 + 4x - 7 \\ y = x^2 + 2x + 1 \end{cases}$

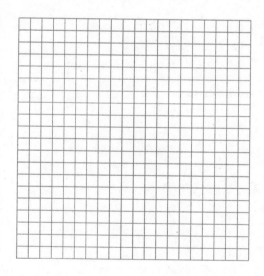

11. $\begin{cases} y = x^2 - 8x + 17 \\ y = -x^2 + 6x - 10 \end{cases}$

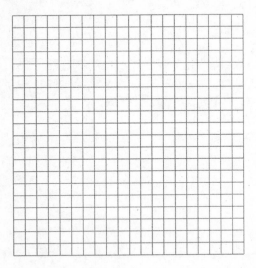

12. $\begin{cases} y = 2x^2 - 3x + 2 \\ y = -2x^2 + x + 1 \end{cases}$

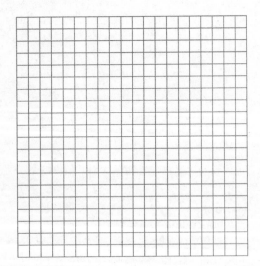

Name _____ Date _____

The Real Numbers . . . For Realsies!
The Numbers of the Real Number System

Vocabulary

Choose the word from the box that best completes each sentence.

counterexample	real numbers	whole numbers
natural numbers	closed	integers
rational numbers	Venn diagram	irrational numbers

1. The set of _____ consists of the set of rational numbers and the set of irrational numbers.

2. The set of _____ consists of the numbers used to count objects.

3. A(n) _____ uses circles to show how elements among sets of numbers or objects are related.

4. A set is said to be _____ under an operation when you can perform the operation on any of the numbers in the set and the result is a number that is also in the same set.

5. The set of _____ consists of all numbers that cannot be written as $\frac{a}{b}$, where a and b are integers.

6. The set of _____ consists of the set of whole numbers and their opposites.

7. The set of _____ consists of all numbers that can be written as $\frac{a}{b}$, where a and b are integers, but b is not equal to 0.

8. The set of _____ consists of the set of natural numbers and the number 0.

9. To show that a set is not closed under an operation, one example that shows the result is not part of that set is needed. This example is called a _____.

14

Problem Set

For each list of numbers, determine which are included in the given set.

1. The set of natural numbers:

10, −12, 0, 31, $\frac{4}{5}$, $\sqrt{5}$, −$\frac{5}{3}$, 1970

The numbers 10, 31, and 1970 are in the set of natural numbers.

2. The set of whole numbers:

−9, 18, 1, $\frac{3}{4}$, 0, 92, $\sqrt{7}$, 2096.5

3. The set of integers:

54, π, $\frac{2}{3}$, −16, $\sqrt{2}$, 3.5, −$\frac{7}{10}$, −594

4. The set of rational numbers:

8, −15, $\frac{3}{8}$, 0, $\sqrt{3}$, 9.5, −$\frac{4}{5}$, 857

5. The set of irrational numbers:

−21, $\frac{7}{8}$, 3, $\sqrt{2}$, 2.5, 0, 99, π

6. The set of real numbers:

−18, 18, 1, $\frac{2}{3}$, $\sqrt{3}$, 1080, 5.4, −42

Identify whether each given number set is closed or not closed under the operations addition, subtraction, multiplication, and division. Explain your reasoning.

7. the set of natural numbers

The set of natural numbers is closed under addition and multiplication because when you add or multiply any two natural numbers, the sum or product is always a natural number.

The set of natural numbers is not closed under subtraction because when you subtract a natural number from a natural number, the difference can be 0 or a negative integer.

The set of natural numbers is not closed under division because when you divide a natural number by a natural number, the quotient can be a fraction.

Name _____ Date _____

8. the set of integers

9. the set of rational numbers

10. the set of real numbers

11. the set of whole numbers

12. the set of irrational numbers

14

Use the given equations to answer each question.

Equation A: $x + 4 = 10$	Equation B: $4x = 24$	Equation C: $x^2 = 16$
Equation D: $8 + x = 8$	Equation E: $x + 7 = 2$	Equation F: $5x = 0$
Equation G: $12x = 3$	Equation H: $x^2 = 3$	Equation J: $5x = 5$

13. Which equations could you solve if the only numbers you knew were natural numbers?

I could solve equations A, B, C, and J.

14. Which equations could you solve if the only numbers you knew were whole numbers?

15. Which equations could you solve if the only numbers you knew were integers?

16. Which equations could you solve if the only numbers you knew were rational numbers?

17. Which equations could you solve if the only numbers you knew were irrational numbers?

18. Which equations could you solve if the only numbers you knew were real numbers?

Represent each given decimal as a fraction.

19. $0.4444\ldots$ **20.** $0.2525\ldots$

Let $x = 0.4444\ldots$

$10x = 4.4444\ldots$

$-x = 0.4444\ldots$

$9x = 4$

$\dfrac{9x}{9} = \dfrac{4}{9}$

$x = \dfrac{4}{9}$

The decimal $0.4444\ldots$ is equal to $\dfrac{4}{9}$.

14

Name _____ Date _____

21. 0.8181 . . .

22. 0.581581 . . .

23. 0.3939 . . .

24. 0.0909 . . .

25. 0.1212 . . .

26. 0.7373 . . .

14

27. 0.4848 . . .

28. 1.400400 . . .

14

Name _____ Date _____

Getting Real, and Knowing How . . .
Real Number Properties

Problem Set

Identify the property demonstrated by each given equation.

1. $4 \cdot (3 \cdot 8) = (4 \cdot 3) \cdot 8$

    Associative Property of Multiplication

2. $9(8 - 5) = 9(8) - 9(5)$

3. $20 + 0 = 20$

4. $10 + 7 + 15 = 10 + 15 + 7$

5. $5 \cdot \dfrac{1}{5} = 1$

6. $4 \cdot 9 = 9 \cdot 4$

7. $99(1) = 99$

8. $12 + (3 + 8) = (12 + 3) + 8$

9. $5(x + 2) = 5x + 5(2)$

10. $8 + (-8) = 0$

14

Each expression has been simplified one step at a time. Next to each step, identify the property, transformation, or simplification used in the step.

11. $8x + 4(3x + 7)$

$8x + (12x + 28)$ <u>Distributive Property of Multiplication over Addition</u>

$(8x + 12x) + 28$ <u>Associative Property of Addition</u>

$20x + 28$ <u>Combine like terms</u>

12. $14(2x + 2 + x)$

$14(2x + x + 2)$ _____

$14(3x + 2)$ _____

$42x + 28$ _____

13. $11(13 - 13 + x - 9)$

$11(0 + x - 9)$ _____

$11(x - 9)$ _____

$11x - 99$ _____

14. $7(x - 4) + 28$

$7x - 28 + 28$ _____

$7x - 0$ _____

$7x$ _____

15. $3(5 + 7x - 5)$

$3(7x + 5 - 5)$ _____

$3(7x + 0)$ _____

$3(7x)$ _____

$21x$ _____

16. $4(10x + 2) - 40x$

$40x + 8 - 40x$ _____

$8 + 40x - 40x$ _____

$8 + 0$ _____

8 _____

14

Name _____ Date _____

Each equation has been solved one step at a time. Next to each step, identify the property, transformation, or simplification used in the step.

17. $x + 19 = 23$

$x + 19 + (-19) = 23 + (-19)$ Addition Property of Equality

$x + 0 = 23 + (-19)$ Combine like terms

$x = 23 + (-19)$ Additive Identity

$x = 4$ Combine like terms

18. $x - 7 = 34$

$x - 7 + 7 = 34 + 7$ _____

$x + 0 = 34 + 7$ _____

$x = 34 + 7$ _____

$x = 41$ _____

19. $13x = 52$

$13x \cdot \dfrac{1}{13} = 52 \cdot \dfrac{1}{13}$ _____

$x(13) \cdot \dfrac{1}{13} = 52 \cdot \dfrac{1}{13}$ _____

$x(1) = 52 \cdot \dfrac{1}{13}$ _____

$x = 52 \cdot \dfrac{1}{13}$ _____

$x = 4$ _____

20. $\dfrac{1}{7}x = 9$

$x\left(\dfrac{1}{7}\right) = 9$ _____

$x\left(\dfrac{1}{7}\right) \cdot 7 = 9 \cdot 7$ _____

$x \cdot 1 = 9 \cdot 7$ _____

$x = 9 \cdot 7$ _____

$x = 63$ _____

14

21. $3(3x - 8) + 2 = 32$

$9x - 24 + 2 = 32$ _____

$9x - 22 = 32$ _____

$9x - 22 + 22 = 32 + 22$ _____

$9x + 0 = 32 + 22$ _____

$9x = 32 + 22$ _____

$9x = 54$ _____

$9x \cdot \dfrac{1}{9} = 54 \cdot \dfrac{1}{9}$ _____

$x(9) \cdot \dfrac{1}{9} = 54 \cdot \dfrac{1}{9}$ _____

$x(1) = 54 \cdot \dfrac{1}{9}$ _____

$x = 54 \cdot \dfrac{1}{9}$ _____

$x = 6$ _____

22. $5(3 + 6x) - 25 = 20$

$15 + 30x - 25 = 20$ _____

$30x + 15 - 25 = 20$ _____

$30x - 10 = 20$ _____

$30x - 10 + 10 = 20 + 10$ _____

$30x + 0 = 20 + 10$ _____

$30x = 20 + 10$ _____

$30x = 30$ _____

$30x \cdot \dfrac{1}{30} = 30 \cdot \dfrac{1}{30}$ _____

$x(30) \cdot \dfrac{1}{30} = 30 \cdot \dfrac{1}{30}$ _____

$x(1) = 1$ _____

$x = 1$ _____

Name _____ Date _____

23.

$$7x + 1 = \frac{12x + 6}{2}$$

$$7x + 1 = \frac{12x}{2} + \frac{6}{2}$$

$$7x + 1 = 6x + 3$$

$$7x + 1 - 1 = 6x + 3 - 1$$

$$7x = 6x + 2$$

$$7x - 6x = 6x + 2 - 6x$$

$$7x - 6x = 2 + 6x - 6x$$

$$x = 2$$

_____

_____

_____

_____

_____

_____

24.

$$\frac{4x - 8}{2} = 11 - 3x$$

$$\frac{4x}{2} - \frac{8}{2} = 11 - 3x$$

$$2x - 4 = 11 - 3x$$

$$2x - 4 + 4 = 11 - 3x + 4$$

$$2x - 4 + 4 = 11 + 4 - 3x$$

$$2x = 15 - 3x$$

$$2x + 3x = 15 - 3x + 3x$$

$$5x = 15$$

$$\frac{1}{5} \cdot 5x = \frac{1}{5} \cdot 15$$

$$x = 3$$

_____

_____

_____

_____

_____

_____

_____

_____

25. $\dfrac{2x - 5}{3} = -2x + 17$

$3\left(\dfrac{2x - 5}{3}\right) = 3(-2x + 17)$

$2x - 5 = 3(-2x + 17)$ _____

$2x - 5 = -6x + 51$ _____

$2x - 5 + 5 = -6x + 51 + 5$ _____

$2x = -6x + 56$ _____

$2x + 6x = -6x + 56 + 6x$ _____

$2x + 6x = -6x + 6x + 56$ _____

$8x = 56$ _____

$\dfrac{1}{8} \cdot 8x = \dfrac{1}{8} \cdot 56$ _____

$x = 7$ _____

26. $2x - 3 = \dfrac{(4x + 9)}{5}$

$5(2x - 3) = 5\left(\dfrac{4x + 9}{5}\right)$

$5(2x - 3) = 4x + 9$ _____

$10x - 15 = 4x + 9$ _____

$10x - 15 + 15 = 4x + 9 + 15$ _____

$10x = 4x + 24$ _____

$10x - 4x = 4x + 24 - 4x$ _____

$10x - 4x = 24 + 4x - 4x$ _____

$6x = 24$ _____

$\dfrac{1}{6} \cdot 6x = \dfrac{1}{6} \cdot 24$ _____

$x = 4$ _____

14

Name _____ Date _____

Imagine the Possibilities
Imaginary and Complex Numbers

Vocabulary

Match each definition to the corresponding term.

1. the set of all numbers written in the form $a + bi$, where a and b are real numbers

   a. exponentiation

2. the set of all numbers written in the form $a + bi$, where a and b are real numbers and b is not equal to 0

   b. the number i

3. the term bi in a complex number written as $a + bi$

   c. imaginary numbers

4. a number equal to $\sqrt{-1}$

   d. pure imaginary number

5. to raise a quantity to a power

   e. complex numbers

6. a number of the form bi where b is a real number and is not equal to 0

   f. real part of a complex number

7. the term a in a complex number written as $a + bi$

   g. imaginary part of a complex number

14

Problem Set

Calculate each power of *i*.

1. i^{12}

$i^{12} = (i^4)^3$

$\quad = (1)^3$

$\quad = 1$

2. i^{13}

3. i^{15}

4. i^{20}

5. i^{22}

6. i^{25}

7. i^{44}

8. i^{46}

9. i^{84}

10. i^{99}

Name _____ Date _____

Simplify each expression using *i*.

11. $\sqrt{-9}$

$\sqrt{-9} = \sqrt{9} \cdot \sqrt{-1}$

$\quad = 3i$

12. $\sqrt{-36}$

13. $\sqrt{-20}$

14. $3 + \sqrt{-18}$

15. $9 - \sqrt{-64}$

16. $\dfrac{10 + \sqrt{-12}}{2}$

17. $\dfrac{8 - \sqrt{-32}}{4}$

18. $\dfrac{16 + \sqrt{-48}}{2}$

Simplify each algebraic expression.

19. $5xi - 2xi$

$5xi - 2xi = 3xi$

20. $10xi + 8i - 6xi - i$

21. $5x + 10i - 2 + 3x - 2i - 7$

22. $(x - i)^2$

23. $(x - i)(x + 3i)$

24. $(4x + i)(2x - 2i)$

14

Name _____ Date _____

Determine the real part and the imaginary part of each complex number.

25. 24

The real part is 24. The imaginary part is 0i.

26. 8i

27. 7 + 3i

28. 8

29. −35i

30. 14 − $\sqrt{5}i$

31. 52

32. 2.5 + 3$\sqrt{2}i$

Identify each given number using words from the box.

natural number	whole number	integer
rational number	irrational number	real number
imaginary number	complex number	

33. −25

integer, rational number, real number, complex number

34. $\sqrt{3}$

35. 9

36. $6 + 7i$

37. $\frac{2}{5}$

38. $14i$

39. $0.\overline{18}$

40. $\sqrt{-4}$

Name _____ Date _____

It's Not Complex—Just Its Solutions Are Complex!
Solving Quadratics with Complex Solutions

Vocabulary

Define the term in your own words.

1. imaginary roots (imaginary zeros)

Problem Set

For each given graph, determine the number of roots for the quadratic equation then determine whether the roots are real or imaginary.

1.

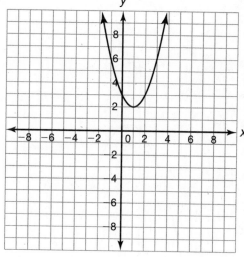

The equation has two imaginary roots.

2.

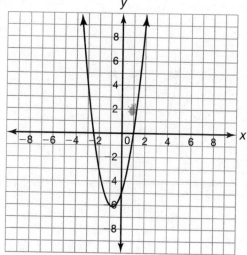

3.

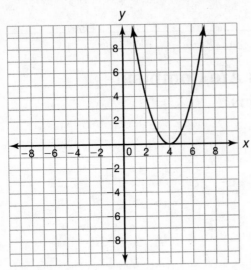

4.

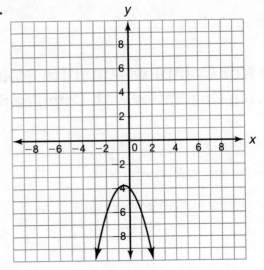

5.

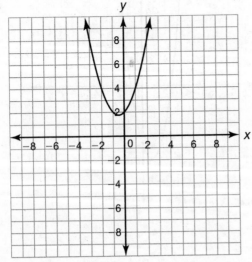

6.

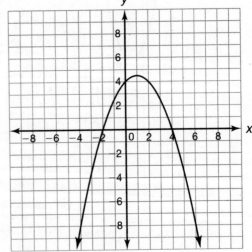

14

Name _____ Date _____

Determine the zeros of each given function.

7. $f(x) = 4x^2 + 1$

$x = \dfrac{-b \pm \sqrt{b^2 - 4ac}}{2a}$

$x = \dfrac{0 \pm \sqrt{0^2 - 4(4)(1)}}{2(4)}$

$x = \dfrac{0 \pm \sqrt{-16}}{8}$

$x = \dfrac{0 \pm 4i}{8}$

$x = \pm \dfrac{1}{2}i$

The zeros are $\dfrac{1}{2}i$ and $-\dfrac{1}{2}i$.

8. $f(x) = x^2 + 9$

9. $f(x) = x^2 + 2x + 5$

10. $f(x) = -x^2 + 4x - 6$

14

11. $f(x) = x^2 + 2x + 2$

12. $f(x) = -x^2 + 6x - 25$

13. $f(x) = x^2 - 4x + 9$

14. $f(x) = 2x^2 + 8x + 10$

14

Name _____ Date _____

I Graph in Pieces
Piecewise Functions

Problem Set

Complete each table. Then, sketch a graph that represents the problem situation.

1. Rosa saved $100 to spend on vacation. For the first 3 days of her vacation she spent $20 each day. Then for the next 2 days, she spent nothing. After those 5 days, she spent $10 each day until her savings were depleted.

Time (days)	Savings (dollars)
0	100
1	80
2	60
3	40
4	40
5	40
6	30
7	20
8	10
9	0

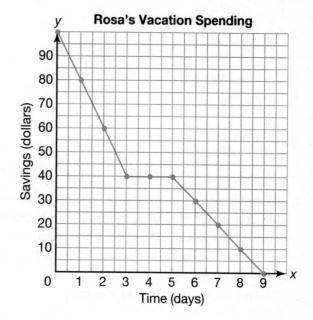

2. Belinda is saving money for a new snowboard. She earns $30 every 5 days she tutors. After 30 days, she takes a break from tutoring and does not earn any money for 10 days. After those 10 days she begins tutoring again and earns $30 every 5 days until she reaches her goal of $300.

Time (days)	Savings (dollars)
0	
5	
10	
15	
20	
25	
30	
35	
40	
45	
50	
55	
60	

3. Shanise starts a new exercise program to lose weight. Before starting the program her weight is 146 pounds. She loses 2 pounds each of the first 4 weeks of her new program. Then, for the next 2 weeks she loses 1 pound per week. After those 2 weeks she adds swimming to her program and again loses 2 pounds per week for the next 2 weeks until she reaches her goal.

Time (weeks)	Weight (pounds)
0	
1	
2	
3	
4	
5	
6	
7	
8	

Name _____ Date _____

4. Carlos is training for a bike race in 30 days. For the first 5 days of his training he bikes 3 miles each day. For the next 10 days he bikes 5 miles each day. For the next 10 days of his training he bikes 8 miles each day. For the last 5 days of his training he bikes 10 miles a day.

Time (days)	Total Distance (miles)
0	
5	
10	
15	
20	
25	
30	

5. Maria earns money delivering newspapers each morning. For the first 3 days she earns $18 each day. For the next 2 days, she takes on an additional route to cover a coworker who is out sick and earns $36 each day. For the next 2 days she returns to her original route and earns $18 each day.

Time (days)	Earnings (dollars)
0	
1	
2	
3	
4	
5	
6	
7	

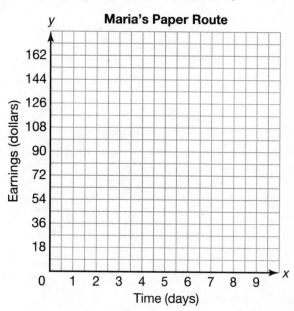

6. Franco saved $200 to spend at an amusement park while on vacation. For the first 2 days of his vacation he spent $36 each day. Then for the next 2 days, he spent nothing. After those 4 days, he stayed 3 more days and spent $40 each day.

Time (days)	Savings (dollars)
0	
1	
2	
3	
4	
5	
6	
7	

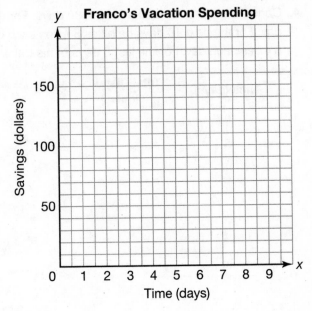

Franco's Vacation Spending

Write a piecewise function to represent the data shown in each table.

7.

x	f(x)
0	60
1	55
2	50
3	45
4	45
5	45
6	45
7	43
8	41
9	39

From 0 to 3:

The y-intercept is 60.

$$m = \frac{y_2 - y_1}{x_2 - x_1}$$

$$= \frac{55 - 60}{1 - 0} = -\frac{5}{1} = -5$$

$$y = mx + b$$
$$y = -5x + 60$$

From 3 to 6:

The slope is 0.

$$y = 45$$

From 6 to 9:

A point is (6, 45).

$$m = \frac{y_2 - y_1}{x_2 - x_1}$$

$$= \frac{41 - 43}{8 - 7} = \frac{-2}{1} = -2$$

$$y - y_1 = m(x - x_1)$$
$$y - 45 = -2(x - 6)$$
$$y - 45 = -2x + 12$$
$$y = -2x + 57$$

$$f(x) = \begin{cases} -5x + 60, & 0 \le x \le 3 \\ 45, & 3 < x \le 6 \\ -2x + 57, & 6 < x \le 9 \end{cases}$$

Name _____ Date _____

8.

x	f(x)
0	0
2	3
4	6
6	9
8	12
10	12
12	12
14	18
16	24
18	30

9.

x	f(x)
0	80
1	75
2	70
3	65
4	64
5	63
6	62
7	61
8	60
9	58

Name _____ Date _____

10.

x	f(x)
0	4
3	6
6	8
9	12
12	16
15	20
18	22
21	24
24	26
27	28

11.

x	f(x)
0	100
2	80
4	60
6	60
8	60
10	60
12	54
14	48
16	42
18	36

12.

x	f(x)
0	74
1	70
2	66
3	62
4	64
5	66
6	68
7	60
8	52
9	44

Name _____ Date _____

Sketch a graph that represents the data shown in each table. Write a function to represent the graph.

13.

x	f(x)
−3	2
−2	6
−1	10
0	14
1	10
2	6
3	2

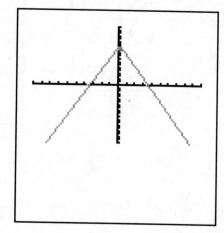

$f(x) = -|4x| + 14$

14.

x	f(x)
−3	−4
−2	−6
−1	−8
0	−10
1	−8
2	−6
3	−4

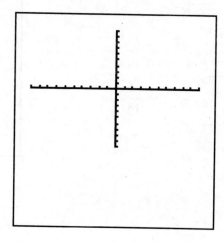

15.

x	f(x)
−6	−2
−4	−4
−2	−6
0	−8
2	−6
4	−4
6	−2

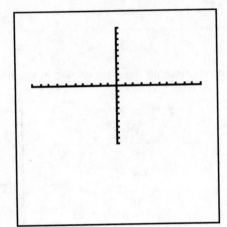

16.

x	f(x)
−15	5
−10	10
−5	15
0	20
5	15
10	10
15	5

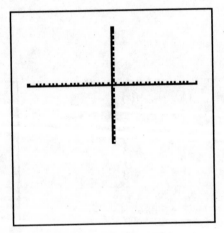

Name _____ Date _____

17.

x	f(x)
−3	14
−2	11
−1	8
0	5
1	8
2	11
3	14

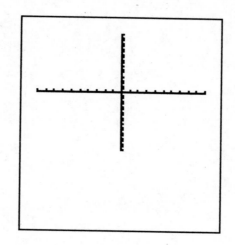

18.

x	f(x)
−3	−5
−2	−4
−1	−3
0	−2
1	−3
2	−4
3	−5

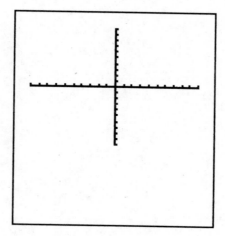

Name _____ Date _____

Step By Step
Step Functions

Vocabulary

For each function, write a definition and give an example.

1. step function

2. greatest integer (floor) function

3. least integer (ceiling) function

Problem Set

Write and graph a function to represent each problem situation.

1. An online mall assigns shipping charges based on the total value of merchandise purchased. The shipping charges are as follows:

   • 18% for purchases more than $0 and up to and including $50,

   • 16% for purchases more than $50 and up to and including $100,

   • 14% for purchases more than $100 and up to and including $150,

   • 12% for purchases more than $150 and up to and including $200, and

   • 10% for purchases more than $200.

$$f(x) = \begin{cases} 0.18x, & 0 < x \le 50 \\ 0.16x, & 50 < x \le 100 \\ 0.14x, & 100 < x \le 150 \\ 0.12x, & 150 < x \le 200 \\ 0.10x, & 200 < x \end{cases}$$

Name _____ Date _____

2. A fundraising company bases the profit returned to organizations on the total value of products sold. The profit returned is calculated as follows:

- 40% for sales more than $0 and up to and including $250,

- 45% for sales more than $250 and up to and including $500,

- 50% for sales more than $500 and up to and including $750,

- 55% for sales more than $750 and up to and including $1000, and

- 60% for sales more than $1000.

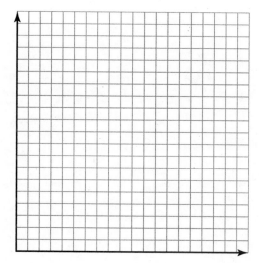

3. A theater company offers discounts based on the value of tickets purchased. The discounts are as follows:

   • 5% for purchases more than $0 and up to and including $20,

   • 10% for purchases more than $20 and up to and including $40,

   • 15% for purchases more than $40 and up to and including $60, and

   • 20% for purchases more than $60.

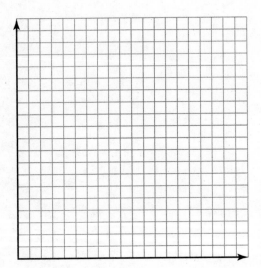

Name _____ Date _____

4. A small clothing company pays its employees a commission based on the total value of clothing sold. The commission for each sale is calculated as follows:

- 6% for sales more than $0 and up to and including $30,

- 9% for sales more than $30 and up to and including $60,

- 12% for sales more than $60 and up to and including $90, and

- 15% for sales more than $90.

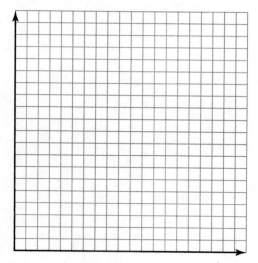

5. A small town calculates its local sales tax rate based on the total value of the goods sold. The local sales tax is calculated as follows:

- 9% for sales more than $0 and up to and including $100,

- 8% for sales more than $100 and up to and including $200,

- 7% for sales more than $200 and up to and including $300, and

- 6% for sales more than $300.

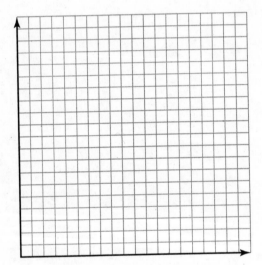

Name _____ Date _____

6. An electronics store rewards customers with in-store reward vouchers. The value of the reward vouchers are based on the total value of merchandise purchased. The rewards are calculated as follows:

- 4% for purchases more than $0 and up to and including $50,

- 8% for purchases more than $50 and up to and including $100,

- 14% for purchases more than $100 and up to and including $150,

- 16% for purchases more than $150 and up to and including $200, and

- 18% for purchases more than $200.

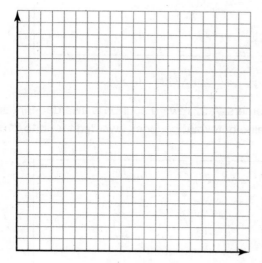

Write a function to represent each problem situation. Then use your graphing calculator to graph the function.

7. To encourage quality and minimize defects, a manufacturer pays his employees a bonus based on the value of defective merchandise produced. The fewer defective merchandise produced, the greater the employee's bonus. The bonuses are calculated as follows:

- $50 for more than $0 and up to and including $100 of defective merchandise,

- $30 for more than $100 and up to and including $200 of defective merchandise,

- $10 for more than $200 and up to and including $300 of defective merchandise, and

- $0 for more than $300 of defective merchandise.

$$f(x) = \begin{cases} 50, & 0 < x \le 100 \\ 30, & 100 < x \le 200 \\ 10, & 200 < x \le 300 \\ 0, & 300 < x \end{cases}$$

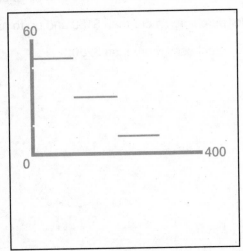

8. A jewelry store offers reward coupons to its customers. A $2 reward coupon is awarded for each $20 spent. Write a function that represents the value of reward coupons awarded for up to $100 spent.

Name _____ Date _____

9. A kids bounce house charges $8 for the first hour and $2 for each additional hour of playtime. Write a function that represents the charges for up to 5 hours of playtime.

10. A fundraising company bases the profit returned to organizations on the total value of products sold. The profit returned is calculated as follows:

- $100 for sales more than $0 and up to and including $250,

- $225 for sales more than $250 and up to and including $500,

- $350 for sales more than $500 and up to and including $750, and

- $475 for sales more than $750 and up to and including $1000.

11. An ice rink charges hockey teams for ice time to practice. The ice rink charges $10 for the first hour and $12 for each additional hour. Write a function that represents the charges for up to 5 hours.

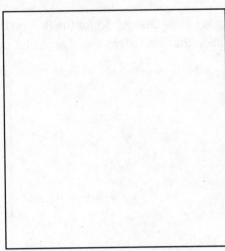

12. Ava is participating in a walk for charity. Her sponsors agree to donate $2.50 plus $2.50 for each whole mile that she walks. Write a function that represents the donation amount for up to 5 miles.

Name _____ Date _____

Evaluate.

13. $\lfloor 4.5 \rfloor$

$\lfloor 4.5 \rfloor = 4$

14. $\lceil 5.1 \rceil$

15. $\lceil -8.3 \rceil$

16. $\lfloor -3.2 \rfloor$

17. $\lfloor 7.3 \rfloor$

18. $\lfloor 0.6 \rfloor$

19. $\lceil 7.9 \rceil$

20. $\lceil 0.03 \rceil$

Name _____ Date _____

The Inverse Undoes What a Function Does
Inverses of Linear Functions

Vocabulary

Match each definition with the corresponding term.

1. inverse operation

   a. the combination of functions such that the output from one function becomes the input for the next function

2. inverse function

   b. working backwards or retracing steps to return to an original value or position

3. composition of functions

   c. a function which takes an output value, performs some operation(s) on the value, and arrives back at the original function's input value

Problem Set

Identify the domain and range of each relationship and the reverse relationship. Determine if the relationship and the reverse relationship are functions.

1. Each student in your school chooses his or her favorite sport.

   Relationship domain: students in your school

   Relationship range: all of the sports chosen

   The relationship is a function because for each student there is exactly one favorite sport.

   Reverse relationship domain: all of the sports chosen

   Reverse range: students in your school

   The reverse relationship is not a function because for each sport there may be more than one student who chose it as their favorite.

2. Each student in your school is assigned a unique student ID number.

3. Each of the 24 students in your class chooses a red, blue, orange, green, or yellow marble from a bag of assorted marbles.

4. Every member of the basketball team is assigned a jersey number.

5. Each member of your family chooses their favorite game for game night.

Name _____ Date _____

6. Each student in your class is assigned a letter grade for their final exam.

Write a phrase, expression, or sentence to describe the inverse of each situation.

7. Close a dresser drawer.

Open the dresser drawer.

8. Light a candle.

9. Jog 3 blocks north and 5 blocks east.

10. Open the garage door and drive out of the garage.

11. Divide a number by 2 then add 7.

12. Multiply a number by 3 then add 1.

Complete each table. Write an equation to represent the relationship. Write an equation for the inverse of the problem situation.

13. One foot is equivalent to 12 inches.

Feet	Inches
1	12
2	24
3	36
4	48
5	60

Let i = the number of inches.

Let f = the number of feet.

$i = 12f$

Inverse: $f = \dfrac{i}{12}$

14. One meter is equivalent to 100 centimeters.

Meters	Centimeters
1	
2	
3	
4	
5	

15. One pint is equivalent to 2 cups.

Pints	Cups
2	
4	
6	
8	
10	

Name _____ Date _____

16. Four quarters is equivalent to 1 dollar.

Quarters	Dollars
4	
16	
32	
64	
128	

17. Three feet is equivalent to 1 yard.

Feet	Yards
3	
9	
12	
18	
24	

18. One US dollar is equivalent to 13 Mexican pesos.

Dollars	Pesos
1	
2	
3	
4	
5	

Determine the inverse of each function. Graph the original function and its inverse.

19. $f(x) = 4x$

$$f(x) = 4x$$
$$y = 4x$$
$$x = 4y$$
$$\frac{x}{4} = y$$
$$f^{-1}(x) = \frac{x}{4}$$

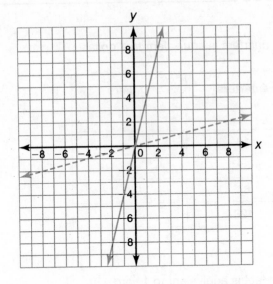

20. $f(x) = \frac{1}{3}x$

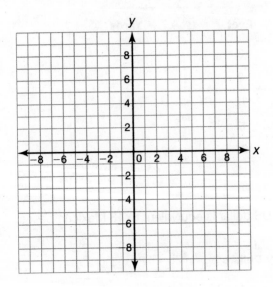

Name _____ Date _____

21. $f(x) = 2x + 1$

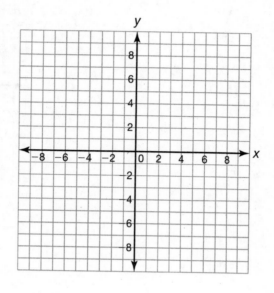

22. $f(x) = -6x - 2$

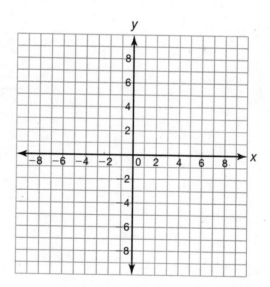

23. $f(x) = \frac{2}{3}x - 8$

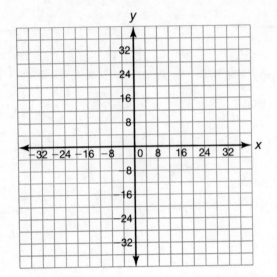

24. $f(x) = -0.5x + 9$

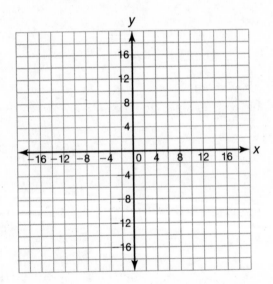

Name _____ Date _____

Determine the corresponding point on the graph of each inverse function.

25. Given that (2, 5) is a point on the graph of $f(x)$, what is the corresponding point on the graph of $f^{-1}(x)$?

The corresponding point on the graph of $f^{-1}(x)$ is (5, 2).

26. Given that (−3, 1) is a point on the graph of $f(x)$, what is the corresponding point on the graph of $f^{-1}(x)$?

27. Given that (−4, −1) is a point on the graph of $f(x)$, what is the corresponding point on the graph of $f^{-1}(x)$?

28. Given that (0, 8) is a point on the graph of $f(x)$, what is the corresponding point on the graph of $f^{-1}(x)$?

29. Given that (1, −7) is a point on the graph of $f(x)$, what is the corresponding point on the graph of $f^{-1}(x)$?

30. Given that (−6, 0) is a point on the graph of $f(x)$, what is the corresponding point on the graph of $f^{-1}(x)$?

Determine if the functions in each pair are inverses.

31. $f(x) = 5x + 1$ and $g(x) = \frac{1}{5}x - \frac{1}{5}$

$\qquad f(x) = 5x + 1 \qquad\qquad\qquad\qquad g(x) = \frac{1}{5}x - \frac{1}{5}$

$\qquad f(g(x)) = f\left(\frac{1}{5}x - \frac{1}{5}\right) \qquad\qquad g(f(x)) = g(5x + 1)$

$\qquad f(g(x)) = 5\left(\frac{1}{5}x - \frac{1}{5}\right) + 1 \qquad\quad g(f(x)) = \frac{1}{5}(5x + 1) - \frac{1}{5}$

$\qquad\qquad = (x - 1) + 1 \qquad\qquad\qquad\quad = \left(x + \frac{1}{5}\right) - \frac{1}{5}$

$\qquad\qquad = x \qquad\qquad\qquad\qquad\qquad\qquad = x$

The functions are inverses because $f(g(x)) = g(f(x)) = x$.

32. $f(x) = 8x - 2$ and $g(x) = \frac{1}{8}x - \frac{1}{4}$

33. $f(x) = -\frac{1}{2}x + 5$ and $g(x) = -2x + 10$

Name _____ Date _____

34. $f(x) = -\frac{2}{3}x - 2$ and $g(x) = -\frac{3}{2}x - 3$

35. $f(x) = 0.4x - 8$ and $g(x) = 2.5x + 20$

36. $f(x) = -0.2x + 6$ and $g(x) = 5x - 30$

Name _____ Date _____

Taking the Egg Plunge!
Inverses of Non-Linear Functions

Vocabulary

Write a definition for each term in your own words.

1. one-to-one function

2. restrict the domain

Problem Set

Complete each table of values for the function and its inverse. Determine whether the function is a one-to-one function.

1. $f(x) = 2x + 5$

x	f(x)
−2	1
−1	3
0	5
1	7
2	9

x	$f^{-1}(x)$
1	−2
3	−1
5	0
7	1
9	2

The function is one-to-one because both the original function and its inverse are functions.

2. $f(x) = -6x + 1$

x	f(x)
−2	
−1	
0	
1	
2	

x	$f^{-1}(x)$
	−2
	−1
	0
	1
	2

3. $f(x) = 5x^2 - 8$

x	f(x)
−2	
−1	
0	
1	
2	

x	$f^{-1}(x)$
	−2
	−1
	0
	1
	2

4. $f(x) = 4^x$

x	f(x)
−2	
−1	
0	
1	
2	

x	$f^{-1}(x)$
	−2
	−1
	0
	1
	2

Name _____ Date _____

5. $f(x) = -3$

x	f(x)
−2	
−1	
0	
1	
2	

x	$f^{-1}(x)$
	−2
	−1
	0
	1
	2

6. $f(x) = |4x|$

x	f(x)
−2	
−1	
0	
1	
2	

x	$f^{-1}(x)$
	−2
	−1
	0
	1
	2

Determine whether each function is a one-to-one function by examining the graph of the function and its inverse.

7. $f(x) = -4x + 7$

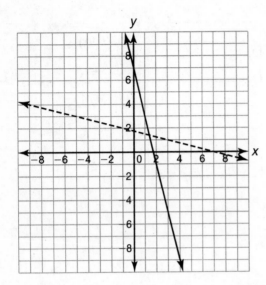

8. $f(x) = 5$

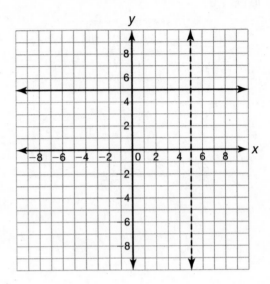

The function is one-to-one because both the original function and its inverse are functions.

9. $f(x) = |3x|$

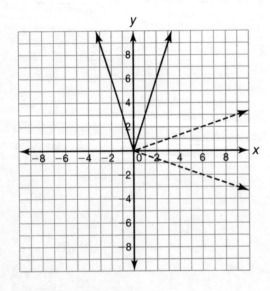

10. $f(x) = -x^2 - 3$

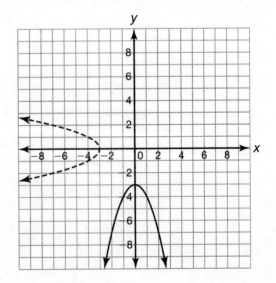

Name _____ Date _____

11. $f(x) = 6x - 3$

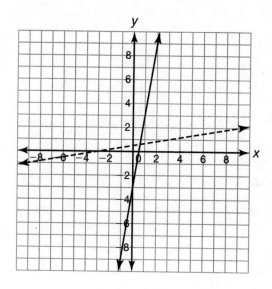

12. $f(x) = 3^x$

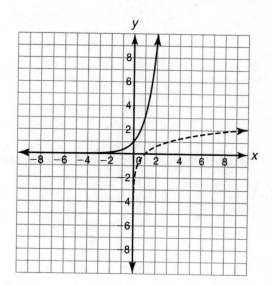

Identify each equation as linear, exponential, quadratic, or linear absolute value. Determine whether the function is a one-to-one function.

13. $f(x) = 2x - 9$

The function is a linear function. A linear function that is not a constant function is a one-to-one function. So, the function is one-to-one.

14. $f(x) = -6$

15. $f(x) = -3x + 10$

16. $f(x) = 5^x$

17. $f(x) = -|6x|$

18. $f(x) = 9x^2 + 3$

Determine the equation of the inverse for each quadratic function.

19. $f(x) = 7x^2$

$$f(x) = 7x^2$$
$$y = 7x^2$$
$$x = 7y^2$$
$$\frac{x}{7} = y^2$$
$$\pm\sqrt{\frac{x}{7}} = y$$

20. $f(x) = -x^2$

21. $f(x) = 6x^2 + 11$

22. $f(x) = 2x^2 - 12$

Name _____ Date _____

23. $f(x) = -4x^2 - 6$ **24.** $f(x) = -3x^2 + 20$

Determine the equation of the inverse for each given function. Graph the function and its inverse. Restrict the domain of the original function and the inverse so that the inverse is also a function.

25. $f(x) = 2x^2$

$$f(x) = 2x^2$$
$$y = 2x^2$$
$$x = 2y^2$$
$$\frac{x}{2} = y^2$$
$$\pm\sqrt{\frac{x}{2}} = y$$

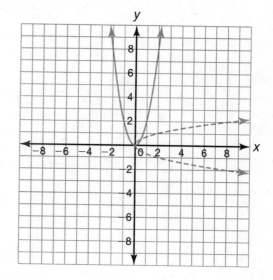

$$f(x) = \begin{cases} 2x^2, & \text{domain: } x \geq 0, \text{ range: } y \geq 0, \\ 2x^2, & \text{domain: } x \leq 0, \text{ range: } y \geq 0, \end{cases}$$

$$\text{Inverse of } f(x) = \begin{cases} \sqrt{\frac{x}{2}}, & \text{domain: } x \geq 0, \text{ range: } y \geq 0, \\ -\sqrt{\frac{x}{2}}, & \text{domain: } x \geq 0, \text{ range: } y \leq 0, \end{cases}$$

For the function $y = 2x^2$ with $x \geq 0$, the inverse is $y = \sqrt{\frac{x}{2}}$.

For the function $y = 2x^2$ with $x \leq 0$, the inverse is $y = -\sqrt{\frac{x}{2}}$.

26. $f(x) = x^2 + 3$

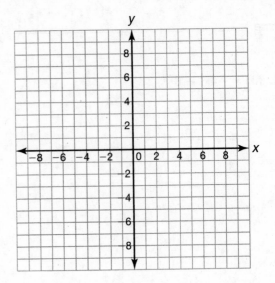

Name _____ Date _____

27. $f(x) = -4x^2 - 2$

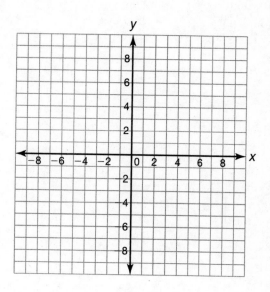

28. $f(x) = |2x|$

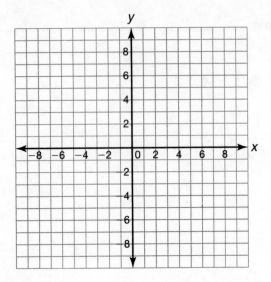

Name _____ Date _____

29. $f(x) = -|x|$

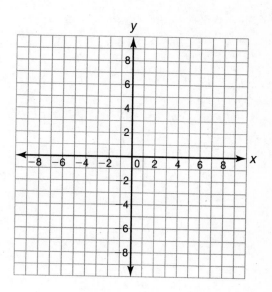

30. $f(x) = -|5x|$

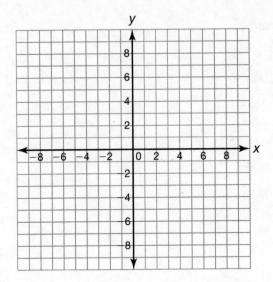

Name _____ Date _____

People, Tea, and Carbon Dioxide
Modeling Using Exponential Functions

Problem Set

For each given data set determine the exponential regression equation and the value of the correlation coefficient, r. Round all values to the hundredths place.

1.

x	y
10	5
20	6
30	8
40	15
50	32
60	70
70	150

$f(x) = 1.88(1.06)^x$

$r = 0.98$

2.

x	y
0	6000
1	2100
2	750
3	275
4	95
5	40
6	15
7	6
8	4

3.

x	5	10	15	20	25	30	35	40
y	12	10	25	21	45	35	80	120

4.

x	100	200	300	400	500	600	700
y	25.4	10.5	4.5	2.1	0.8	0.3	0.4

5.

x	0.5	1.0	1.5	2.0	2.5	3.0	3.5	4.0
y	1200	585	272	126	42	40	14	12

6.

x	0	100	200	300	400	500	600
y	10	50	110	160	220	290	350

Evaluate each function for the given value of x. Round your answer to the hundredths place.

7. Evaluate $f(x) = 2.45(1.05)^x$ when $x = 6$.

$f(6) = 2.45(1.05)^6$

≈ 3.28

8. Evaluate $f(x) = 55(0.82)^x$ when $x = 10$.

9. Evaluate $f(x) = 200(1.11)^x$ when $x = 20$.

10. Evaluate $f(x) = 10(2)^x$ when $x = 11$.

11. Evaluate $f(x) = 1200(0.99)^x$ when $x = 100$.

12. Evaluate $f(x) = 0.5(1.094)^x$ when $x = 25$.

13. Evaluate $f(x) = 5000(0.485)^x$ when $x = 7$.

14. Evaluate $f(x) = 180(0.35)^x$ when $x = 5$.

15. Evaluate $f(x) = 2.5(1.5)^x$ when $x = 30$.

16. Evaluate $f(x) = 9000(0.95)^x$ when $x = 90$.

Name _____ Date _____

Determine the exponential regression equation that models each situation. Use the equation to make the associated prediction. Round all values to the hundredths place.

17. Tamara deposited $500 into a savings account in 1970. The table shows the value of Tamara's savings account from 1970 to 2010. Predict the account's value in 2020.

Time Since 1970 (years)	0	5	10	15	20	25	30	35	40
Account Value (dollars)	500	650	900	1150	1600	2100	2750	3850	4800

$f(x) = 497.63(1.06)^x$

$f(50) = 497.63(1.06)^{50}$

≈ 9166.42

The account's value will be approximately $9166.42 in 2020.

18. Tamika deposited $1000 into a savings account in 1980. The table shows the value of Tamika's savings account from 1980 to 2010. Predict when the account's value will be $5000.

Time Since 1980 (years)	0	5	10	15	20	25	30
Account Value (dollars)	1000	1200	1480	1800	2200	2720	3250

19. A marine biologist monitors the population of sunfish in a small lake. He records 800 sunfish in his first year, 600 sunfish in his fourth year, 450 sunfish in his sixth year, and 350 sunfish in his tenth year. Predict the population of sunfish in the lake in his sixteenth year.

16

20. A marine biologist monitors the population of catfish in a small lake. He records 50 catfish in his first year, 170 catfish in his fourth year, 380 catfish in his sixth year, and 1900 catfish in his tenth year. Predict when the population of catfish in the lake will be 6000.

21. Every hour, a scientist records the number of cells in a colony of bacteria growing in her lab. The sample begins with 15 cells. Predict the number of cells in the colony after 7 hours.

Hour	Number of Cells
0	15
1	40
2	110
3	300
4	850

22. Every hour, a scientist records the number of cells in a colony of bacteria growing in her lab. The sample begins with 50 cells. Predict how long it will take the sample to grow to 2000 cells.

Hour	Number of Cells
0	50
1	90
2	160
3	290
4	530

Name _____ Date _____

Stop! What Is Your Reaction?
Modeling Stopping Distances and Reaction Times

16

Problem Set

Determine the regression equation which best fits each given data set. Create a scatter plot of the data and graph the regression equation on the same grid.

1. The table shows the height of a supply kit dropped from a helicopter at various times.

Time Since Release (seconds)	0	1	2	3	4	5
Height (feet)	900	880	830	750	650	500

The quadratic regression equation $f(x) = -15.18x^2 - 3.25x - 898.93$, where the function represents the height of the supply kit x seconds after it is released, best fits the data.

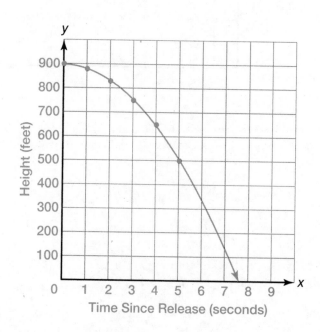

2. The table shows the population of river otters in a river over a period of time.

Time Since 2005 (years)	0	1	2	3	4	5
River Otter Population	6	8	12	17	26	40

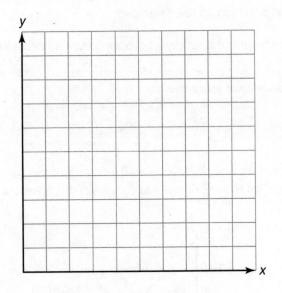

Name _____ Date _____

3. The table shows a runner's speed at different distance markers during a marathon.

Distance (miles)	0	5	10	15	20	25
Runner's Speed (miles per hour)	9.0	8.8	8.2	7.8	7.2	7.0

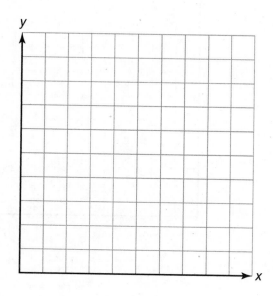

16

4. The table shows the population of bald eagles in a particular county over a period of time.

Time Since 2000 (years)	0	1	2	3	4	5
Bald Eagle Population	50	55	65	90	110	150

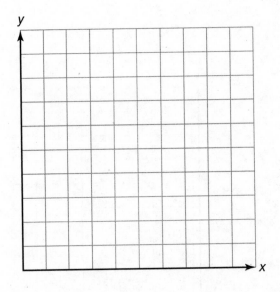

Name _____ Date _____

5. The table shows the population of ash trees in a forest over a period of time.

Time Since 1980 (years)	0	5	10	15	20	25	30
Ash Tree Population	450	350	290	230	184	147	120

16

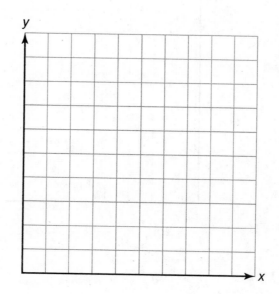

16

6. The table shows the height of a burning candle over a period of time.

Time (minutes)	0	5	10	15	20	25	30
Height (centimeters)	12	11.5	11	10.5	10	9.5	9

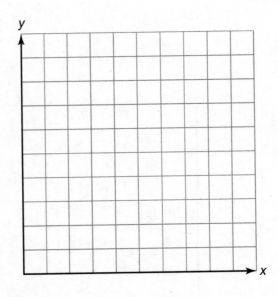

Name _____ Date _____

The function modeling each problem situation is given. Sketch the inverse of each function on the grid provided and label the axes. Then, describe the domain and range of both functions as they relate to the problem situation.

7. The function models a mountain climber's elevation over his 10-day mountain climb.

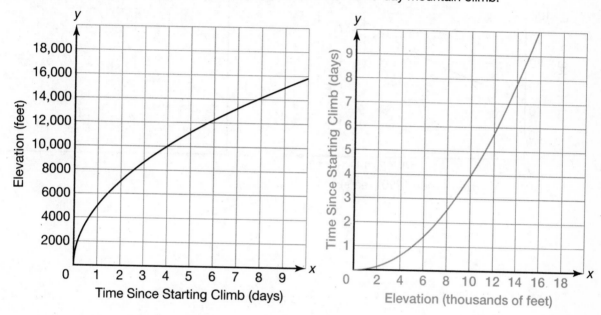

For the given function, the domain is all real numbers greater than or equal to 0 and less than or equal to 10, because it represents the time, in days, since the climber started his climb. The range is all real numbers greater than or equal to 0 and less than or equal to about 15,800, because it represents the climber's elevation from his starting point of 0 feet to his ending point of about 15,800 feet.

For the inverse function, the domain is all real numbers greater than or equal to 0 and less than or equal to about 15,800, because it represents the climber's elevation from his starting point of 0 feet to his ending point of about 15,800 feet. The range is all real numbers greater than or equal to 0 and less than or equal to 10, because it represents the time, in days, since the climber started his climb.

8. In the year 1990, park rangers stocked an unpopulated lake with 50 channel catfish. The function models the channel catfish population over a period of time.

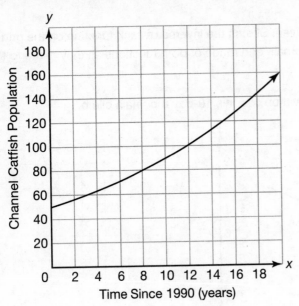
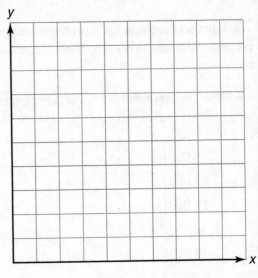

Name _____ Date _____

9. Twenty years ago, Daniel deposited $150.00 in a savings account. The function models the balance in the savings account in dollars.

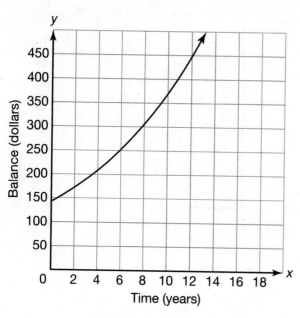

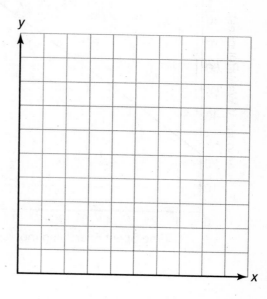

16

10. On a day when he does not exercise, Carl drinks 24.3 ounces of water. The function models the amount of water Carl drinks while exercising.

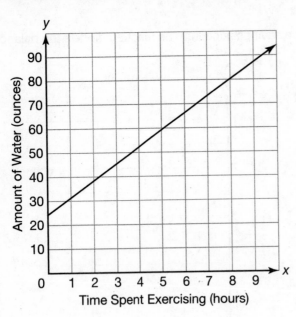

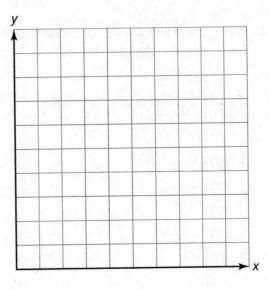

Name _____ Date _____

11. The function models the relationship between the number of wool hats sold and the amount of money earned.

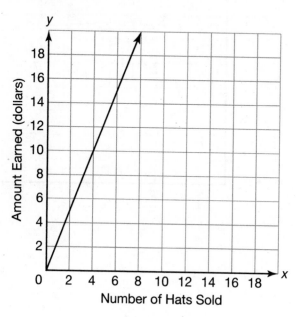

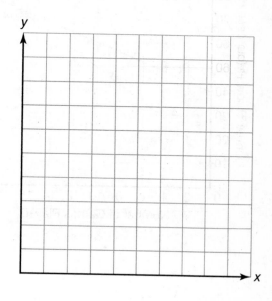

12. The function models a basketball player's free throw percentage during the course of the season.

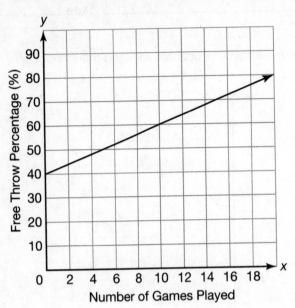

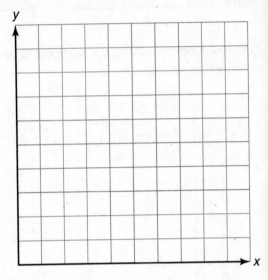

Name _____ Date _____

The graph displays the average scores of bowlers in the Spare Time Bowling League throughout their 10-game season. The function $L(x)$ models the left-handed bowlers' average scores after x games. The function $R(x)$ models the right-handed bowlers' average scores after x games. Analyze the graph to answer each question.

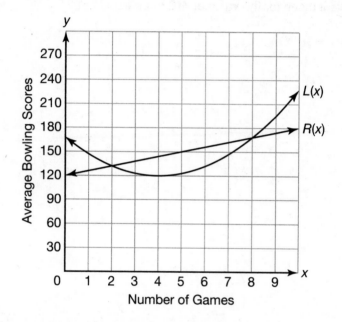

13. Which function family does each function appear to belong to?

The function $L(x)$ appears to be a quadratic function, because it is a smooth curve which decreases and then increases over the domain. The function $R(x)$ appears to be a linear function, because it is a straight line.

14. Describe how each group's average scores changed throughout the season.

15. At which point(s) during the season did both groups have the same average scores?

16. Consider the function $A(x)$, where $A(x) = L(x) - R(x)$. What does $A(x)$ mean in terms of the problem situation? What does it mean for the value of $A(x)$ to be equal to 0?

Name _____ Date _____

Modeling Data Helps Us Make Predictions
Using Quadratic Functions to Model Data

Problem Set

A quadratic regression equation is given for the amount of profit, P, in dollars that a number of produced items, n, generates. Predict the profit for each given number of produced items.

1. $P = -n^2 + 150n - 300$ for $n = 20$

   $P = -(20)^2 + 150(20) - 300$

   $P = -400 + 3000 - 300$

   $P = 2300$

   The profit when 20 items are produced should be $2300.

2. $P = -n^2 + 150n - 300$ for $n = 100$

3. $P = -2n^2 + 500n - 800$ for $n = 200$

4. $P = -2n^2 + 500n - 800$ for $n = 125$

16

5. $P = -4n^2 + 2000n - 1500$ for $n = 300$

6. $P = -4n^2 + 2000n - 1500$ for $n = 450$

Use a graphing calculator to determine the quadratic regression equation for each data set.
Round decimals to the nearest thousandth.

7.

x	y
1	22
6	6
20	20
42	64
80	99

$y = 0.002x^2 + x + 9.259$

8.

x	y
12	38
24	12
30	3
40	16
54	54

9.

x	y
25	60
50	80
75	140
100	210
125	250
150	322
175	400

10.

x	y
10	14
20	36
30	70
40	120
50	180
60	240
70	350

Name _____ Date _____

16.

x	y
0.1	8
0.2	12
0.3	14
0.4	16
0.5	18
0.6	10
0.7	2

12.

x	y
0.1	2.2
0.2	3.1
0.3	4
0.4	4.8
0.5	5.4
0.6	6
0.7	4.2

Determine the y-intercept, x-intercept(s), and vertex of the graph of each given quadratic regression equation. Then determine what these values mean in terms of the problem situation and tell whether the values make sense.

13. The speed, s, of a car and the car's average fuel efficiency, G, in miles per gallon at that speed can be modeled by the linear regression equation $G = -0.014s^2 + 1.502s - 9.444$.

The y-intercept is the point (0, −9.444). The y-intercept represents the fuel efficiency of the car when it is traveling at 0 miles per hour (at a stop). Because the fuel efficiency is a negative number, this value does not make sense.

The x-intercepts are the points (6.707, 0) and (100.579, 0). The x-intercepts represent the speed of the car when the fuel efficiency is zero. The fuel efficiency would be zero when the car is not moving, not when the car is traveling 6.707 miles per hour or 100.579 miles per hour. So, these values do not make sense.

The vertex is the point (53.643, 30.842). The vertex represents the speed at which the car is getting the highest fuel efficiency. So, when the car is traveling at 53.643 miles per hour, it gets its highest fuel efficiency, which is 30.842 miles per gallon. This value makes sense.

14. An athlete throws a disc upward at an angle. The height in feet, *h*, of the disc can be modeled by the linear regression equation $h = -0.002x^2 + 0.440x + 5.621$, where *x* represents the distance in feet that the disc has traveled horizontally.

15. Martin and his friend are playing catch with a baseball. Martin tosses the ball to his friend, but he overthrows it, and it hits the ground. The height in feet, *h*, of the baseball can be modeled by the quadratic regression equation $h = -0.005x^2 + 0.752x + 5.220$, where *x* represents the distance in feet that the baseball has traveled horizontally.

Name _____ Date _____

16. A company's profit in dollars, p, can be modeled by the quadratic regression equation $p = -116.938x^2 + 4010.166x - 10{,}590.863$, where x represents the number of years since the company was started.

17. The temperatures, t, in degrees Fahrenheit recorded during a 10-hour winter snow storm can be modeled by the quadratic regression equation $t = 0.74x^2 - 8.12x + 35.07$ where x represents the number of hours the storm has lasted.

18. A company's daily profit, p, from selling calculators can be modeled by the quadratic regression equation $p = -9.67x^2 + 1625.20x - 48{,}793.33$ where x represents the price of the calculator.

Use the given regression equation to answer each question.

19. A farmer finds that his crop yield per acre can be modeled by the quadratic regression equation $y = -0.02x^2 + 1.08x + 3.89$, where x represents the amount of fertilizer applied in pounds per hundred square feet and y represents the crop yield in bushels. What is the approximate yield when 20 pounds of fertilizer are applied per hundred square feet?

    $y = -0.02(20)^2 + 1.08(20) + 3.89$

    $y = -8 + 21.6 + 3.89$

    $y = 17.49$

    The farmer should have a yield of 17.49 bushels per hundred square feet.

20. The growth of soybean plants in inches over a certain time is tested with different amounts of fertilizer. The growth can be modeled by the quadratic regression equation $y = -0.001x^2 + 0.12x + 5.6$, where y represents the growth in inches and x represents the amount of fertilizer per plant in milligrams. How much growth could be expected from a plant given 40 milligrams of fertilizer?

21. The height of a ball thrown at an angle is measured photographically. The height of the ball can be modeled by the quadratic regression equation $h = -16.2t^2 + 46t + 4$, where h is the height of the ball after t seconds. At what time should the ball reach a height of 30 feet?

22. The quadratic regression equation $y = -20x^2 + 600x + 2250$ models the relationship between the selling price of a necklace, x, in dollars and the profit earned each month, y, in dollars. To reach a profit of $300 per month from the necklaces, what should the selling price be?

Name _____   Date _____

23. A company manufactures bicycles. The relationship between the number of bicycles made and the cost to produce those bicycles can be modeled by the quadratic regression equation $y = x^2 + 36.7x + 4756$, where y represents the total cost to make the bicycles and x represents the number of bicycles made. What would be the cost to manufacture 50 bicycles?

24. A model rocket is launched into the air. The height of the model rocket can be modeled by the quadratic regression equation $y = -4.1x^2 + 272.8x + 2.7$, where y represents the height of the model rocket in feet and x represents the time in seconds. At what time should the model rocket reach a height of 2000 feet?

Name _____ Date _____

BAC Is BAD News
Choosing a Function to Model BAC

16

Problem Set

Use a graphing calculator to determine the indicated regression equation for each data set. Explain the meaning of each variable in the regression equation.

1. Determine a quadratic regression equation that shows the relationship between the length of time in months that a new television has been for sale and the price of the television in dollars.

Time (months)	0	6	8	12
Price (dollars)	750	530	450	275

$y = -0.5x^2 - 33.6x + 749.9$

x represents the time in months the television has been for sale

y represents the price in dollars of the television

2. Determine a quadratic regression equation that shows the relationship between the number of years since a collector purchased an antique table and the value of the table in dollars.

Time (years)	0	22	50	100
Price (dollars)	25	9755	15,750	8550

3. Determine an exponential regression equation that shows the relationship between the time in months and the population of a town.

Time (months)	1	2	3	4	5
Population	1000	1050	1175	1340	1450

4. Determine an exponential regression equation that shows the relationship between the time in months and the rabbit population in a park.

Time (months)	1	2	3	4
Rabbit Population	4	5	8	12

5. Determine a quadratic regression equation that shows the relationship between a vehicle's mileage in thousands of miles and the cost for repairs in dollars during the vehicle's last inspection.

Mileage (thousands of miles)	50	100	150	200
Cost for Repairs (dollars)	200	350	675	1425

6. Determine an exponential regression equation that shows the relationship between the time in years and the amount of interest on a mortgage in dollars.

Time (years)	1	5	10	15	20
Interest (dollars)	3500	4750	3200	8525	10,450

Name _____ Date _____

Determine which regression equation is the best fit for each set of data points. Explain your reasoning.

7. Quadratic graph has equation $y = 0.0077056x^2 - 0.161558x + 2.142424$

Exponential graph has equation $y = (1.0851)(1.045)^x$

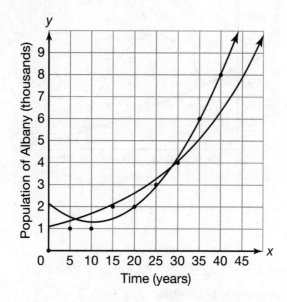

The exponential regression equation fits the data better than the quadratic regression equation. The exponential regression equation is closer to more points in the data set.

8. Quadratic graph has equation $y = -0.220238x^2 + 16.369x - 57.14285$

   Exponential graph has equation $y = (172.2555)(0.9926)^x$

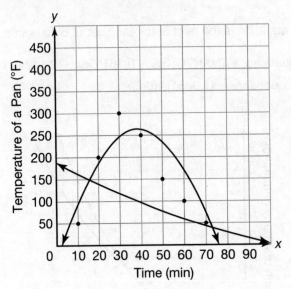

9. Quadratic graph has equation $y = 7.42857x^2 - 44.5714x + 78.4$

   Exponential graph has equation $y = (23.202)(1)^x$

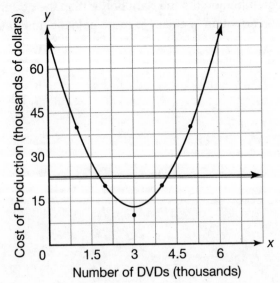

Name _____ Date _____

10. Quadratic graph has equation $y = 0.00205357x^2 + -0.2380357x + 8.05$

Exponential graph has equation $y = (7.98796)(0.965952)^x$

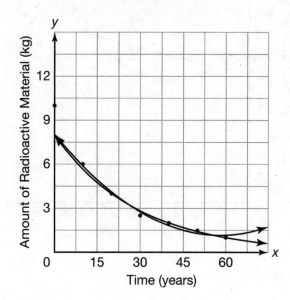

11. The quadratic regression equation is $y = 0.24x^2 - 6.43x + 171$.

The exponential regression equation is $y = (133.56)(1.01)^x$.

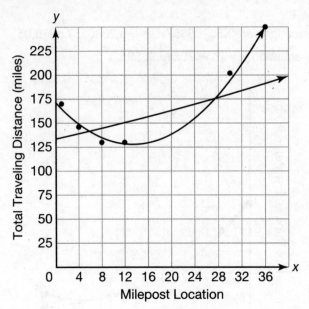

12. The quadratic regression equation is $y = 0.617x^2 - 3.48x + 4.66$.

The exponential regression equation is $y = 1.12(1.345562)^x$.

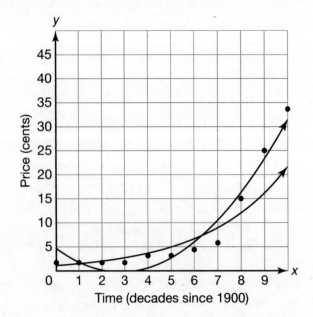

Name _____ Date _____

Use the given regression equation to answer each question.

13. The height of a ball in feet t seconds after it is projected upward can be modeled by the regression equation $h(t) = -16t^2 + 160t + 5$. What is the height of the ball after 2 seconds?

$h(2) = -16(2)^2 + 160(2) + 5$

$\quad = -16(4) + 320 + 5$

$\quad = -64 + 325$

$\quad = 261$

The height of the ball is 261 feet after 2 seconds.

14. The population of a town after t years can be modeled by the regression equation $p(t) = 15,000(1.07)^t$. What will the population of the town be after 5 years?

15. A boiling pot of water is removed from a burner. Its temperature in degrees Fahrenheit can be modeled by the regression equation $t(x) = 72 + 140(0.98)^x$, where x represents the number of minutes after the pot is removed from the burner. When does the temperature reach 152 degrees?

16. The balance in a bank account can be modeled by the regression equation $b(t) = 2t^2 - 20t + 400$, where t represents the time in months. When is the balance in the bank account $382?

17. The population of polar bears in a park after t years can be modeled by the regression equation $p(t) = 350(0.98)^t$. What is the population of the polar bears after 20 years?

16

18. The height of a rocket in feet t seconds after it is launched can be modeled by the regression equation $h(t) = -16t^2 + 800t + 15$. What is the height of the rocket 40 seconds after it is launched?

Ralph purchased a new 1970 Chevy Nova in the year it was manufactured for $3000. The scatter plot shows the car's value over a period of time since 1970. The quadratic regression equation that best fits the data is $f(x) = 20.77x^2 - 470.98x + 3685.45$, where $f(x)$ represents the value of the car in dollars and x represents the time since 1970 in years. The function is graphed on the grid. Analyze this information to answer each question.

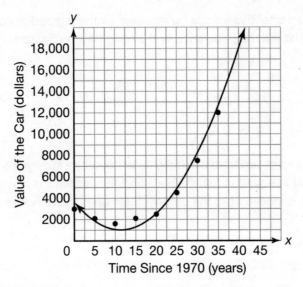

19. Discuss the domain and range of the function as they relate to the problem situation.

The domain is all real numbers greater than or equal to 0, because the car did not have a value prior to the year of its manufacture. The range is all real numbers greater than or equal to approximately $1000, because the function's value starts at approximately $3685, and then drops to approximately $1000 before rising from that point onward.

20. Discuss the intervals of increase and decrease as they relate to the problem situation.

21. Discuss the x- and y-intercepts of the function as they relate to the problem situation.

Name _____ Date _____

22. Discuss any minimums and maximums as they relate to the problem situation.

23. Predict the value of the car in 2010.

24. Why do you think the value of this car is best represented by a quadratic function? Do you think this is true of all cars?

The scatter plot shows the number of wild Burmese pythons captured in a Florida county over a period of time. The exponential regression equation that best fits the data is $p(x) = 4.96(1.68)^x$, where p represents the number of wild Burmese pythons captured and x represents the number of years since 2005. The function is graphed on the grid. Analyze this information to answer each question.

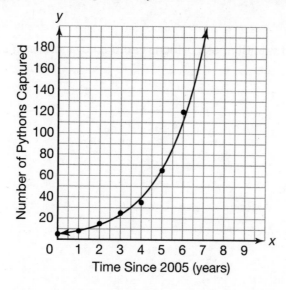

25. Discuss any minimums and maximums as they relate to the problem situation.

The function does not have a maximum value. Even though the given exponential function has no minimum value, the function as it relates to the problem has a minimum value of approximately 5 in the year 2005.

26. Discuss the domain and range of the function as they relate to the problem situation.

27. Discuss the intervals of increase and decrease as they relate to the problem situation.

28. Discuss the *x*- and *y*-intercepts of the function as they relate to the problem situation.

29. Predict the number of wild Burmese pythons captured in Florida in 2012.

30. Why might the number of wild Burmese pythons captured by increasing exponentially?

Name _____ Date _____

Cell Phone Batteries, Gas Prices, and Single Family Homes
Modeling with Piecewise Functions

Problem Set

Write a possible scenario to model each piecewise function graph. Determine the slope, x-intercept(s) and y-intercept and explain what each means in terms of the problem situation.

1. The graph shows the depth at which a shark swims after a tracking device is attached to its dorsal fin.

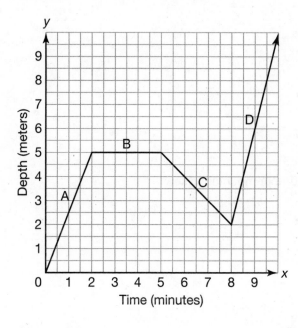

Answers will vary.

The shark is released into the water after having the device attached. It swims downward to a depth of 5 meters over a two minute period. It remains at this depth for 3 minutes before swimming upward to a depth of 2 meters over the next 3 minutes. Finally, it swims downward past the a depth of 10 meters over the next 2 minutes. The slope in this situation represents the rate at which the shark's depth is changing over time. When the slope is positive, the shark is going deeper. When the slope is negative, the shark is going towards the surface. When the slope is 0, the shark's depth is remaining constant. The slope of part A is $\frac{5}{2}$, the slope of part B is 0, the slope of part C is -1, and the slope of part D is 4. The x-intercept in this situation represents the time at which the shark is at the surface. The only x-intercept is (0, 0) which means the shark was only at the surface at the moment it was released. The y-intercept is (0, 0) and represents the depth of the shark when it was first released. In this case, the depth of the shark was 0 meters when it was released.

2. Mercedes leaves her beach house for a walk along the beach. The graph shows her distance from home for the duration of her walk.

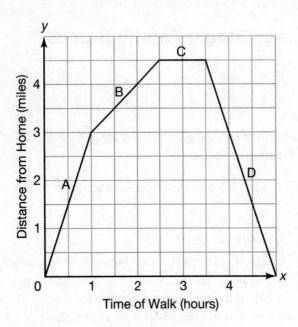

3. The graph shows a hiker's elevation during his 10-hour mountain hike.

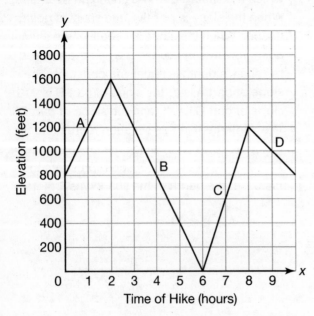

Name _____ Date _____

4. John goes for a bike ride early in the morning and returns home later that day. The graph shows his distance from home for the duration of his ride.

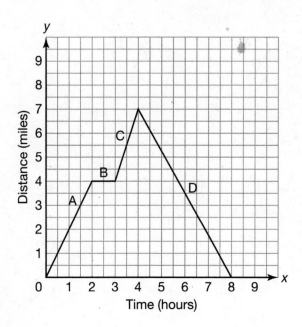

5. Peyton takes her dog for a long walk on Saturday. The graph shows her distance from home for the duration of the walk.

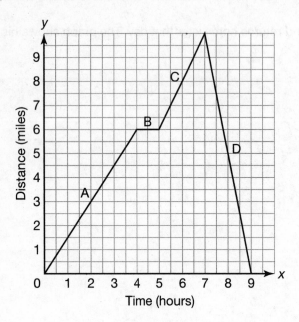

6. Tonya travels to her friend Alexandra's house, stays awhile, and then returns home. The graph shows her distance from home for the duration of her trip.

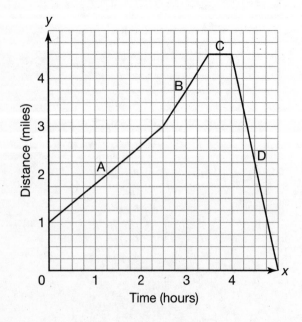

Name _____ Date _____

Determine a piecewise function to model each given data set and define the variables used. Then, graph the piecewise function on the grid provided. Round decimals to the nearest thousandth.

7. The table and the scatter plot show the number of employees employed by a company over a period of time.

Time Since 1995 (years)	Number of Employees
0	300
1	370
2	500
3	630
4	700
5	650
6	620
7	580
8	550
9	500

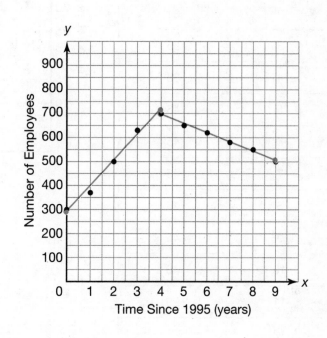

Answers will vary.

Let $f(x)$ represent the number of employees employed by the company x years since 1995.

$$f(x) = \begin{cases} 106x + 288, & 0 \le x \le 4 \\ -38.286x + 848.857, & 4 < x \le 9 \end{cases}$$

8. The table and the scatter plot show the outdoor temperature in Washington, DC over a period of time.

Time Since 8 AM (hours)	Temperature (°F)
0	20
1	23
2	31
3	35
4	38
5	45
6	45
7	45
8	45
9	45
10	40
11	29
12	27
13	16
14	11

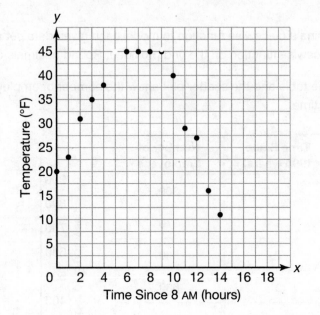

Name _____   Date _____

9. The table and the scatter plot show the population of black bears in a Tennessee county over a
period of time.

Time Since 1980 (years)	Black Bear Population
0	20
2	26
4	32
6	44
8	58
10	75
12	65
14	55
16	45
18	35
20	25

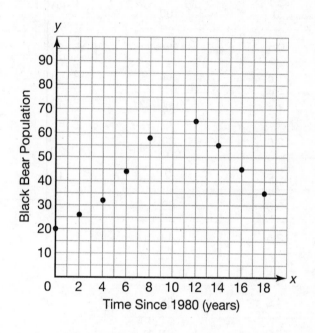

10. The table and the scatter plot show the height of a bouncing ball dropped from a building over a period of time.

Time Since Release (seconds)	Height of Ball (feet)
0	100
0.5	96
1.0	84
1.5	64
2.0	36
2.5	0
3.0	29
3.5	49
4.0	61
4.5	65
5.0	61
5.5	49
6.0	29
6.5	0
7.0	24
7.5	36
8.0	40
8.5	36
9.0	24
9.5	4

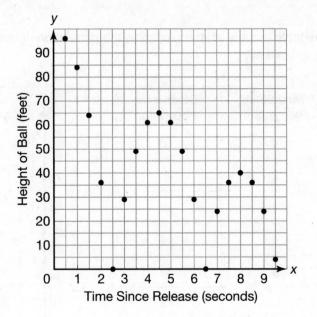

Name _____ Date _____

11. The table and the scatter plot show a bookstore's yearly profit over a period of time.

Time Since 2001 (years)	Profit (dollars)
0	10,000
1	15,000
2	22,500
3	34,000
4	50,000
5	76,000
6	60,000
7	55,000
8	48,000
9	39,000
10	28,000

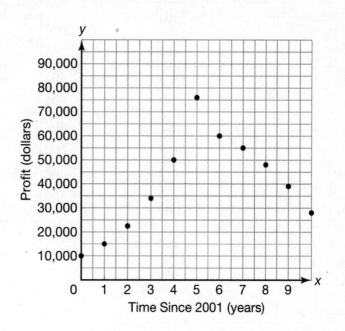

16

12. The table and the scatter plot show the number of yearly subscriptions to a small town newspaper over a period of time.

Time Since 1990 (years)	Number of Subscriptions
0	500
1	750
2	900
3	900
4	750
5	550
6	300
7	350
8	400
9	450
10	500
11	550
12	600
13	500
14	450
15	450
16	500
17	650
18	900

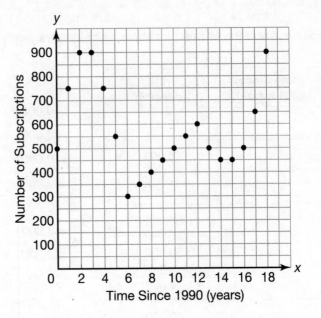

Odd-Numbered Answers

Chapter 1

LESSON 1.1

1. Independent quantity: time (hours) Dependent quantity: distance (miles)

3. Independent quantity: number of cups Dependent quantity: cost (dollars)

5. Independent quantity: time (hours) Dependent quantity: distance (miles)

7. Graph A

9. Graph B

11. Graph C

13.
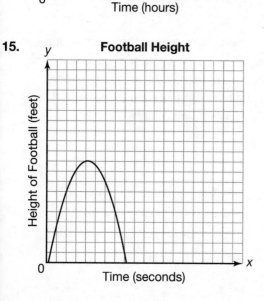
Distance Madison Bikes

15.
Football Height

17.
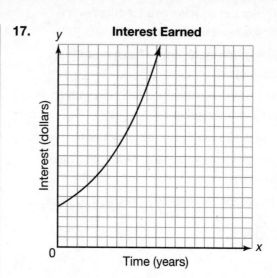
Interest Earned

LESSON 1.2

1. Both graphs are always decreasing from left to right. Both graphs are functions. Both graphs are made up of straight lines.

3. Both graphs have an increasing and a decreasing interval. Both graphs have a minimum value. Both graphs are functions.

5. Both graphs are increasing from left to right. Both graphs are functions.

7. The graph is discrete.

9. The graph is continuous.

11. The graph is discrete.

13. Yes. The graph is a function.

15. No. The graph is not a function.

17. No. The graph is not a function.

LESSON 1.3

1. $f(x) = 3x - 8$

3. $P(x) = 3^x + 8$

5. $A(m) = -\frac{1}{2}m + 5$

7. Graph A

9. Graph B

11. Graph A

13. The graph represents an increasing function.

15. The graph represents a function with a combination of an increasing interval and a decreasing interval.

17. The graph represents a constant function.

19. The graph represents a function with an absolute minimum.

21. The graph represents a function with an absolute maximum.

23. The graph represents a function with an absolute maximum.

25. The graph represents an exponential function.

27. The graph represents a linear piecewise function.

29. The graph represents a constant function.

LESSON 1.4

11. $f(x) = x^2$

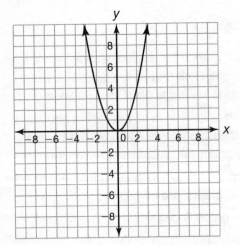

13. $f(x) = x^2$

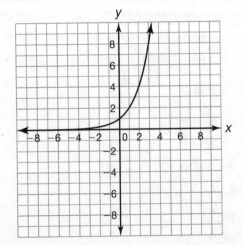

15. $f(x) = 3$

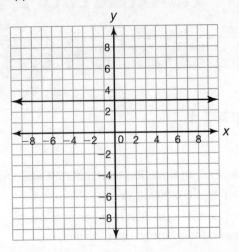

17. The graph represents a quadratic function.

19. The graph represents a linear absolute value function.

21. The graph represents a linear piecewise function.

Chapter 2
LESSON 2.1

1. The distance Nathan travels depends on the time. Distance, D, is the dependent quantity and time, t, is the independent quantity.

$D(t) = 6t$

3. The total number of envelopes Mario stuffs depends on the time. The total number of envelopes, E, is the dependent quantity and time, t, is the independent quantity.

$E(t) = 5t$

5. The amount of money the booster club earns depends on the number of cups sold. The amount of money, M, is the dependent quantity and the number of cups sold, c, is the independent quantity.

$M(c) = 2c$

7.

	Independent Quantity	Dependent Quantity
Quantity	Time	Distance
Units	hours	miles
Expression	t	$7t$
	0	0
	0.5	3.5
	1	7
	1.5	10.5
	2	14

$(0.5, 3.5)$ and $(1, 7)$

$$\frac{7 - 3.5}{1 - 0.5} = \frac{3.5}{0.5}$$

$$= \frac{7}{1}$$

The unit rate of change is 7.

9. Noah is stuffing envelopes with invitations to the school's Harvest Festival. He stuffs 4 envelopes each minute.

	Independent Quantity	Dependent Quantity
Quantity	Time	Number of Envelopes
Units	minutes	envelopes
Expression	t	$4t$
	5	20
	10	40
	15	60
	20	80
	25	100

$(5, 20)$ and $(10, 40)$

$$\frac{40 - 20}{10 - 5} = \frac{20}{5}$$

$$= \frac{4}{1}$$

The unit rate of change is 4.

11. The volleyball boosters sell bags of popcorn during the varsity matches to raise money for new uniforms. Each bag of popcorn costs $3.

	Independent Quantity	Dependent Quantity
Quantity	Number of bags of popcorn sold	Amount of money raised
Units	bags	dollars
Expression	b	$3b$
	5	15
	10	30
	15	45
	20	60
	25	75

(5, 15) and (10, 30)

$$\frac{30 - 15}{10 - 5} = \frac{15}{5}$$
$$= \frac{3}{1}$$

The unit rate of change is 3.

13. The input value is t.

    The output value is $4t$.

    The rate of change is 4.

15. The input value is e.

    The output value is $15e$.

    The rate of change is 15.

17. The input value is b.

    The output value is $35b$.

    The rate of change is 35.

19. Carmen earns $21 when she babysits for 3 hours.

21. Carmen earns $35 when she babysits for 5 hours.

23. Carmen earns $24.50 when she babysits for 3.5 hours.

25. $t = 3$

27. $t = 6$

29. $t = 2$

1.

	Independent Quantity	Dependent Quantity
Quantity	Time	Height
Units	minutes	feet
	0	1000
	2	1400
	4	1800
	6	2200
	8	2600
Expression	t	$200t + 1000$

3.

	Independent Quantity	Dependent Quantity
Quantity	Time	Height
Units	minutes	feet
	0	4125
	1	3575
	2	3025
	3	2475
	4	1925
Expression	t	$-550t + 4125$

5.

	Independent Quantity	Dependent Quantity
Quantity	Time	Depth
Units	minutes	feet
	0	−300
	2	−244
	4	−188
	6	−132
	8	−76
Expression	t	$28t - 300$

7. The input value is t, time in minutes. The output value is $f(t)$, height in feet.

The y-intercept is 130. The rate of change is 160.5.

9. The input value is t, time in minutes. The output value is $f(t)$, depth in feet.

The y-intercept is 0. The rate of change is −17.

11. The input value is t, time in minutes. The output value is $f(t)$, volume in gallons.

The y-intercept is 5. The rate of change is 4.25.

13.

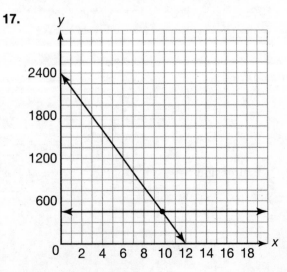

$f(x) = 720$ at $x = 12$

15.

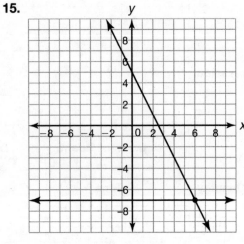

$f(x) = -7$ at $x = 6$

17.

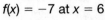

$f(x) = 450$ at $x \approx 10$

19. $12 = x$

21. $6 = x$

23. $9.75 = x$

1. $x \geq 8$

3. $x < 3$

5. $x > 10$

7. Elena must sell at least 50 tickets. $x \geq 50$

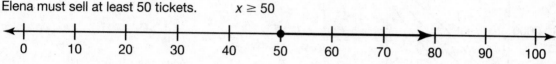

9. Elena must sell at least 70 tickets. $x \geq 70$

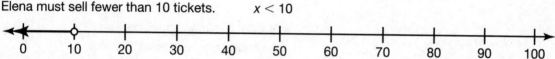

11. Elena must sell fewer than 10 tickets. $x < 10$

13. $5 \leq x$

Leon must play in 5 or more games to score at least 117 points.

15. $7 < x$

Leon must play in more than 7 games to score more than 143 points.

17. $2.54 > x$

Leon must play in 2 or fewer games to score fewer than 85 points.

19.

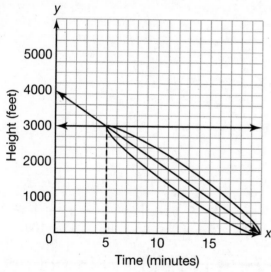

More than 5 minutes have passed if the balloon is below 3000 feet.

$x > 5$

Answers

21.

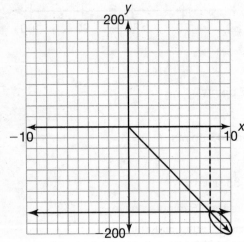

Distance (feet) vs. Time (minutes)

Less than 12 minutes have passed if Lea still has more than 2000 feet to walk.

$x < 12$

23.

At least 8 minutes have passed if the submarine is at least 160 feet below the surface.

$x \geq 8$

LESSON 2.4

1. $22 \geq x > -4$

3. $0 \leq x \leq 6$

5. $87 \geq x \geq 83$

7. $-8 < x \leq 11$

9. $7 < x < 25$

11. $-14 \leq x \leq 5$

13.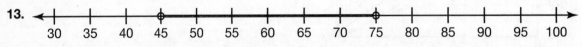

15.

17. $-35 \leq x \leq 50$

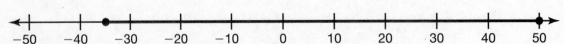

19. $x \geq 6$ or $x < 3$

21. $x > 31$ or $x \leq 26$

23. $x > 1000$ or $x < 10$

25.
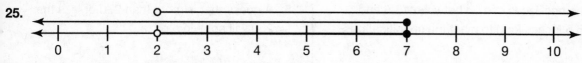

27.
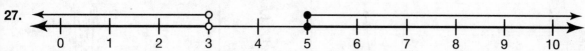

29.
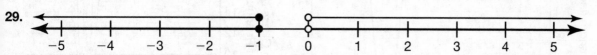

31.
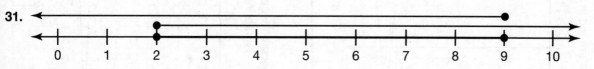

$2 \leq x \leq 9$

33.

Solution: $-10 < x \leq 10$

35.
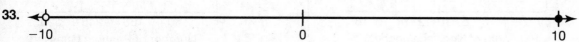

Solution: $x > 9$ or $x < 3$

37.
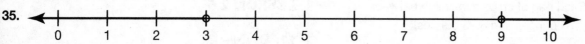

Solution: $32 \leq x < 48$

LESSON 2.5

1. $|3| = 3$

3. $\left|\dfrac{1}{4}\right| = \dfrac{1}{4}$

5. $|3.7| = 3.7$

7. There is only one solution.

$x = -9$

9. There are two solutions.

$x = 4$ or $x = -4$

11. There is only one solution.

$x = 0$

13. $x = -7$

15. $x = 17$

17. There are no solutions.

19. $x = 33$ $x = -33$

21. $x = 30$ $x = -18$

23. $x = 15$ $x = -15$

25.
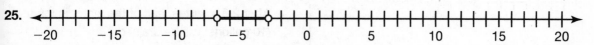

27.
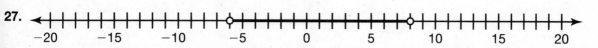

29.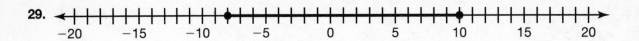

31. The necklaces can be between 15.5 and 16.5 inches long to meet the specifications.

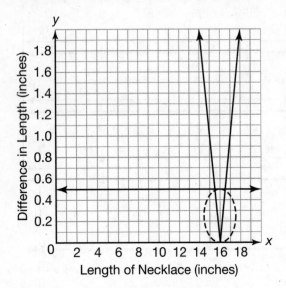

33. Each bag of chips can weigh between 7.75 ounces and 8.25 ounces.

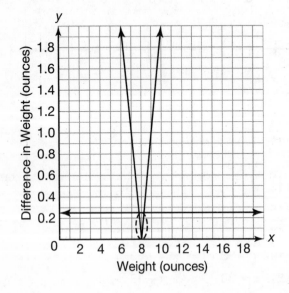

35. A guess that is more than 270 or less than 250 will not win a prize.

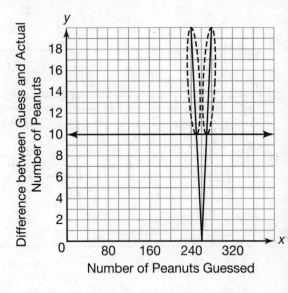

LESSON 2.6

1. B $f(x) = 3x$

3. C $f(x) = 25,000\left(\frac{5}{6}\right)^x$

5. B $f(x) = -32x^2 + 25x$

7.

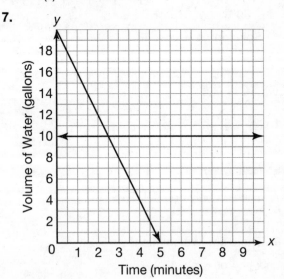

After 2.5 minutes, half of the water in the tank (10 gallons) will be drained.

9.

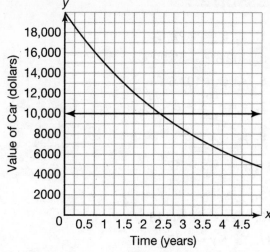

Ronna can own the car for almost 2.5 years before reselling and will still make at least $10,000.

11.

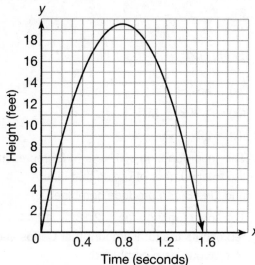

The softball is in the air for about 1.5 seconds.

Chapter 3

LESSON 3.1

1. The attendance during Game 9 will be 2620 people.

3. The average price of gas in August will be $3.44.

5. In 2014, Kata will travel 5623 miles.

1. a = pounds of apples

   b = pounds of oranges

   $0.75a + 0.89b$

3. m = matinee

   n = evening

   $7m + 10.5n$

5. d = daisies

   r = roses

   $8.99d + 15.99r$

7. c = carnations

   f = lilies

   $10.99c + 12.99f = 650$

9. q = pounds of oranges

   r = pounds of peaches

   $0.79q + 1.05r = 325$

11. d = DVDs

    b = Blu-ray discs

    $15.99d + 22.99b = 2000$

13. The booster club must sell 75 hot dogs to reach their goal.

15. The booster club must sell 360 hamburgers to reach their goal.

17. The booster club must sell 132 hot dogs to reach their goal.

19. The x-intercept is (12, 0) and the y-intercept is (0, 30).

21. The x-intercept is $(-21, 0)$ and the y-intercept is (0, 168).

23. The x-intercept is approximately (24.43, 0) and the y-intercept is (0, 13.68).

25.

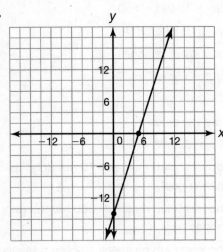

$x = 18$ $\qquad$ $y = 15$

27.

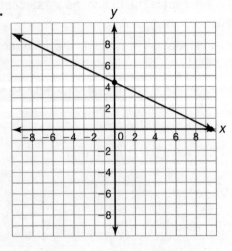

$5 = x$ $\qquad$ $y = -15$

29.

$x = 9.5$ $\qquad$ $y \approx 4.4$

LESSON 3.3

1. $72°F \approx 22.22°C$

3. $102.6°F \approx 39.22°C$

5. $42°C = 107.6°F$

7. $y = -\dfrac{2}{3}x + 8$

9. $y = \dfrac{4}{9}x + 5$

11. $y = -\dfrac{1}{8}x - 12$

13. $-5x + y = 8$

15. $-2x + 3y = -18$

17. $5x + y = -13$

19. $\dfrac{2A}{b} = h$

21. $\sqrt{\dfrac{A}{\pi}} = r$

23. $\dfrac{3V}{lh} = w$

LESSON 3.4

1. $f(x) = 35x - 105$

3. $f(x) = 1.99x - 3.98$

5. $f(x) = 20x - 20$

7. The linear function $c(x) = \dfrac{5}{2}x - 24$ represents the total number of boxes that Line A and Line B can produce combined.

9. The linear function $f(x) = 2.16x - 12.44$ represents the total amount that Carlos and Hector can earn combined.

11. The linear function $c(x) = 47.75x - 279$ represents the total amount that Line A and Line B can make combined.

Chapter 4

LESSON 4.1

1. The second figure has 2 more squares than the first, the third figure has 3 more squares than the second, and the fourth figure has 4 more squares than the third.

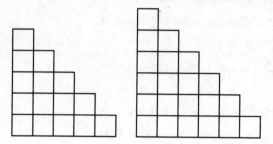

3. Each figure has 2 more circles than the previous figure.

5. Each figure has twice as many triangles as the previous figure.

7. 1000, 995, 990, 985, 980, 975, 970

9. $40, $80, $120, $160, $200, $240

11. 1, 3, 7, 15, 31, 63, 127

13. 200, 225, 250, 275, 300, 325, 350

15. 50, 47, 44, 41, 38, 35, 32, 29

LESSON 4.2

1. $d = 5 - 1$
$d = 4$

3. $d = 13 - 10.5$
$d = 2.5$

5. $d = 91.5 - 95$
$d = -3.5$

7. $d = 1190 - 1250$
$d = -60$

9. $d = 9 - 8\frac{1}{2}$
$d = \frac{1}{2}$

11. $r = 10 \div 5$
$r = 2$

13. $r = -6 \div 3$
$r = -2$

15. $r = -30 \div 10$
$r = -3$

17. $r = 40 \div 5$
$r = 8$

19. $r = -1 \div 0.2$
$r = -5$

21. 8, 14, 20, 26, __32__, __38__, __44__, . . .

23. −24, −14, −4, 6, __16__, __26__, __36__, . . .

25. 20, 11, 2, −7, __−16__, __−25__, __−34__, . . .

27. −101, −112, −123, −134, __−145__, __−156__, __−167__, . . .

29. −500, −125, 250, 625, __1000__, __1375__, __1750__, . . .

31. 3, 9, 27, 81, __243__, __729__, __2187__, . . .

33. 5, −10, 20, −40, __80__, __−160__, __320__, . . .

35. 2, −2, 2, −2, __2__, __−2__, __2__, . . .

37. −8000, 4000, −2000, 1000, __−500__, __250__, __−125__, . . .

39. 156.25, 31.25, 6.25, 1.25, $\underline{0.25}$, $\underline{0.05}$, $\underline{0.01}$, . . .

41. The sequence is arithmetic. The next 3 terms are 20, 24, and 28.

43. The sequence is geometric. The next 3 terms are 768, 3072, and 12,288.

45. The sequence is neither arithmetic nor geometric.

47. The sequence is arithmetic. The next 3 terms are 23.9, 28.0, and 32.1.

49. The sequence is geometric. The next 3 terms are 1280, −5120, and 20,480.

LESSON 4.3

1. $a_{20} = 58$

3. $a_{25} = 29.7$

5. $a_{42} = 104.50$

7. $a_{34} = 98.7$

9. $a_{57} = 0$

11. $g_{10} = 1536$

13. $g_{12} = 885{,}735$

15. $g_{20} = -65{,}536$

17. $g_{14} = 32{,}768$

19. $g_{12} \approx 46.57$

21. The sequence is geometric.

$g_5 = 64$

23. The sequence is geometric.

$g_4 = -54$ $g_6 = -486$

25. The sequence is arithmetic.

$a_4 = 590$ $a_5 = 680$

27. The sequence is arithmetic.

$a_4 = -113$ $a_5 = -128$ $a_6 = -143$

29. $a_{20} = 790$

31. $a_{30} = 248$

33. $a_{30} = 10{,}500$

35. $a_{24} = 68.9$

37. $a_{20} = 13{,}900$

LESSON 4.4

1.

Term Number (n)	Value of Term (a_n)
1	15
2	18
3	21
4	24
5	27
6	30
7	33
8	36
9	39
10	42

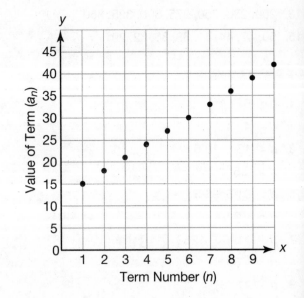

3.

Term Number (n)	Value of Term (a_n)
1	50
2	42
3	34
4	26
5	18
6	10
7	2
8	−6
9	−14
10	−22

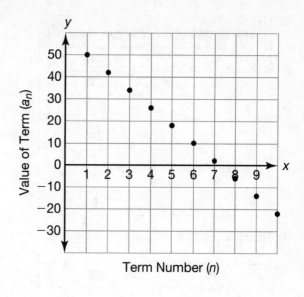

5.

Term Number (n)	Value of Term (a_n)
1	−24
2	−18
3	−12
4	−6
5	0
6	6
7	12
8	18
9	24
10	30

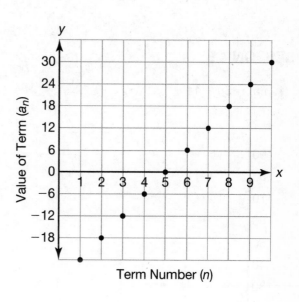

7.

Term Number (n)	Value of Term (a_n)
1	75
2	100
3	125
4	150
5	175
6	200
7	225
8	250
9	275
10	300

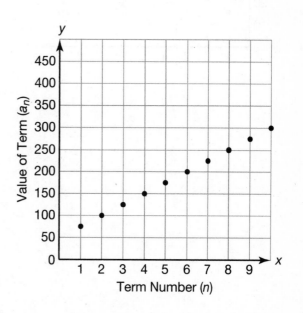

9.

Term Number (n)	Value of Term (a_n)
1	400
2	320
3	240
4	160
5	80
6	0
7	−80
8	−160
9	−240
10	−320

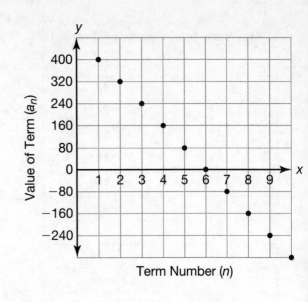

LESSON 4.5

1. $f(n) = 5n + 11$

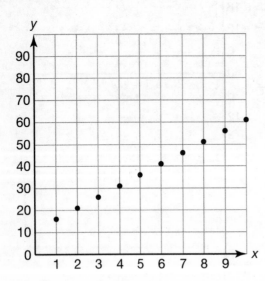

3. $f(n) = -20n + 120$

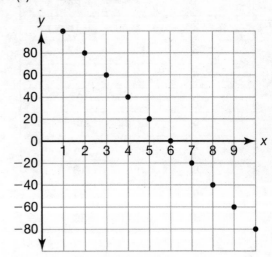

5. $f(n) = -50n + 600$

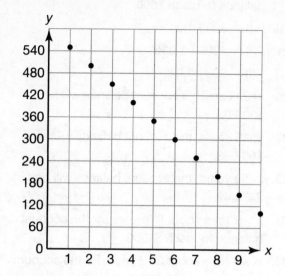

9. $f(n) = 8 \cdot 2.5^n$

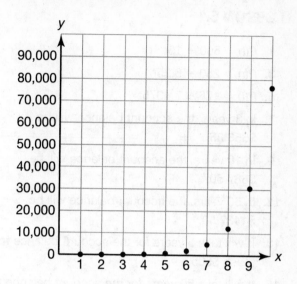

7. $f(n) = \dfrac{5}{2} \cdot 2^n$

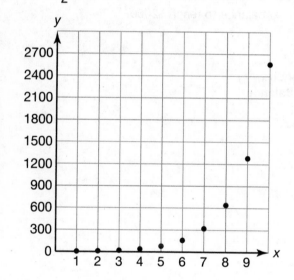

11. $f(n) = -0.25 \cdot 2^n$

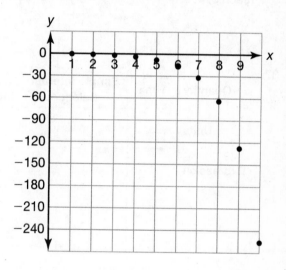

Chapter 5

LESSON 5.1

1. $P(t) = 500 + 15t$

3. $P(t) = 250 + 6.25t$

5. $P(t) = 175 + 7.4375t$

7. In 3 years, the account balance will be $556.25.

9. In 10 years, the account balance will be $687.50.

11. In 50 years, the account balance will be $1437.50.

13. It will take 5 years for the account balance to reach $505.

15. It will take 50 years for the account balance to reach $1450.

17. It will take about 19 years for the account balance to reach $800.

19. $P(t) = 500 \cdot 1.04$

21. $P(t) = 1200 \cdot 1.035^t$

23. $P(t) = 300 \cdot 1.0175^t$

25. In 2 years, the account balance will be $533.03.

27. In 15 years, the account balance will be $807.83.

29. In 50 years, the account balance will be 2474.42.

31. It will take about 8.3 years for the account balance to reach $1500.

33. It will take about 36.7 years for the account balance to reach $6000.

35. It will take about 14.2 years for the account balance to reach $2000.

37.

Quantity	Time	Simple Interest Balance	Compound Interest Balance
Units	years	dollars	dollars
Expression	t	$300 + 12t$	$300 \cdot 1.04^t$
	0	300.00	300.00
	2	324.00	324.48
	6	372.00	379.60
	10	420.00	444.07

A-18 ■ Answers

39.

Quantity	Time	Simple Interest Balance	Compound Interest Balance
Units	years	dollars	dollars
Expression	t	$1100 + 38.5t$	$1100 \cdot 1.035^t$
	0	1100.00	1100.00
	5	1292.50	1306.45
	10	1485.00	1551.66
	30	2255.00	3087.47

41.

Quantity	Time	Simple Interest Balance	Compound Interest Balance
Units	years	dollars	dollars
Expression	t	$2300 + 86.25t$	$2300 \cdot 1.0375^t$
	0	2300.00	2300.00
	2	2472.50	2475.73
	5	2731.25	2764.83
	15	3593.75	3995.30

LESSON 5.2

1. $P(t) = 7000 \cdot 1.014^t$

3. $P(t) = 8000 \cdot 0.9825^t$

5. $P(t) = 9500 \cdot 0.028^t$

7. The population after 1 year will be 16,240.

9. The population after 5 years will be about 17,237.

11. The population after 20 years will be about 21,550.

13. It will take about 4.7 years for the population to reach 17,000.

15. It will take about 57.4 years for the population to reach 9000.

17. The range of the function is all numbers greater than 0. The function never actually reaches 0.

19.

x	f(x)
−2	$\frac{1}{4}$
−1	$\frac{1}{2}$
0	1
1	2
2	4

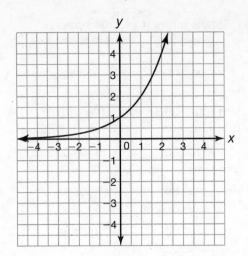

x-intercept: none

y-intercept: (0, 1)

asymptote: $y = 0$

domain: all real numbers

range: $y > 0$

interval(s) of increase or decrease: increasing over the entire domain

21.

x	f(x)
−2	9
−1	3
0	1
1	$\frac{1}{3}$
2	$\frac{1}{9}$

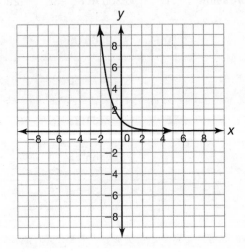

x-intercept: none

y-intercept: (0, 1)

asymptote: $y = 0$

domain: all real numbers

range: $y > 0$

interval(s) of increase or decrease: decreasing over the entire domain

23.

x	f(x)
-2	$-\dfrac{1}{2}$
-1	-1
0	-2
1	-4
2	-8

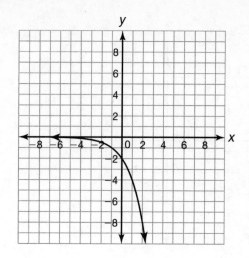

x-intercept: none

y-intercept: (0, -2)

asymptote: $y = 0$

domain: all real numbers

range: $y < 0$

interval(s) of increase or decrease: decreasing over the entire domain

LESSON 5.3

1. $g(x) = f(x) + 4$

3. $g(x) = f(x) - 8$

5. $g(x) = f(x) + 2$

7. $(x, y) \rightarrow (x, y + 8)$

9. $(x, y) \rightarrow (x, y - 4)$

11. $(x, y) \rightarrow (x, y + 6)$

13. $g(x) = 3^{(x + 1)} = f(x + 1)$

15. $g(x) = 2^{(x - 1)} = f(x - 1)$

17. $g(x) = 2(x - 3) = f(x - 3)$

19. $(x, y) \rightarrow (x + 2, y)$

21. $(x, y) \rightarrow (x - 1, y)$

23. $(x, y) \rightarrow (x + 1, y)$

25. The graph of f(x) is b units below the graph of h(x).

27. The graph of f(x) is b units to the right of h(x).

29. The graph of f(x) is k units up from the graph of h(x).

31.

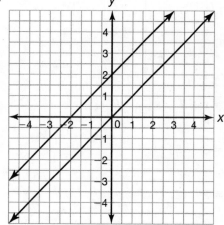

33.

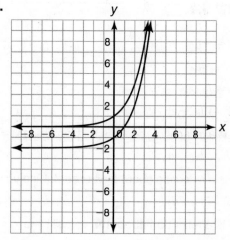

35.

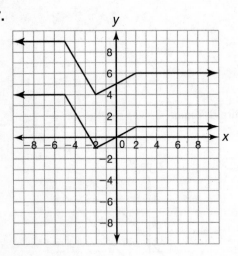

37.

39. $g(x) = x + 2$

41. $g(x) = 3^{x-4}$

43. $g(x) = 3^x - 5$

45. $g(x) = x - 3$

47. $g(x) = 2^x + 2$

49. $g(x) = 2^{x-3}$

LESSON 5.4

1. $g(x) = -f(x)$

3. $g(x) = -f(x)$

5. $g(x) = f(-x)$

7. $(x, y) \to (x, -y)$

   $g(x)$ is a reflection about the horizontal line $y = 0$.

9. $(x, y) \to (x, -y)$

   $g(x)$ is a reflection about the horizontal line $y = 0$.

11. $(x, y) \to (-x, y)$

   $g(x)$ is a reflection about the vertical line $x = 0$.

13.

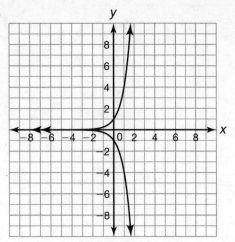

15.

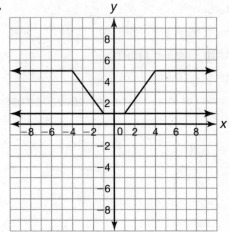

17.

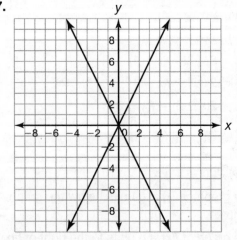

19. $g(x) = -3^x$

21. $g(x) = 12x$

23. $g(x) = -(2^x + 9)$

25. $g(x) = -5^x$

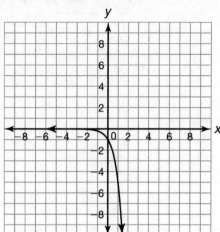

27. $g(x) = 3^x + 2$

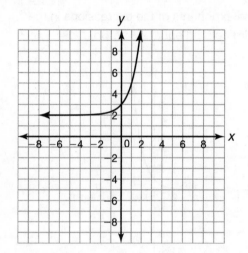

29. $g(x) = 4^x - 4$

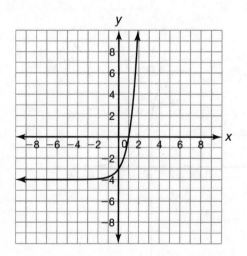

31. $g(x)$ is a reflection of $f(x)$ over the line $x = 0$.

33. $g(x)$ is a translation of $f(x)$ up 10 units or $g(x)$ is a translation of $f(x)$ left 5 units.

35. $g(x)$ is a translation of $f(x)$ right 4 units.

37. $g(x)$ is a reflection of $f(x)$ over the line $y = 0$.

39. $g(x)$ is a translation of $f(x)$ down 5 units.

41. $g(x)$ is a translation of $f(x)$ up 2 units.

LESSON 5.5

1. $\dfrac{10^5}{10^8} = 10^{5-8} = 10^{-3}$

3. $\dfrac{10^2}{10^5} = 10^{2-5} = 10^{-3}$

5. $\dfrac{5^3}{5^{10}} = 5^{3-10} = 5^{-7}$

7. $\sqrt[3]{216} = 6$

9. $\sqrt[3]{-125} = -5$

11. $\sqrt[3]{729} = 9$

13. $\sqrt[5]{32} = 2$

15. $\sqrt[6]{729} = 3$

17. $\sqrt[7]{-128} = -2$

19. $\sqrt[4]{15} = 15^{\frac{1}{4}}$

21. $\sqrt[4]{31} = 31^{\frac{1}{4}}$

23. $\sqrt[6]{y} = y^{\frac{1}{6}}$

25. $12^{\frac{1}{3}} = \sqrt[3]{12}$

27. $18^{\frac{1}{4}} = \sqrt[4]{18}$

29. $d^{\frac{1}{5}} = \sqrt[5]{d}$

31. $5^{\frac{2}{3}} = \sqrt[3]{5^2}$

33. $18^{\frac{3}{4}} = \sqrt[4]{18^3}$

35. $y^{\frac{4}{3}} = \sqrt[3]{y^4}$

37. $\sqrt[4]{6^3} = 6^{\frac{3}{4}}$

39. $\sqrt[3]{12^2} = 12^{\frac{2}{3}}$

41. $\sqrt[4]{p^7} = p^{\frac{7}{4}}$

1.

x	f(x)	Expression
0	1	3^0
1	3	3^1
2	9	3^2
3	27	3^3
4	81	3^4
5	243	3^5
x	3^x	-----

The exponents of the expressions in the third column equal x. So, $f(x) = 3x$.

3.

x	f(x)	Expression
0	−1	-2^0
1	−2	-2^1
2	−4	-2^2
3	−8	-2^3
4	−16	-2^4
5	−32	-2^5
x	-2^x	-----

The exponents of the expressions in the third column equal x. So, $f(x) = -2^x$.

5.

x	f(x)	Expression
0	$-\dfrac{1}{25}$	-5^{-2}
1	$-\dfrac{1}{5}$	-5^{-1}
2	−1	-5^0
3	−5	-5^1
4	−25	-5^2
5	−125	-5^3
x	-5^{x-2}	-----

The exponents of the expressions in the third column equal $x - 2$. So, $f(x) = -5^{x-2}$.

7.

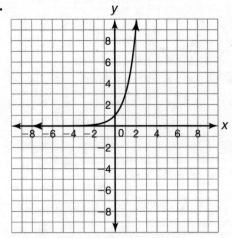

9.

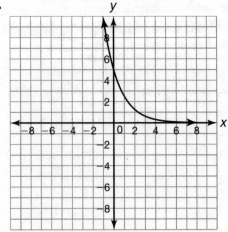

11.

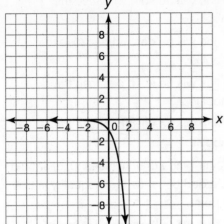

13. $f(x) = 7776$ when $x = 6$.

15. $f(x) = 625$ when $x = -3$.

17. $f(x) > -9$ when $x < 1$.

19. $x = 4$

21. $x = 9$

23. $x = -2$

25. $x = -2$

27. $2^{-1} \cdot 2s$

  2^{s-1}

29. $2^1 \cdot 2^{2x}$

  2^{2x+1}

31. $64^x \cdot 4$

  $4(64)^x$

33. $f(x) = 2\left(\dfrac{1}{2}\right)^x$

35. $f(x) = \left(\dfrac{3}{4}\right)^x$

37. $f(x) = 3\left(\dfrac{1}{3}\right)^x$

Chapter 6

LESSON 6.1

1. The break-even point is between 6 and 7 model cars. Eric must sell more than 6 model cars to make a profit.

3. The break-even point is between 11 and 12 yards mowed. Chen must mow more than 11 yards to make a profit.

5. The break-even point is between 13 and 14 boxes of fruit. The Spanish Club must sell more than 13 boxes of fruit to make a profit.

7. $x + 3y = 8 \qquad 2x - y = 21$

9. $15x - 36 = 2y \qquad 2x + y = 9$

11. $2x - 4y = 20 \qquad -x - 5y = 11$

13. The solution is (4, 5). The system is consistent.

15. There is no solution. The system is inconsistent.

17. The solution is (2, 0.5). The system is consistent.

LESSON 6.2

1. $\begin{cases} 10x + 15y = 20 \\ 5x + 6y = 8.50 \end{cases}$

The solution is (0.5, 1). The band charges $0.50 for each apple and $1.00 for each orange.

3. $\begin{cases} 3x + 2y = 30 \\ 4x + 3y = 41 \end{cases}$

The solution is (8, 3). The Pizza Barn sells each pepperoni pizza for $8 and each order of breadsticks for $3.

5. $\begin{cases} 4x + 2y = 63.8 \\ 9x + 4y = 139.8 \end{cases}$

The solution is (12.2, 7.5). Each large block is 12.2 inches tall and each small block is 7.5 inches tall.

7. The solution is (6, −2).

9. The solution is (−3, −4).

11. The solution is (0, 7).

13. The solution is (2, −2).

LESSON 6.3

1. $\begin{cases} 4x + 10y = 200 \\ 6x + 5y = 200 \end{cases}$

The solution is (25, 10). Each large plate weighs 25 pounds. Each small plate weighs 10 pounds.

3. $\begin{cases} y = 0.25x + 2.50 \\ y = 0.50x + 1.50 \end{cases}$

The solution is (4, 3.50). Both vendors charge $3.50 for a sundae with 4 toppings. If Raja wants fewer than 4 toppings, then Colder & Creamier Sundaes is the better buy. If Raja wants more than 4 toppings, Cold & Creamy Sundaes is the better buy.

5. $\begin{cases} 10x + 6y = 193 \\ 8x + 10y = 183 \end{cases}$

The solution is (16, 5.5). Alicia charges $16 for each purse and $5.50 for each wallet.

LESSON 6.4

1. $\begin{cases} y = 0.02x + 20{,}000 \\ y = 0.01x + 25{,}000 \end{cases}$

The solution is (500,000, 30,000). Both real estate companies will pay Jun $30,000 per year for $500,000 in real estate sales. If Jun expects to sell less than $500,000 of real estate per year, then he should accept the offer from Amazing Homes. If Jun expects to sell more than $500,000 of real estate per year, then he should accept the offer from Dream Homes.

3. $\begin{cases} y = 25x + 15{,}000 \\ y = 21x + 18{,}000 \end{cases}$

The solution is (750, 33,750). Both companies will pay Renee $33,750 for selling 750 food processors. If Renee expects to sell fewer than 750 food processors in one year, then she should accept the offer from Puree Processors. If Renee expects to sell more than 750 food processors in one year, then she should accept the offer from Pro Process Processors.

5. $\begin{cases} y = 0.01x + 22{,}000 \\ y = 0.025x + 13{,}000 \end{cases}$

The solution is (600,000, 28,000). Both dealerships will pay Serena $28,000 for $600,000 in car sales. If Serena expects to have fewer than $600,000 in car sales in one year, then she should accept the offer from Classic Cars. If Serena expects to have more than $600,000 in car sales in one year, then she should accept the offer from Sweet Rides.

Chapter 7

LESSON 7.1

1. $x + y \geq 500$

3. $y > 6x + 20$

5. $7x + 3y > 28$

7. The line will be solid because the symbol is $\leq$.

9. The line will be dashed because the symbol is $<$.

11. The line will be solid because the symbol is $\geq$.

13. The line will be solid because the symbol is $\geq$.

15. The half-plane that includes (0, 0) should be shaded because the inequality is true for that point.

17. The half-plane that does not include (0, 0) should be shaded because the inequality is false for that point.

19. The half-plane that does not include (0, 0) should be shaded because the inequality is false for that point.

21.

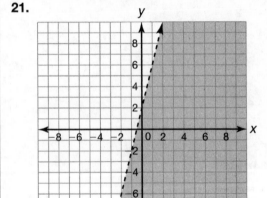

23.

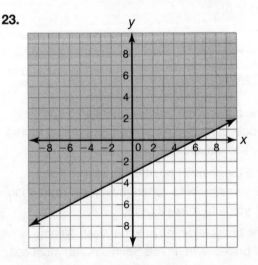

25.

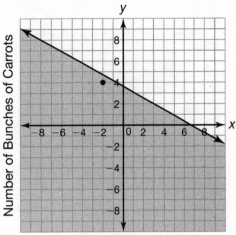

27. No. The ordered pair (6, 3) is not a solution to the inequality. It is not in the shaded half-plane.

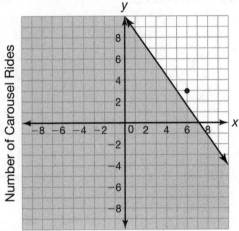

Number of Ferris Wheel Rides

29. No. The ordered pair (6, −1) is not a solution for the problem situation.

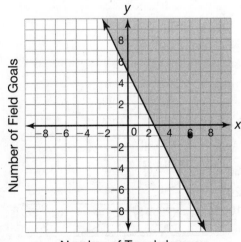

Number of Touchdowns

31. No. The ordered pair (−2, 4) is not a solution for the problem situation.

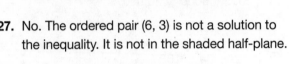

Number of Squash

LESSON 7.2

1. $\begin{cases} 3x + 2y \geq 24 \\ 200x + 100y \leq 1200 \end{cases}$

3. $\begin{cases} x + y \leq 15 \\ 200x + 100y \leq 3000 \end{cases}$

5. $\begin{cases} 10x + 25y \geq 200 \\ 15x + 45y \leq 480 \end{cases}$

7. The point (−2, −10) is a solution to the system of inequalities.

9. The point (3, 7) is not a solution to the system of inequalities.

11. The point (14, 8) is not a solution to the system of inequalities.

13. Answers will vary. (2, 3) and (6, 0)

15. Answers will vary. (1, 2) and (−2, 2)

17. Answers will vary. (−1, 6) and (1, 10)

LESSON 7.3

1. $\begin{cases} r \geq 65 \\ r \leq 180 \\ s \leq 0.65r \end{cases}$

3. $\begin{cases} r \geq 55 \\ r \leq 325 \\ c \leq 0.80r \\ c \geq 0.60r \end{cases}$

5. $\begin{cases} t \geq 5 \\ q \geq 5 \\ t + q \leq 20 \end{cases}$

7.

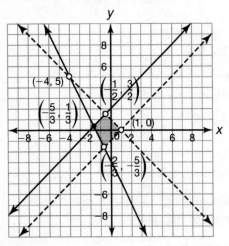

Answers will vary. A solution to the system of inequalities would be (0, 0).

9.

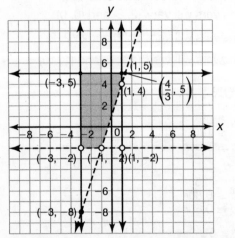

Answers will vary. A solution to the system of inequalities would be (0, 0).

11.

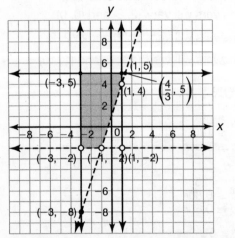

Answers will vary. A solution to the system of inequalities would be (−1, 1).

13. The most Pedro can save is $240 represented by the point (400, 240).

15. The most he will pay is $320.

17. The least he will pay is $160.

LESSON 7.4

1. $\begin{cases} t \ge 0 \\ f \ge 0 \\ t + f \le 40 \\ t + 2f \le 72 \end{cases}$

3. $\begin{cases} t \ge 0 \\ p \ge 0 \\ t + p \le 50 \\ 300t + 600p \le 20{,}000 \end{cases}$

5. $\begin{cases} i \ge 0 \\ a \ge 0 \\ 2i + 3a \le 168 \\ 65i + 85a \le 5000 \\ i + a \le 65 \end{cases}$

7.

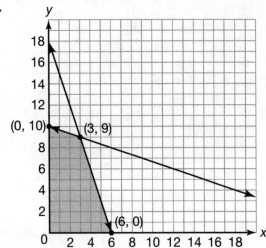

9.

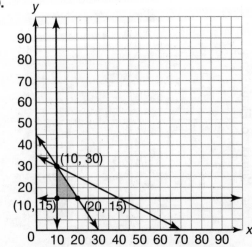

11.

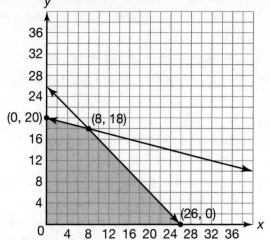

13. The minimum daily cost is $1080. To minimize their daily cost, the company should produce 3 basic models and 8 touch screen models.

15. The maximum profit is $960. To maximize their profit, the company should produce 12 basic models and 12 touch screen models.

17. The minimum number of work hours utilized is 60 hours per day. To minimize the number of work hours utilized per day, the company should produce 3 basic models and 8 touch screen models.

Chapter 8
LESSON 8.1

1.

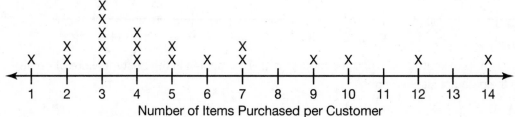

The data are skewed left.

3.

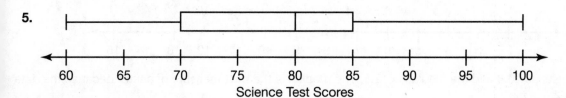

The data are skewed right.

5.

The data are symmetric.

7.

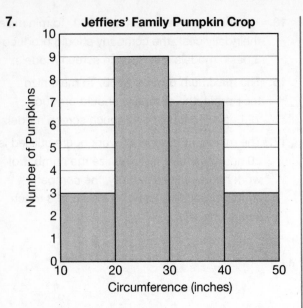

Jeffiers' Family Pumpkin Crop

The data are symmetric.

9. The data are skewed right, because a majority of the data values are on the left of the plot and only a few of the data values are on the right of the plot. This means that a majority of the players on the softball team hit a small number of home runs, while only a few players on the team hit a large number of home runs.

11. Five players hit more than 2 home runs.

13. Six players hit more than 1 and fewer than 9 home runs.

15. The middle 50 percent of the surveyed adults are at least 65 inches and at most 72 inches tall.

17. Fifty percent of the surveyed adults are 68 inches tall or shorter.

19. One hundred percent of the surveyed adults are at least 58 inches tall. Therefore, all 40 of the surveyed adults are at least 58 inches tall.

21. There are a total of 31 students represented by the histogram.

23. It is not possible to determine the number of students who scored exactly 25.

25. Twenty-six students had an ACT composite score less than 30.

LESSON 8.2

1.

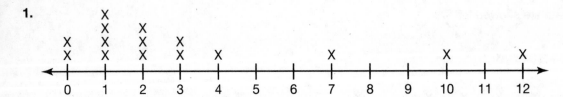

The mean is approximately 3.27 and the median is 2. The median is the best measure of center because the data are skewed right.

3.

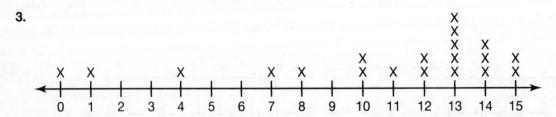

The mean is 10.6 and the median is 12.5. The median is the best measure of center because the data are skewed left.

5.

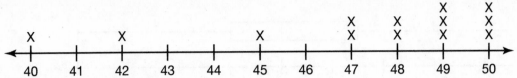

The mean is approximately 47.53 and the median is 49. The median is the best measure of center because the data are skewed left.

7. The mean is the best measure of center to describe the data because the data are symmetric. The mean and median cannot be determined because the data values are not given.

9. The median is the best measure of center to describe the data because the data are skewed right. The median number of movies watched last month is 6. The mean cannot be determined because the data values are not given.

11. The median is the best measure of center to describe the data because the data are skewed right. The mean number of fish caught is approximately 3.14 and the median number of fish caught is 2.

LESSON 8.3

1. $IQR = Q3 - Q1$
$= 14 - 5$
$= 9$

The value 30 is an outlier because it is greater than the upper fence.

3. $IQR = Q3 - Q1$
$= 40 - 28$
$= 12$

The value 9 is an outlier because it is less than the lower fence. The value 59 is an outlier because it is greater than the upper fence.

5. $IQR = Q3 - Q1$
$= 25 - 18.5$
$= 6.5$

The value 8 is an outlier because it is less than the lower fence.

7. $IQR = Q3 - Q1$
$= 10 - 7$
$= 3$

There is at least 1 outlier less than the lower fence because the minimum value of the data set is 1.

9. $IQR = Q3 - Q1$
$= 60 - 45$
$= 15$

There is at least 1 outlier less than the lower fence because the minimum value of the data set is 15. There is at least 1 outlier greater than the upper fence because the maximum value of the data set is 90.

11. $IQR = Q3 - Q1$
$= 550 - 350$
$= 200$

There is at least 1 outlier less than the lower fence because the minimum value of the data set is 0.

LESSON 8.4

1. The mean is 5. The standard deviation is approximately 3.16.

3. The mean is 13. The standard deviation is approximately 7.56.

5. The mean is 4. The standard deviation is approximately 1.15.

7. The mean is approximately 6.56. The standard deviation is approximately 3.34.

9. The mean is approximately 104.45. The standard deviation is approximately 1.44.

11. The mean is 7.9. The standard deviation is approximately 3.42.

1.

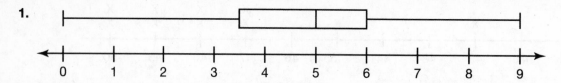

The most appropriate measure of center is the mean, and the most appropriate measure of spread is the standard deviation because the data are symmetric. The mean is 4.75 and the standard deviation is approximately 2.35.

3.

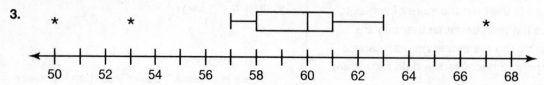

The most appropriate measure of center is the mean, and the most appropriate measure of spread is the standard deviation because the data are symmetric. The mean is 59.2 and the standard deviation is approximately 3.85.

5.

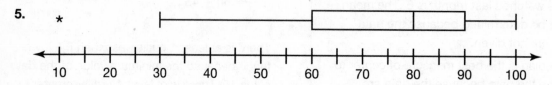

The most appropriate measure of center is the median, and the most appropriate measure of spread is the IQR because the data are skewed left. The median is 80 and the IQR is 30.

7. For each data set, the most appropriate measure of center is the median and the most appropriate measure of spread is the IQR, because the data are skewed right. For Data Set 1, the median is 11 and the IQR is 14. For Data Set 2, the median is 11 and the IQR is 15.

9. For Data Set 1, the most appropriate measure of center is the mean, and the most appropriate measure of spread is the standard deviation because the data are symmetric. For Data Set 1, the mean is 69.9 and the standard deviation is approximately 8.40. For Data Set 2, the most appropriate measure of center is the median, and the most appropriate measure of spread is the IQR because the data are skewed left. For Data Set 2, the median is 74 and the IQR is 16.5.

11. For Data Set 1, the most appropriate measure of center is the median, and the most appropriate measure of spread is the IQR because the data are skewed right. For Data Set 1, the median is 42 and the IQR is 11. For Data Set 2, the most appropriate measure of center is the mean, and the most appropriate measure of spread is the standard deviation because the data are symmetric. For Data Set 2, the mean is 49.5 and the standard deviation is approximately 7.98.

Chapter 9

LESSON 9.1

1. The least squares regression line for the points is $y = 1.13x - 1.02$.

3. The least squares regression line for the points is $y = -0.83x + 0.61$.

5. The least squares regression line for the points is $y = 1.00x + 1.25$.

7. The total number of T-shirts sold in 2008 should be about 143. The actual number of T-shirts sold was 175, so the predicted value is fairly close to the actual value.

9. The total number of T-shirts sold in 2012 should be about 371. The actual number of T-shirts sold was 375, so the predicted value is very close to the actual value.

11. The total number of T-shirts sold in 2020 should be about 829. The prediction is reasonable.

LESSON 9.2

1. These data have a positive correlation. Because of this the *r-value* must be positive. Also, the data are fairly close to forming a straight line, so $r = 0.8$ (A) would be the most accurate.

3. These data have no correlation. Because there is not a linear relationship in the data, the *r*-value will be close to 0, so $r = 0.01$ (A) would be the most accurate.

5. These data have a positive correlation. Because of this the *r*-value must be positive. Also, the data are fairly close to forming a straight line, so $r = 0.7$ (D) would be the most accurate.

7. The correlation coefficient of this data set is 0.8846.

9. The correlation coefficient of this data set is 0.9226.

11. The correlation coefficient of this data set is -0.4193.

13. $y = 34{,}571.4286x + 50{,}238.0952$

$r = 0.9571$

Because the *r*-value is close to 1, the linear regression equation is appropriate for the data set.

15. $y = -0.6286x + 20.2381$

$r = -0.0915$

Because the *r*-value is close to 0, the linear regression equation is not appropriate for the data set.

17. $y = -311.1429x + 9304.5238$

$r = -0.0857$

Because the *r*-value is close to 0, the linear regression equation is not appropriate for the data set.

LESSON 9.3

1.

x	y	Predicted Value	Residual Value
5	3	2.5	0.5
10	4	5	−1
15	9	7.5	1.5
20	7	10	−3
25	13	12.5	0.5
30	15	15	0

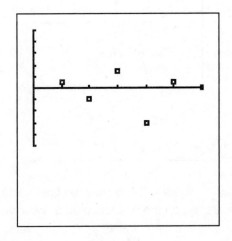

3.

x	y	Predicted Value	Residual Value
1	1.5	0.9	0.6
3	6.5	6.9	−0.4
5	12.5	12.9	−0.4
7	19.5	18.9	0.6
9	24.5	24.9	−0.4
11	31.5	30.9	0.6

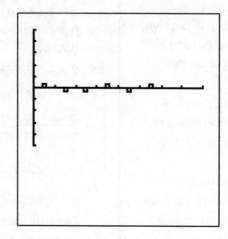

5.

x	y	Predicted Value	Residual Value
100	505	506.4	−1.4
90	460	457.4	2.6
80	415	408.4	6.6
70	360	359.4	0.6
60	305	310.4	−5.4
50	265	261.4	3.6

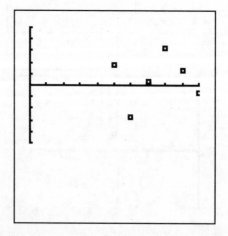

7. Based on the shape of the scatter plot and the correlation coefficient, a linear model appears to be appropriate for the data. Based on the residual plot, a linear model appears to be appropriate for the data.

9. Based on the shape of the scatter plot and the correlation coefficient, a linear model appears to be appropriate for the data. Based on the residual plot, there may be a more appropriate model than linear for the data.

11. Based on the shape of the scatter plot and the correlation coefficient, a linear model appears to be appropriate for the data. Based on the residual plot, a linear model appears to be appropriate for the data.

LESSON 9.4

1. Linear regression equation: $y = 24.98x + 100.86$, $r = 1.0000$

Scatter Plot & Line of Best Fit   Residual Plot

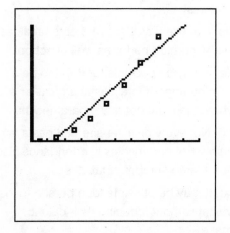 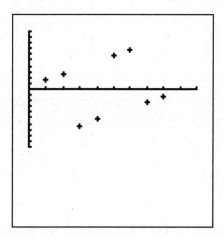

Based on the shape of the scatter plot and the correlation coefficient, a linear model appears to be appropriate for the data. Based on the residual plot, a linear model appears to be appropriate for the data.

3. Linear regression equation: $y = 16x - 42$, $r = 0.9701$

Scatter Plot & Line of Best Fit   Residual Plot

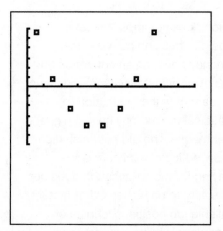

Based on the shape of the scatter plot and the correlation coefficient, a linear model may possibly be appropriate for the data. Based on the residual plot, there may be a more appropriate model than linear for the data.

5. Linear regression equation: $y = -2.51x + 40.18$, $r = -0.9993$

Scatter Plot & Line of Best Fit

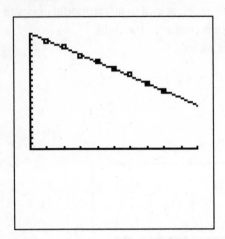

Residual Plot

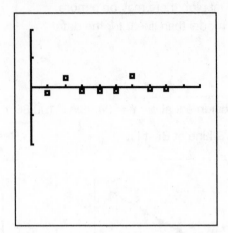

Based on the shape of the scatter plot and the correlation coefficient, a linear model appears to be appropriate for the data. Based on the residual plot, a linear model appears to be appropriate for the data.

LESSON 9.5

1. The correlation does not imply causation. There may be a correlation between ice cream sales and soup sales. For instance, ice cream sales may increase as soup sales decrease because ice cream sales typically increase in warmer weather and soup sales typically decrease in warmer weather. However, this trend does not mean that an increase in ice cream sales causes the soup sales to decrease.

3. The correlation does not imply causation. There may be a correlation between the amount of money spent on an education and a person's salary. For instance, someone who pays for 10 years of higher education to become a medical doctor may have a higher salary than someone who did not finish high school and is working at minimum wage. However, paying for more education does not cause one's salary to be higher. Other factors, such as available job positions, choice of career, and personal abilities impact the amount of annual salary a person receives.

5. The correlation does not imply causation. There may be a correlation between the number of hours a student plays video games per day and the grades a student receives at school. However, playing video games does not cause bad grades. There may be other factors such as poor study habits or a lack of attention that result in a student receiving bad grades.

7. a. Yes. It is very difficult for a student to perform well in school without a healthy breakfast.

   b. No. Not every student who eats breakfast every morning performs well at school.

9. a. No. It may be possible for there to be a large number of fatalities at a disaster site where there are not many paramedics.

   b. No. Not every disaster site that has a large number of paramedics in attendance also has a large number of fatalities.

11. a. No. It may be possible for a person to lose weight without reducing their caloric intake.

   b. Yes. Reducing caloric intake results in weight loss.

Chapter 10

LESSON 10.1

1. Two-way frequency table:

Favorite Color of Students

		Red	Blue	Purple	Green
Class	**Class A**	////	///	/	/
	Class B	/	////	///	///

Frequency marginal distribution:

Favorite Color of Students

		Red	Blue	Purple	Green	Total
Class	**Class A**	4	3	1	1	9
	Class B	1	4	3	3	11
	Total	5	7	4	4	20

3. Two-way frequency table:

Favorite Fruit of Students

		Apple	Banana	Grapes	Orange
Class	**5th Grade**	////	////	//	/
	6th Grade	///	//	/	///

Frequency marginal distribution:

Favorite Fruit of Students

		Apple	Banana	Grapes	Orange	Total
Class	**5th Grade**	4	4	2	1	11
	6th Grade	3	2	1	3	9
	Total	7	6	3	4	20

5. Two-way frequency table:

Favorite Sports Girls Play

Class	Soccer	Softball	Swimming	Basketball
Class A	/	///	/	///
Class B	///	/	//	
Class C	/	/	/	///

Frequency marginal distribution:

Favorite Sports Girls Play

Class	Soccer	Softball	Swimming	Basketball	Total
Class A	1	3	1	3	8
Class B	3	1	2	0	6
Class C	1	1	1	3	6
Total	5	5	4	6	20

7.

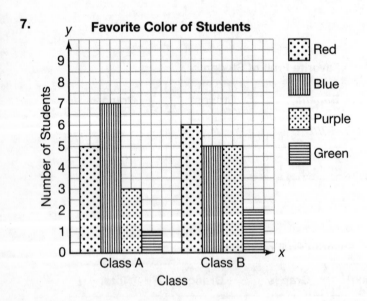

9.

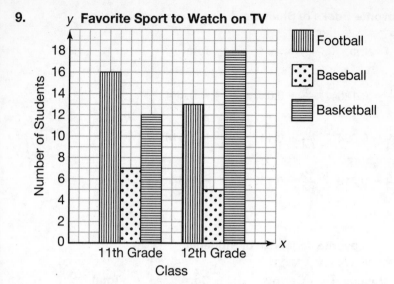

11.

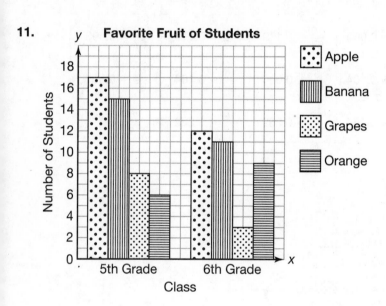

LESSON 10.2

1.

<table>
<tr><th colspan="6">Favorite Music of Students</th></tr>
<tr><th></th><th>Pop</th><th>Rap</th><th>Country</th><th>Rock</th><th>Total</th></tr>
<tr><td rowspan="3" style="writing-mode: vertical-rl;">Class</td></tr>
<tr><td>Class A</td><td>$\frac{15}{76} \approx 0.197$</td><td>$\frac{10}{76} \approx 0.132$</td><td>$\frac{4}{76} \approx 0.053$</td><td>$\frac{7}{76} \approx 0.092$</td><td>$\frac{36}{76} \approx 0.474$</td></tr>
<tr><td>Class B</td><td>$\frac{12}{76} \approx 0.158$</td><td>$\frac{17}{76} \approx 0.224$</td><td>$\frac{6}{76} \approx 0.079$</td><td>$\frac{5}{76} \approx 0.066$</td><td>$\frac{40}{76} \approx 0.526$</td></tr>
<tr><td>Total</td><td>$\frac{27}{76} \approx 0.355$</td><td>$\frac{27}{76} \approx 0.355$</td><td>$\frac{10}{76} \approx 0.132$</td><td>$\frac{12}{76} \approx 0.158$</td><td>$\frac{76}{76} = 1$</td></tr>
</table>

3.

Favorite Books of Students

Class		Comedy	Drama	Horror	Total
	Class A	$\frac{20}{64} \approx 0.313$	$\frac{8}{64} \approx 0.125$	$\frac{3}{64} \approx 0.047$	$\frac{31}{64} \approx 0.484$
	Class B	$\frac{18}{64} \approx 0.281$	$\frac{6}{64} \approx 0.094$	$\frac{9}{64} \approx 0.141$	$\frac{33}{64} \approx 0.516$
	Total	$\frac{38}{64} \approx 0.594$	$\frac{14}{64} \approx 0.219$	$\frac{12}{64} \approx 0.188$	$\frac{64}{64} = 1$

5.

Favorite Vegetable of Students

Class		Green Beans	Broccoli	Carrots	Corn	Total
	Class A	$\frac{9}{67} \approx 0.134$	$\frac{4}{67} \approx 0.060$	$\frac{12}{67} \approx 0.179$	$\frac{8}{67} \approx 0.119$	$\frac{33}{67} \approx 0.493$
	Class B	$\frac{10}{67} \approx 0.149$	$\frac{7}{67} \approx 0.104$	$\frac{6}{67} \approx 0.090$	$\frac{11}{67} \approx 0.164$	$\frac{34}{67} \approx 0.507$
	Total	$\frac{19}{67} \approx 0.284$	$\frac{11}{67} \approx 0.164$	$\frac{18}{67} \approx 0.269$	$\frac{19}{67} \approx 0.284$	$\frac{67}{67} = 1$

7.

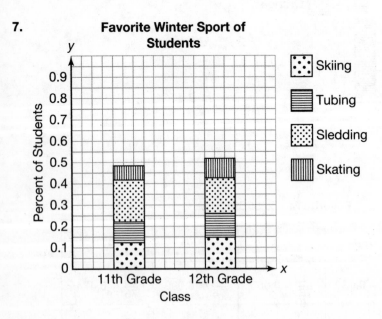

9.

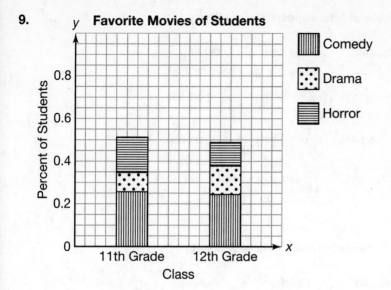

11.

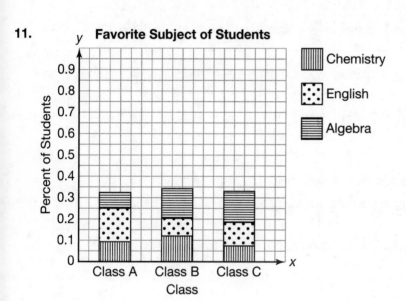

LESSON 10.3

1.

Grades of Students

		A	B	C	D	F	Total
Class	**Algebra**	$\frac{6}{20} = 30\%$	$\frac{4}{20} = 20\%$	$\frac{8}{20} = 40\%$	$\frac{1}{20} = 5\%$	$\frac{1}{20} = 5\%$	$\frac{20}{20} = 100\%$
	Geometry	$\frac{6}{30} = 20\%$	$\frac{11}{30} \approx 36.7\%$	$\frac{9}{30} = 30\%$	$\frac{2}{30} \approx 6.7\%$	$\frac{2}{30} \approx 6.7\%$	$\frac{30}{30} = 100\%$
	Trigonometry	$\frac{3}{30} = 10\%$	$\frac{7}{30} \approx 23.3\%$	$\frac{12}{30} \approx 40\%$	$\frac{5}{30} \approx 16.7\%$	$\frac{3}{30} = 10\%$	$\frac{30}{30} = 100\%$

3.

Student's Choice of Shakespeare Play to Study

		Hamlet	Macbeth	King Lear	Othello
Class	**Class A**	$\frac{9}{23} \approx 39.1\%$	$\frac{10}{18} \approx 55.6\%$	$\frac{13}{20} = 65\%$	$\frac{5}{13} \approx 38.5\%$
	Class B	$\frac{14}{23} \approx 60.9\%$	$\frac{8}{18} \approx 44.4\%$	$\frac{7}{20} = 35\%$	$\frac{8}{13} \approx 61.5\%$
	Total	$\frac{23}{23} = 100\%$	$\frac{18}{18} = 100\%$	$\frac{20}{20} = 100\%$	$\frac{13}{13} = 100\%$

5.

Favorite Lunch Item of Students

		Pizza	Salad	Chicken	Burger	Total
Class	**Class A**	$\frac{12}{33} \approx 36.4\%$	$\frac{3}{33} \approx 9.1\%$	$\frac{10}{33} \approx 30.3\%$	$\frac{8}{33} \approx 24.2\%$	$\frac{33}{33} = 100\%$
	Class B	$\frac{9}{35} \approx 25.7\%$	$\frac{8}{35} \approx 22.9\%$	$\frac{13}{35} \approx 37.1\%$	$\frac{5}{35} \approx 14.3\%$	$\frac{35}{35} = 100\%$
	Class C	$\frac{7}{35} = 20\%$	$\frac{9}{35} \approx 25.7\%$	$\frac{7}{35} = 20\%$	$\frac{12}{35} \approx 34.3\%$	$\frac{35}{35} = 100\%$

7. Of the female students, 25.9% participate in track & field.

9. Among female students, swimming is the most popular sport with 36.5% of female students participating.

11. Among female students, soccer is the least popular sport with 16.5% of female students participating.

LESSON 10.4

1. Frequency marginal distribution table:

Favorite Senior Picnic Location of Students

		Beach	Amusement Park	Water Park	Total
Class	**Class A**	⧻ //// 9	/// 2	// 2	13
	Class B	//// 4	// 2	⧻ ⧻ 10	16
	Class C	/// 3	⧻ // 7	/// 3	13
	Total	16	11	15	42

The beach is the most popular location among all three classes.

3. Frequency marginal distribution table:

Favorite Senior Picnic Location of Students

	Beach	Amusement Park	Water Park	Total
Class A	~~////~~//// 9	/// 2	// 2	13
Class B	//// 4	// 2	~~////~~ ~~////~~ 10	16
Class C	/// 3	~~////~~// 7	/// 3	13
Total	16	11	15	42

In Class B, the water park is the most preferred location.

5. Relative frequency conditional distribution:

Favorite Senior Picnic Location of Students

	Beach	Amusement Park	Water Park	Total
Class A	$\frac{9}{13} \approx 69.2\%$	$\frac{2}{13} \approx 15.4\%$	$\frac{2}{13} \approx 15.4\%$	$\frac{13}{13} = 100\%$
Class B	$\frac{4}{16} = 25\%$	$\frac{2}{16} = 12.5\%$	$\frac{10}{16} = 62.5\%$	$\frac{16}{16} = 100\%$
Class C	$\frac{3}{13} \approx 23.1\%$	$\frac{7}{13} \approx 53.8\%$	$\frac{3}{13} \approx 23.1\%$	$\frac{13}{13} = 100\%$

At 62.5%, Class B had the highest percentage of students choose the water park as their favorite senior picnic location.

7. Relative frequency conditional distribution:

Favorite Senior Picnic Location of Students

	Beach	Amusement Park	Water Park	Total
Class A	$\frac{9}{13} \approx 69.2\%$	$\frac{2}{13} \approx 15.4\%$	$\frac{2}{13} \approx 15.4\%$	$\frac{13}{13} = 100\%$
Class B	$\frac{4}{16} = 25\%$	$\frac{2}{16} = 12.5\%$	$\frac{10}{16} = 62.5\%$	$\frac{16}{16} = 100\%$
Class C	$\frac{3}{13} \approx 23.1\%$	$\frac{7}{13} \approx 53.8\%$	$\frac{3}{13} \approx 23.1\%$	$\frac{13}{13} = 100\%$

Class A, with 69.2%, had the highest percentage of students within their class choose their preferred location, the beach.

9. Relative frequency conditional distribution:

Favorite Senior Picnic Location of Students

		Beach	Amusement Park	Water Park
Class	**Class A**	$\frac{9}{16} \approx 56.3\%$	$\frac{2}{11} \approx 18.2\%$	$\frac{2}{15} \approx 13.3\%$
	Class B	$\frac{4}{16} = 25\%$	$\frac{2}{11} \approx 18.2\%$	$\frac{10}{15} \approx 66.7\%$
	Class C	$\frac{3}{16} \approx 18.8\%$	$\frac{7}{11} \approx 63.6\%$	$\frac{3}{15} = 20\%$
	Total	$\frac{16}{16} = 100\%$	$\frac{11}{11} = 100\%$	$\frac{15}{15} = 100\%$

At 63.6%, Class C had the highest percent of students who supported the least popular overall location, the amusement park.

Chapter 11

LESSON 11.1

1. $f(x) = x^2 + 3x$

3. $g(s) = s^2 + 4s - 2$

5. $f(n) = 2n^2 - 4n$

7. $-2x^2 + 300x$

9. $-x^2 + 50x$

11. $-2x^2 + 24x$

13. The absolute maximum of the function is at (100, 20,000).

The x-coordinate of 100 represents the width in feet that produces the maximum area.

The y-coordinate of 20,000 represents the maximum area in square feet of the parking lot.

15. The absolute maximum of the function is at about (1.31, 32.56).

The x-coordinate of 1.31 represents the time in seconds after the baseball is thrown that produces the maximum height.

The y-coordinate of 32.56 represents the maximum height in feet of the baseball.

17. The absolute maximum of the function is at (45, 2025).

The x-coordinate of 45 represents the width in feet that produces the maximum area.

The y-coordinate of 2025 represents the maximum area in square feet of the skating rink.

LESSON 11.2

1. The function represented by the graph is a linear function.

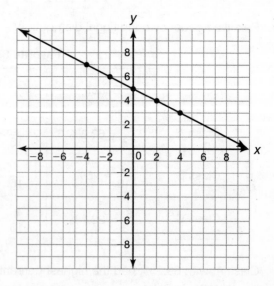

3. The function represented by the graph is a quadratic function.

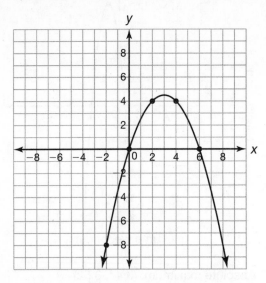

5. The function represented by the graph is a linear function.

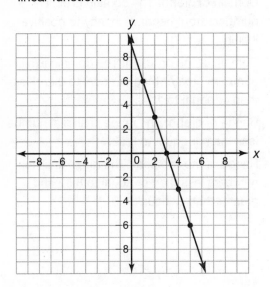

7.

x	y	First Differences	Second Differences
-2	-6		
		3	
-1	-3		0
		3	
0	0		0
		3	
1	3		0
		3	
2	6		

The function represented by the table is a linear function.

9.

x	y	First Differences	Second Differences
-3	3		
		1	
-2	4		0
		1	
-1	5		0
		1	
0	6		0
		1	
1	7		

The function represented by the table is a linear function.

11.

x	y	First Differences	Second Differences
-4	-48		
		21	
-3	-27		-6
		15	
-2	-12		-6
		9	
-1	-3		-6
		3	
0	0		

The function represented by the table is a quadratic function.

Answers

1.

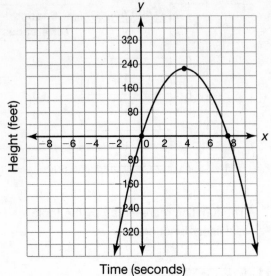

Time (seconds)

Absolute maximum: (3.75, 225)

Zeros: (0, 0), (7.5, 0)

Domain of graph: The domain is all real numbers from negative infinity to positive infinity.

Domain of the problem: The domain is all real numbers greater than or equal to 0 and less than or equal to 7.5.

Range of graph: The range is all real numbers less than or equal to 225.

Range of the problem: The range is all real numbers less than or equal to 225 and greater than or equal to 0.

3.

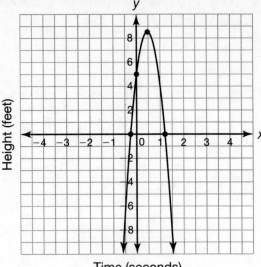

Time (seconds)

Absolute maximum: (0.47, 8.52)

Zeros: (−0.26, 0), (1.20, 0)

Domain of graph: The domain is all real numbers from negative infinity to positive infinity.

Domain of the problem: The domain is all real numbers greater than or equal to 0 and less than or equal to 1.20.

Range of graph: The range is all real numbers less than or equal to 8.52.

Range of the problem: The range is all real numbers less than or equal to 8.52 and greater than or equal to 0.

Answers

5.

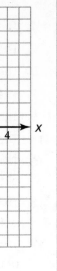

Time (seconds)

Absolute maximum: (0, 25)

Zeros: (−1.25, 0), (1.25, 0)

Domain of graph: The domain is all real numbers from negative infinity to positive infinity.

Domain of the problem: The domain is all real numbers greater than or equal to 0 and less than or equal to 1.25.

Range of graph: The range is all real numbers less than or equal to 25.

Range of the problem: The range is all real numbers less than or equal to 25 and greater than or equal to 0.

7. [−3, 5)

9. (−36, 14]

11. [c, d]

13. Interval of increase: (−3, ∞)

Interval of decrease: (−∞, −3)

15. Interval of increase: (−∞, 1)

Interval of decrease: (1, ∞)

17. Interval of increase: (0, ∞)

Interval of decrease: (−∞, 0)

LESSON 11.4

1. $6(x − 4)$

3. $5(2x + 3)$

5. $−(x + 9)$

7. The x-intercepts are (2, 0) and (8, 0).

9. The x-intercepts are (−4, 0) and (2, 0).

11. The x-intercepts are (−15, 0) and (−5, 0).

13. Answers will vary but functions should be in the form:

$f(x) = a(x + 2)(x − 5)$ for $a < 0$

15. Answers will vary but functions should be in the form:

$f(x) = a(x + 8)(x + 1)$ for $a > 0$

17. Answers will vary but functions should be in the form:

$f(x) = a(x + 5)(x − 2)$ for $a < 0$

19. x-intercepts: (1, 0) and (7, 0)

factored form: $f(x) = (x − 1)(x − 7)$

21. x-intercepts: (−5, 0) and (−15, 0)

factored form: $f(x) = −(x + 5)(x + 15)$

23. x-intercepts: (−4, 0) and (1, 0)

factored form: $f(x) = −3(x + 4)(x − 1)$

25. factored form: $f(x) = 3(x + 6)(x − 2)$

x-intercepts: (−6, 0) and (2, 0)

27. factored form: $f(x) = −2(x − 4)(x − 14)$

x-intercepts: (4, 0) and (14, 0)

29. factored form: $f(x) = (x − 0)(x + 7)$

x-intercepts: (0, 0) and (−7, 0)

LESSON 11.5

1. $h(t) = −16t^2 + 82t + 36$

3. $h(t) = −16t^2 + 110t + 49$

5. $h(t) = −16t^2 + 46t + 25$

7. The vertex of the graph is (2.5, 124).

The axis of symmetry is $x = 2.5$.

9. The vertex of the graph is (2, 104).

The axis of symmetry is $x = 2$.

11. The vertex of the graph is (1.5, 56).

The axis of symmetry is $x = 1.5$.

13. The axis of symmetry is $x = 6$.

15. The axis of symmetry is $x = −7$.

17. The axis of symmetry is $x = −1$.

19. The vertex is (−1, −16).

21. The vertex is (−2, −16).

23. The vertex is (4, 36).

25. Another point on the parabola is (5, 4).

27. Another point on the parabola is (5, 2).

29. Another point on the parabola is (−4, 3).

LESSON 11.6

1. The vertex is (3, 8).

3. The vertex is (1, −8).

5. The vertex is (−9, −1).

7. The vertex is (3, −36).

The function in vertex form is
$f(x) = (x − 3)^2 − 36$.

9. The vertex is (1, −8).

The function in vertex form is
$f(x) = 2(x − 1)^2 − 8$.

11. The vertex is (7.5, 2.25).

The function in vertex form is
$f(x) = −(x − 7.5)^2 + 2.25$.

13. The x-intercepts are (2, 0) and (−4, 0).

The function in factored form is
$f(x) = (x − 2)(x + 4)$.

15. The x-intercepts are (1, 0) and (2, 0).

The function in factored form is
$f(x) = −4(x − 1)(x − 2)$.

17. The x-intercepts are (−2, 0) and (3, 0).

The function in factored form is
$f(x) = \frac{1}{2}(x + 2)(x − 3)$.

19. The function is in vertex form.

The parabola opens up and the vertex
is (3, 12).

21. The function is in standard form.

The parabola opens down and the y-intercept
is (0, 0).

23. The function is in vertex form.

The parabola opens down and the vertex
is (−2, −7).

25. $f(x) = a(x + 1)2 + 4$, for $a < 0$

27. $f(x) = a(x − 3)2 − 2$, for $a > 0$

29. $f(x) = a(x − 5)(x − 12)$, for $a > 0$

LESSON 11.7

1. The graph of g(x) is translated down 5 units.

3. The graph of g(x) is translated up 6 units.

5. The graph of g(x) is translated down 3 units.

7. The graph of g(x) is translated left 4 units.

9. The graph of g(x) is translated left 1 unit.

11. The graph of g(x) is translated left 3 units.

13. The graph of p(x) is a horizontal reflection
of the graph of g(x).

15. The graph of p(x) is a horizontal reflection
of the graph of g(x).

17. The graph of p(x) is a vertical reflection
of the graph of g(x).

19. $(x, y) \rightarrow (x, 4y)$

21. $(x, y) \rightarrow (x, 5y)$

23. $(x, y) \rightarrow (x, 2y)$

25. $g(x) = −(x − 0)^2 + 3$

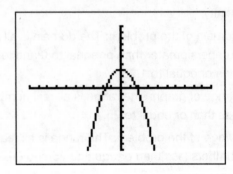

27. $g(x) = 6(x − 4)^2 + 1$

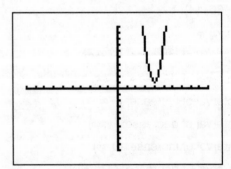

29. $g(x) = -3(x - 4)^2 - 2$

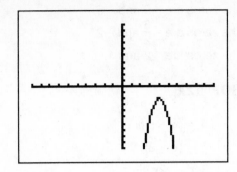

31. The function $g(x)$ is translated 7 units up from $f(x) = x^2$.

33. The function $g(x)$ is translated 8 units up and 2 units right from $f(x) = x^2$.

35. The function $g(x)$ is vertically dilated with a dilation factor of $\frac{2}{3}$ and then translated 9 units down and 4 units left from $f(x) = x^2$.

Chapter 12

LESSON 12.1

1. The terms are $5x$ and 8. The coefficients are 5 and 8.

3. The terms are x^2 and $-4x$. The coefficients are 1 and -4.

5. The term is -18. The coefficient is -18.

7. The expression is a polynomial.

9. The expression is not a polynomial. The first term can be rewritten as $3x^{-1}$ which has an exponent that is not a whole number.

11. The expression is a polynomial.

13. The expression is not a polynomial. The first term can be rewritten as $x^{1/3}$ which has an exponent that is not a whole number.

15. The polynomial is a binomial with a degree of 1.

17. The polynomial is a binomial with a degree of 2.

19. The polynomial is a monomial with a degree of 0.

21. $6x^2 + 2x$

The polynomial is a binomial with a degree of 2.

23. $-5x + 10$

The polynomial is a binomial with a degree of 1.

25. $-w^3 + 4w + 15$

The polynomial is a trinomial with a degree of 3.

27. $-p^4 - 1$

The polynomial is a binomial with a degree of 4.

29. $-18a^3 - 22a^2 + 54a$

The polynomial is a trinomial with a degree of 3.

31. $12x + 2$

33. $x^2 + 5x - 18$

35. $10w^2 - w + 3$

37. $a^2 - 7a + 7$

39. $-6x^5 + 3x^4 + 9x^3 + 3x^2 - 5$

41. $h(2) = (2)^2 + 3(2) - 2$
$$= 4 + 6 - 2$$
$$= 8$$

43. $h(0) = (0)^2 + 3(0) - 2$
$$= 0 + 0 - 2$$
$$= -2$$

45. $h(-2) = (-2)^2 + 3(-2) - 2$
$$= 4 - 6 - 2$$
$$= -4$$

LESSON 12.2

1. $x^2 + 2x + 1$

3. $x^2 + 4x + 4$

5. $2x^2 + 7x + 3$

7. $6x^2 + 14x + 8$

9. $42t^2 + 5t - 25$

11. $90w^2 + 71w - 8$

13. $2x^2 + 12x$

15. $7x^2 - 35x$

17. $x^3 + 3x^2 - x - 3$

19. $3x^3 + 15x^2 - 3x$

21. $x^3 + 8x^2 + 11x - 2$

LESSON 12.3

1. $x(x + 9)$

3. $5(x^2 + 4x - 3)$

5. $y(y^2 - 7)$

7. There is no greatest common factor.

9. $7(m^3 - 3)$

11. $x^2 + 4x + 3 = (x + 1)(x + 3)$

13. $x^2 - x - 6 = (x + 2)(x - 3)$

15. $x^2 + 7x + 10 = (x + 2)(x + 5)$

17. $x^2 - 2x - 8 = (x - 4)(x + 2)$

19. $m^2 + 6m - 7 = (m + 7)(m - 1)$

21. $4w^2 + 12w - 40 = 4(w + 5)(w - 2)$

23. $3m^3 + 36m^2 + 60m = 3m(m + 10)(m + 2)$

25. $x^2 + 11x + 10 = (x + 1)(x + 10)$

27. $m^2 + 2m - 35 = (m + 7)(m - 5)$

29. $3n^2 - 27n + 60 = 3(n - 5)(n - 4)$

31. $x^2 + 11x + 28 = \underline{(x + 4)(x + 7)}$

   $x^2 - 11x + 28 = \underline{(x - 4)(x - 7)}$

   $x^2 + 3x - 28 = \underline{(x - 4)(x + 7)}$

   $x^2 - 3x + 28 = \underline{(x + 4)(x - 7)}$

33. $x^2 + 12x + 27 = \underline{(x + 3)(x + 9)}$

   $x^2 - 12x + 27 = \underline{(x - 3)(x - 9)}$

   $x^2 + 6x - 27 = \underline{(x - 3)(x + 9)}$

   $x^2 - 6x - 27 = \underline{(x + 3)(x - 9)}$

35. $x^2 + 12x + 11 = \underline{(x + 1)(x + 11)}$

   $x^2 - 12x + 11 = \underline{(x - 1)(x - 11)}$

   $x^2 + 10x - 11 = \underline{(x - 1)(x + 11)}$

   $x^2 - 10x - 11 = \underline{(x + 1)(x - 11)}$

37. $x^2 + 4x + 4 = (x + 2)(x + 2)$

39. $-32 - 12m - m^2 = -(m + 4)(m + 8)$

41. $5x^2 + 10x - 15 = 5(x + 3)(x - 1)$

LESSON 12.4

1. The roots are -3 and -2.

3. The roots are -7 and 5.

5. The roots are 0 and -8.

7. The roots are 4 and 8.

9. The roots are $-\dfrac{3}{2}$ and 1.

11. The zeros are 0 and 5.

13. The zeros are -6 and -5.

15. The zeros are $-\dfrac{5}{2}$ and -2.

17. The zeros are -2 and 1.

LESSON 12.5

1. $x^2 - 25 = (x + 5)(x - 5)$

3. $x^3 + 27 = (x + 3)(x^2 - 3x + 9)$

5. $5(x + 2)(x^2 - 2x + 4)$

7. $(2a - 3)(4a^2 + 6a + 9)$

9. $x^2 + 16x + 64 = (x + 8)(x + 8)$

11. $2(x - 7)(x - 7)$

13. $z(z + 9)(z + 9)$

15. The roots are -10 and 10.

17. The root is -2.

19. The root is -11.

21. The zeros are -15 and 15.

23. The zeros are $-\dfrac{1}{3}$ and $\dfrac{1}{3}$.

25. The zeros are $-\dfrac{5}{2}$ and $\dfrac{5}{2}$.

LESSON 12.6

1. $\sqrt{25} = \pm 5$

3. $\sqrt{400} = \pm 20$

5. $\pm 4\sqrt{2}$

7. $\pm 10\sqrt{3}$

9. $\sqrt{7} \approx 2.6$

11. $\sqrt{96} \approx 9.8$

13. $\sqrt{109} \approx 10.4$

15. The roots are approximately 6.3 and -6.3.

17. The roots are approximately 3.9 and -3.9.

19. The roots are approximately 0.3 and 9.7.

21. The roots are $4\sqrt{3}$ and $-4\sqrt{3}$.

23. The roots are $3\sqrt{3}$ and $-3\sqrt{3}$.

25. The roots are $12 + 2\sqrt{2}$ and $12 - 2\sqrt{2}$.

LESSON 12.7

1. $x^2 + 2x + 1 = (x + 1)^2$

3. $x^2 + 12x + 36 = (x + 6)^2$

5. $x^2 + 11x + \dfrac{121}{4} = \left(x + \dfrac{11}{2}\right)^2$

7. $\underline{25}$

9. $\underline{6}$

11. $\underline{\dfrac{49}{4}}$

13. $\underline{26}$

15. The roots are approximately 1.16 and -5.16.

17. The roots are approximately -0.20 and -9.80.

19. The roots are approximately 0.30 and -3.30.

Chapter 13

LESSON 13.1

1. $x \approx 1.193$ or $x \approx -4.193$

3. $x \approx 1.098$ or $x \approx -4.098$

5. $x = -0.25$ or $x = 0.5$

7. $x = -2 - \dfrac{3}{2}\sqrt{2}$ or $x = -2 + \dfrac{3}{2}\sqrt{2}$

9. $x = 1 - \dfrac{\sqrt{30}}{3}$ or $x = 1 + \dfrac{\sqrt{30}}{3}$

11. $x = \dfrac{-5 + \sqrt{17}}{-4}$ or $x = \dfrac{-5 - \sqrt{17}}{-4}$

13. Because $b^2 - 4ac > 0$ the function has two zeros.

    $x = -1$ or $x = 7$

15. Because $b^2 - 4ac < 0$ the function has no zeros.

17. Because $b^2 - 4ac = 0$ the function has one zero.

    $x = -1$

LESSON 13.2

1. $y = -0.97x^2 + 4.84x + 0.03$

    $r^2 \approx 0.99$

    Because the r^2 value is close to 1, the quadratic regression equation is a good fit for the data.

3. $y = -0.73x^2 - 2.93x + 3.84$

    $r^2 \approx 0.55$

    Because the r^2 value is not close to 1, the quadratic regression equation is not a good fit for the data.

5. $y = 0.71x^2 - 4.10x + 6.77$

    $r^2 \approx 0.86$

    Because the r^2 value is close to 1, the quadratic regression equation is a good fit for the data.

LESSON 13.3

1. $x = 6$ or $x = 1$

    Solution: $x \in (-\infty, 1]$ or $x \in [6, \infty)$

3. $x \approx 3.887$ or $x \approx -4.887$

    Solution: $x \in (-4.887, 3.887)$

5. $x = 1$ or $x = 3$

    Solution: $x \in (-\infty, 1]$ or $x \in [3, \infty)$

7. It will take just over 2.3 seconds for the balloon to reach the ground.

9. The balloon is more than 10 feet above the ground between 0.1536 seconds and 2.034 seconds.

11. The balloon is more than 20 feet above the ground between 0.5850 seconds and 1.602 seconds.

LESSON 13.4

1. The system has two solutions: $(7, 14)$ and $(1, 2)$.

3. The system has two solutions: $\left(-6\dfrac{1}{2}, 4\dfrac{1}{2}\right)$ and $(-2, 0)$.

5. The system has one solution: $\left(-\dfrac{3}{2}, 3\right)$.

7. The system has two solutions: $\left(-\dfrac{1}{2}, 2\dfrac{1}{4}\right)$ and $(3, 4)$.

9. The system has no real solutions.

11. The system has no real solutions.

Chapter 14

LESSON 14.1

1. The numbers 10, 31, and 1970 are in the set of natural numbers.

3. The numbers 54, 216, and 2594 are in the set of integers.

5. The numbers $\sqrt{2}$ and π are in the set of irrational numbers.

7. The set of natural numbers is closed under addition and multiplication because when you add or multiply any two natural numbers, the sum or product is always a natural number.

The set of natural numbers is not closed under subtraction because when you subtract a natural number from a natural number, the difference can be 0 or a negative integer.

The set of natural numbers is not closed under division because when you divide a natural number by a natural number, the quotient can be a fraction.

9. The set of rational numbers is closed under each of the four operations because when you add, subtract, multiply, or divide two rational numbers, the result is always a rational number. Note that division by zero is not defined to allow division to be closed for the set of rational numbers.

11. The set of whole numbers is closed under addition and multiplication because when you add or multiply any whole numbers, the result is always a whole number.

The set of whole numbers is not closed under subtraction because when you subtract a whole number from a whole number, the difference can be a negative number.

The set of whole numbers is not closed under division because when you divide a whole number by a whole number, the quotient can be a fraction.

13. I could solve equations A, B, C, and J.

15. I could solve equations A, B, C, D, E, F, and J.

17. I could solve equation H.

19. The decimal 0.4444 . . . is equal to $\frac{4}{9}$.

21. The decimal 0.8181 . . . is equal to $\frac{9}{11}$.

23. The decimal 0.3939 . . . is equal to $\frac{13}{33}$.

25. The decimal 0.1212 . . . is equal to $\frac{4}{33}$.

27. The decimal 0.4848 . . . is equal to $\frac{16}{33}$.

LESSON 14.2

1. Associative Property of Multiplication

3. Additive Identity

5. Multiplicative Inverse

7. Multiplicative Identity

9. Distributive Property of Multiplication over Addition

11. $8x + (12x + 28)$ — Distributive Property of Multiplication over Addition

$(8x + 12x) + 28$ — Associative Property of Addition

$20x + 28$ — Combine like terms

13. $11(0 + x - 9)$ — Subtract

$11(x - 9)$ — Additive Identity

$11x - 99$ — Distributive Property of Multiplication over Subtraction

15. $3(7x + 5 - 5)$ — Commutative Property of Addition

$3(7x + 0)$ — Combine like terms

$3(7x)$ — Additive Identity

$21x$ — Multiply

17. $x + 19 + (-19) = 23 + (-19)$ Addition Property of Equality

$x + 0 = 23 + (-19)$ Combine like terms

$x = 23 + (-19)$ Additive Identity

$x = 4$ Combine like terms

19. $13x \cdot \dfrac{1}{13} = 52 \cdot \dfrac{1}{13}$ Multiplication Property of Equality

$x(13) \cdot \dfrac{1}{13} = 52 \cdot \dfrac{1}{13}$ Commutative Property of Multiplication

$x(1) = 52 \cdot \dfrac{1}{13}$ Multiply

$x = 52 \cdot \dfrac{1}{13}$ Multiplicative Identity

$x = 4$ Multiply

21. $9x - 24 + 2 = 32$ Distributive Property of Multiplication over Subtraction

$9x - 22 = 32$ Combine like terms

$9x - 22 + 22 = 32 + 22$ Addition Property of Equality

$9x + 0 = 32 + 22$ Combine like terms

$9x = 32 + 22$ Additive Identity

$9x = 54$ Combine like terms

$9x \cdot \dfrac{1}{9} = 54 \cdot \dfrac{1}{9}$ Multiplication Property of Equality

$x(9) \cdot \dfrac{1}{9} = 54 \cdot \dfrac{1}{9}$ Commutative Property of Multiplication

$x(1) = 54 \cdot \dfrac{1}{9}$ Multiply

$x = 54 \cdot \dfrac{1}{9}$ Multiplicative Identity

$x = 6$ Multiply

23. $7x + 1 = \dfrac{12x}{2} + \dfrac{6}{2}$ Distributive Property of Division over Addition

$7x + 1 = 6x + 3$ Simplify

$7x + 1 - 1 = 6x + 3 - 1$ Addition Property of Equality

$7x = 6x + 2$ Combine like terms

$7x - 6x = 6x + 2 - 6x$ Addition Property of Equality

$7x - 6x = 2 + 6x - 6x$ Commutative Property of Addition

$x = 2$ Combine like terms

25.

$3\left(\dfrac{2x-5}{3}\right) = 3(-2x+17)$	Multiplication Property of Equality
$2x - 5 = 3(-2x + 17)$	Simplify
$2x - 5 = -6x + 51$	Distributive Property of Multiplication over Addition
$2x - 5 + 5 = -6x + 51 + 5$	Addition Property of Equality
$2x = -6x + 56$	Combine like terms
$2x + 6x = -6x + 56 + 6x$	Addition Property of Equality
$2x + 6x = -6x + 6x + 56$	Commutative Property of Addition
$8x = 56$	Combine like terms
$\dfrac{1}{8} \cdot 8x = \dfrac{1}{8} \cdot 56$	Multiplication Property of Equality
$x = 7$	Multiply

LESSON 14.3

1. 1

3. $-i$

5. -1

7. 1

9. 1

11. $3i$

13. $2\sqrt{5}i$

15. $9 - 8i$

17. $2 - \sqrt{2}i$

19. $3xi$

21. $8x + 8i - 9$

23. $x^2 + 2xi + 3$

25. The real part is 24. The imaginary part is $0i$.

27. The real part is 7. The imaginary part is $3i$.

29. The real part is 0. The imaginary part is $-35i$.

31. The real part is 52. The imaginary part is $0i$.

33. integer, rational number, real number, complex number

35. natural number, whole number, integer, rational number, real number, complex number

37. rational number, real number, complex number

39. rational number, real number, complex number

LESSON 14.4

1. The equation has two imaginary roots.

3. The equation has a one real root.

5. The equation has two imaginary roots.

7. The zeros are $\dfrac{1}{2}i$ and $-\dfrac{1}{2}i$.

9. The zeros are $-1 + 2i$ and $-1 - 2i$.

11. The zeros are $-1 + i$ and $-1 - i$.

13. The zeros are $2 + \sqrt{5}i$ and $2 - \sqrt{5}i$.

Chapter 15

LESSON 15.1

1.

Time (days)	Savings (dollars)
0	100
1	80
2	60
3	40
4	40
5	40
6	30
7	20
8	10
9	0

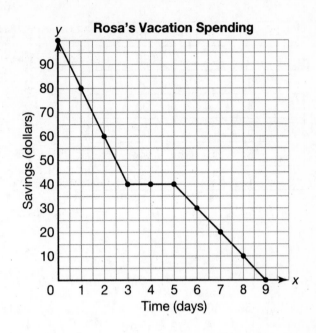

3.

Time (weeks)	Weight (pounds)
0	146
1	144
2	142
3	140
4	138
5	137
6	136
7	134
8	132

5.

Time (days)	Earnings (dollars)
0	0
1	18
2	36
3	54
4	90
5	126
6	144
7	162

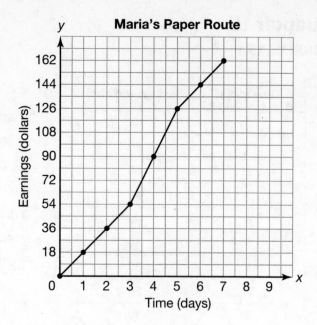

Maria's Paper Route

7. $f(x) = \begin{cases} -5x + 60, & 0 \le x \le 3 \\ 45, & 3 < x \le 6 \\ -2x + 57, & 6 < x \le 9 \end{cases}$

9. $f(x) = \begin{cases} -5x + 80, & 0 \le x \le 3 \\ -x + 68, & 3 < x \le 8 \\ -2x + 76, & 8 < x \le 9 \end{cases}$

11. $f(x) = \begin{cases} -10x + 100, & 0 \le x \le 4 \\ 60, & 4 < x \le 10 \\ -3x + 90, & 10 < x \le 18 \end{cases}$

13.

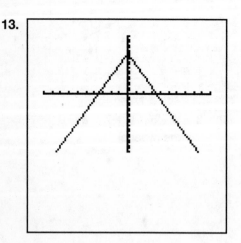

$f(x) = -|4x| + 14$

15.

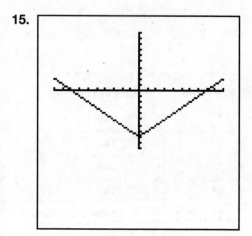

$f(x) = |x| - 8$

17.

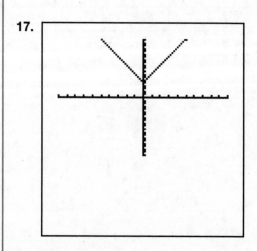

$f(x) = |3x| + 5$

LESSON 15.2

1. $f(x) = \begin{cases} 0.18x, & 0 < x \le 50 \\ 0.16x, & 50 < x \le 100 \\ 0.14x, & 100 < x \le 150 \\ 0.12x, & 150 < x \le 200 \\ 0.10x, & 200 < x \end{cases}$

Online Mall Shipping Charges

y-axis: Shipping Charge (dollars)
x-axis: Purchase Amount (dollars)

3. $f(x) = \begin{cases} 0.05x, & 0 < x \le 20 \\ 0.10x, & 20 < x \le 40 \\ 0.15x, & 40 < x \le 60 \\ 0.20x, & 60 < x \end{cases}$

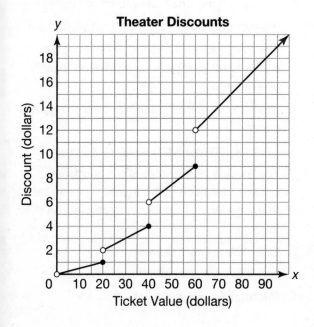

Theater Discounts

y-axis: Discount (dollars)
x-axis: Ticket Value (dollars)

5. $f(x) = \begin{cases} 0.09x, & 0 < x \le 100 \\ 0.08x, & 100 < x \le 200 \\ 0.07x, & 200 < x \le 300 \\ 0.06x, & 300 < x \end{cases}$

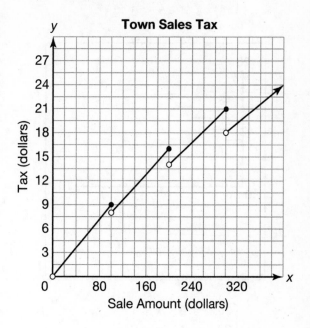

Town Sales Tax

y-axis: Tax (dollars)
x-axis: Sale Amount (dollars)

7. $f(x) = \begin{cases} 50, & 0 < x \le 100 \\ 30, & 100 < x \le 200 \\ 10, & 200 < x \le 300 \\ 0, & 300 < x \end{cases}$

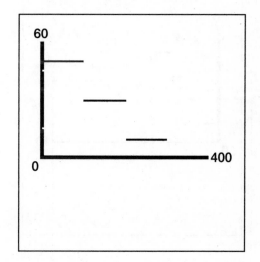

9. $f(x) = \begin{cases} 8, & 0 < x \le 1 \\ 10, & 1 < x \le 2 \\ 12, & 2 < x \le 3 \\ 14, & 3 < x \le 4 \\ 16, & 4 < x \le 5 \end{cases}$

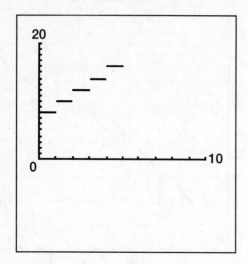

11. $f(x) = \begin{cases} 10, & 0 < x \le 1 \\ 22, & 1 < x \le 2 \\ 34, & 2 < x \le 3 \\ 46, & 3 < x \le 4 \\ 58, & 4 < x \le 5 \end{cases}$

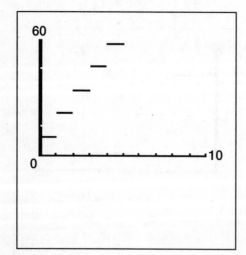

13. $\lfloor 4.5 \rfloor = 4$

15. $\lceil -8.3 \rceil = -8$

17. $\lfloor 7.3 \rfloor = 7$

19. $\lceil 7.9 \rceil = 8$

LESSON 15.3

1. Relationship domain: students in your school

   Relationship range: all of the sports chosen

   The relationship is a function because for each student there is exactly one favorite sport.

   Reverse relationship domain: all of the sports chosen

   Reverse range: students in your school

   The reverse relationship is not a function because for each sport there may be more than one student who chose it as their favorite.

3. Relationship domain: students in your class

   Relationship range: red, blue, orange, green, and yellow marbles

   The relationship is a function because for each student there is exactly one marble chosen.

   Reverse relationship domain: red, blue, orange, green, and yellow marbles

   Reverse range: students in your class

   The relationship is not a function because for each color of marble there may be more than one student who chose it.

5. Relationship domain: members of your family

   Relationship range: all of the games chosen

   The relationship is a function because for each member of your family there is exactly one favorite game.

   Reverse relationship domain: all of the games chosen

   Reverse range: members of your family

   The reverse relationship is not a function because for each game there may be more than one family member who chose it as their favorite.

7. Open the dresser drawer.

9. Jog 5 blocks west and 3 blocks south.

11. Subtract 7 then multiply by 2.

13.

Feet	Inches
1	12
2	24
3	36
4	48
5	60

Let i = the number of inches.

Let f = the number of feet.

$i = 12f$

Inverse: $f = \dfrac{i}{12}$

15.

Pints	Cups
2	4
4	8
6	12
8	16
10	20

Let p = the number of pints.

Let c = the number of cups.

$c = 2p$

Inverse: $p = \dfrac{c}{2}$

17.

Feet	Yards
3	1
9	3
12	4
18	6
24	8

Let f = the number of feet.

Let y = the number of yards.

$y = \dfrac{f}{3}$

Inverse: $f = 3y$

19. $f^{-1}(x) = \dfrac{x}{4}$

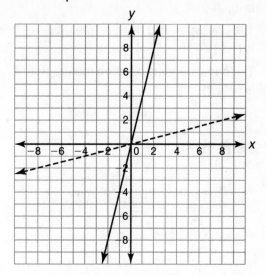

21. $f^{-1}(x) = \dfrac{1}{2}x - \dfrac{1}{2}$

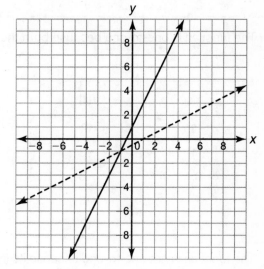

23. $f^{-1}(x) = \dfrac{3}{2}x + 12$

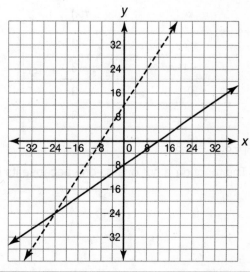

25. The corresponding point on the graph of $f^{-1}(x)$ is $(5, 2)$.

27. The corresponding point on the graph of $f^{-1}(x)$ is $(-1, -4)$.

29. The corresponding point on the graph of $f^{-1}(x)$ is $(-7, 1)$.

31. The functions are inverses because $f(g(x)) = g(f(x)) = x$.

33. The functions are inverses because $f(g(x)) = g(f(x)) = x$.

35. The functions are inverses because $f(g(x)) = g(f(x)) = x$.

LESSON 15.4

1.

x	$f(x)$
-2	1
-1	3
0	5
1	7
2	9

x	$f^{-1}(x)$
1	-2
3	-1
5	0
7	1
9	2

The function is one-to-one because both the original function and its inverse are functions.

3.

x	$f(x)$
-2	12
-1	-3
0	-8
1	-3
2	12

x	$f^{-1}(x)$
12	-2
-3	-1
-8	0
-3	1
12	2

The function is not one-to-one because its inverse is not a function.

5.

x	$f(x)$
-2	-3
-1	-3
0	-3
1	-3
2	-3

x	$f^{-1}(x)$
-3	-2
-3	-1
-3	0
-3	1
-3	2

The function is not one-to-one because its inverse is not a function.

7. The function is one-to-one because both the original function and its inverse are functions.

9. The inverse function does not pass the Vertical Line Test. So, the function is not one-to-one because its inverse is not a function.

11. The function is one-to-one because both the original function and its inverse are functions.

13. The function is a linear function. A linear function that is not a constant function is a one-to-one function. So, the function is one-to-one.

15. The function is a linear function. A linear function that is not a constant function is a one-to-one function. So, the function is one-to-one.

17. The function is a linear absolute value function. A linear absolute value function is never a one-to-one function. So, the function is not one-to-one.

19. $f^{-1}(x) = \pm\sqrt{\dfrac{x}{7}}$

21. $f^{-1}(x) = \pm\sqrt{\dfrac{x - 11}{6}}$

23. $f^{-1}(x) = \pm\sqrt{\dfrac{x + 6}{-4}}$

25. $f^{-1}(x) = \pm\sqrt{\dfrac{x}{2}}$

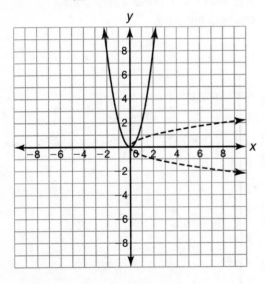

For the function $y = 2x^2$ with $x \geq 0$, the inverse is $y = \sqrt{\dfrac{x}{2}}$.

For the function $y = 2x^2$ with $x \leq 0$, the inverse is $y = -\sqrt{\dfrac{x}{2}}$.

27. $f^{-1}(x) = \pm\sqrt{\dfrac{x + 2}{-4}}$

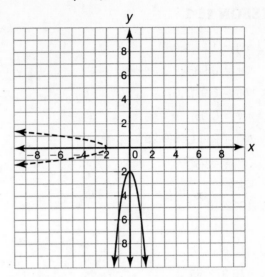

For the function $y = -4x^2 - 2$ with $x \geq 0$, the inverse is $y = \sqrt{\dfrac{x + 2}{-4}}$.

For the function $y = -4x^2 - 2$ with $x \leq 0$, the inverse is $y = -\sqrt{\dfrac{x + 2}{-4}}$.

29. $x = y \qquad x = -y$

$-x = y$

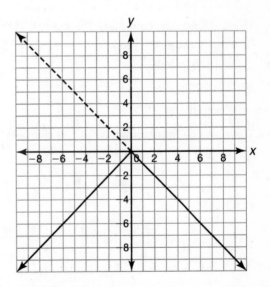

For the function $y = x$ with $x \leq 0$, the inverse is $y = x$.

For the function $y = -x$ with $x \geq 0$, the inverse is $y = -x$.

Chapter 16

LESSON 16.1

1. $f(x) = 1.88(1.06)^x$

   $r = 0.98$

3. $f(x) = 6.91(1.07)^x$

   $r = 0.95$

5. $f(x) = 2101.58(0.25)^x$

   $r = -0.99$

7. 3.28

9. 1612.46

11. 439.24

13. 31.56

15. 479,377.65

17. $f(x) = 497.63(1.06)^x$

   $f(50) = 497.63(1.06)^{50}$

   ≈ 9166.42

   The account's value will be approximately $9166.42 in 2020.

19. $f(x) = 856.83(0.91)^x$

   $f(16) = 856.83(0.91)^{16}$

   ≈ 189.48

   There will be approximately 189 sunfish in the lake in his sixteenth year.

21. $f(x) = 14.75(2.74)^x$

   $f(7) = 14.75(2.74)^7$

   $\approx 17,101.96$

   There will be approximately 17,102 bacteria cells in the colony after 7 hours.

LESSON 16.2

1. The quadratic regression equation $f(x) = -15.18x^2 - 3.25x - 898.93$, where the function represents the height of the supply kit x seconds after it is released, best fits the data.

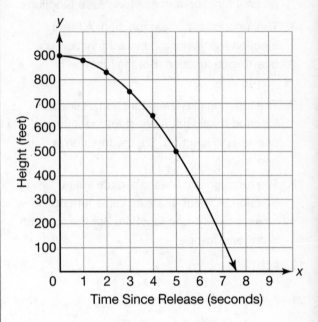

3. The linear regression equation $f(x) = -0.09x + 9.09$, where the function represents the runner's speed after x miles, best fits the data.

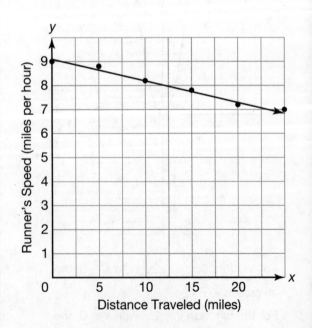

5. The exponential regression equation $f(x) = 444.87(0.96)^x$, where the function represents the ash tree population x years since 1980, best fits the data.

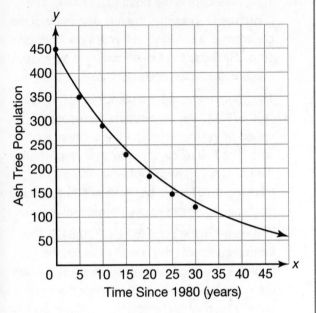

7.

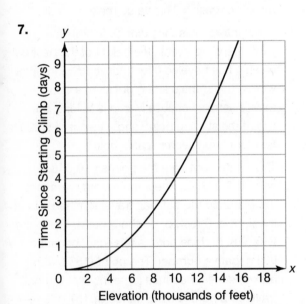

For the given function, the domain is all real numbers greater than or equal to 0 and less than or equal to 10, because it represents the time, in days, since the climber started his climb. The range is all real numbers greater than or equal to 0 and less than or equal to about 15,800, because it represents the climber's elevation from his starting point of 0 feet to his ending point of about 15,800 feet.

For the inverse function, the domain is all real numbers greater than or equal to 0 and less than or equal to about 15,800, because it represents the climber's elevation from his starting point of 0 feet to his ending point of about 15,800 feet. The range is all real numbers greater than or equal to 0 and less than or equal to 10, because it represents the time, in days, since the climber started his climb.

9.

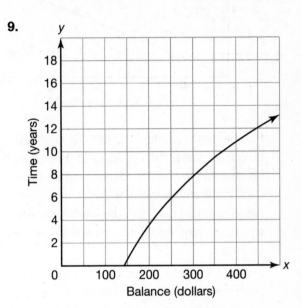

For the given function, the domain is all real numbers greater than or equal to 0 and less than 20 because it represents the time, in years, the money has been in the account. The range is all real numbers greater than or equal to 150 because it represents the amount of money in the account from the initial deposit of $150.

For the inverse function, the domain is all real numbers greater than or equal to 150 because it represents the amount of money in the account from the initial deposit of $150. The range is all real numbers greater than or equal to 0 and less than 20 because it represents the time, in years, the money has been in the account.

11.

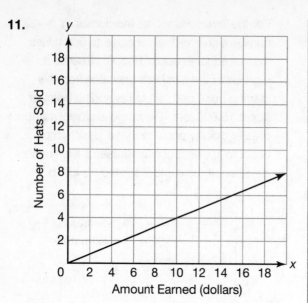

Amount Earned (dollars)

For the given function, the domain is all real numbers greater than or equal to 0 because it represents the number of hats sold and you cannot sell a negative number of hats. The range is all real numbers greater than or equal to 0 because it represents the amount earned, in dollars.

For the inverse function, the domain is all real numbers greater than or equal to 0 because it represents the amount earned, in dollars. The range is all real numbers greater than or equal to 0 because it represents the number of hats sold and you cannot sell a negative number of hats.

13. The function $L(x)$ appears to be a quadratic function, because it is a smooth curve which decreases and then increases over the domain. The function $R(x)$ appears to be a linear function, because it is a straight line.

15. During their second and eighth games, both groups had the same average scores.

LESSON 16.3

1. The profit when 20 items are produced should be $2300.

3. The profit when 200 items are produced should be $19,200.

5. The profit when 300 items are produced should be $238,500.

7. $y = 0.002x^2 + x + 9.259$

9. $y = 0.006x^2 + 1.201x + 19.714$

11. $y = -130.952x^2 + 98.333x - 1.714$

13. The y-intercept is the point $(0, -9.444)$. The y-intercept represents the fuel efficiency of the car when it is traveling at 0 miles per hour (at a stop). Because the fuel efficiency is a negative number, this value does not make sense.

The x-intercepts are the points $(6.707, 0)$ and $(100.579, 0)$. The x-intercepts represent the speed of the car when the fuel efficiency is zero. The fuel efficiency would be zero when the car is not moving, not when the car is traveling 6.707 miles per hour or 100.579 miles per hour. So, these values do not make sense.

The vertex is the point $(53.643, 30.842)$. The vertex represents the speed at which the car is getting the highest fuel efficiency. So, when the car is traveling at 53.643 miles per hour, it gets its highest fuel efficiency, which is 30.842 miles per gallon. This value makes sense.

15. The y-intercept is the point $(0, 5.220)$. The y-intercept represents the height of the baseball when it has traveled 0 feet horizontally. In other words, this is the starting point. This value makes sense, because Martin is holding the ball at the starting point, and a height of 5.220 feet for Martin seems reasonable.

The x-intercepts are the points $(-6.648, 0)$ and $(157.048, 0)$. The x-intercepts represent the distance the ball has traveled when it is at a height of 0 feet, or on the ground. The point $(-6.648, 0)$ does not make sense, because it is a negative number. The point $(157.048, 0)$ makes sense, because it means that the ball traveled a horizontal distance of 157.048 feet after Martin threw it and it hit the ground.

The vertex is the point $(75.2, 33.495)$. The vertex represents the horizontal distance the ball traveled when it is at its highest point vertically. So, when the ball travels 75.2 feet, it is at its highest point, which is 33.495 feet. This value makes sense.

17. The *y*-intercept is the point (0, 35.07). The *y*-intercept represents the temperature at the beginning of the storm. In other words, this is the starting point. This value makes sense because the temperature is cold enough for a winter storm.

There are no *x*-intercepts for this graph. This means that the temperature never reached 0°. This makes sense because it would be rare for the temperature to drop from 35 to 0 degrees in a short amount of time.

The vertex is the point (5.5, 13). The vertex represents the lowest temperature during the storm. This makes sense because after 5.5 hours, the temperature dropped to 13°F.

19. The farmer should have a yield of 17.49 bushels per hundred square feet.

21. The ball should reach a height of 30 feet about 0.779 seconds after it is thrown and again about 2.061 seconds after it is thrown.

23. The cost to manufacture 50 bicycles should be $9091.

LESSON 16.4

1. $y = -0.5x^2 - 33.6x + 749.9$

   x represents the time in months the television has been for sale

   y represents the price in dollars of the television

3. $y = (885.8)(1.1)^x$

   x represents the time in months

   y represents the population of a town

5. $y = 0.06x^2 - 7x + 412.5$

   x represents the vehicle's mileage in thousands of miles

   y represents the cost for repairs in dollars

7. The exponential regression equation fits the data better than the quadratic regression equation. The exponential regression equation is closer to more points in the data set.

9. The quadratic regression equation fits the data better than the exponential regression equation. The quadratic regression equation is closer to more points in the data set.

11. The quadratic regression equation fits the data better than the exponential regression equation. The quadratic regression equation is closer to more points in the data set.

13. The height of the ball is 261 feet after 2 seconds.

15. The point where $t(x) = 72 + 140(0.98)^x$ intersects $g(x) = 152$ is approximately (27.7, 152). The temperature reaches 152 degrees Fahrenheit about 27.7 minutes after the pot is removed from the stove.

17. The polar bear population is about 234 after 20 years.

19. The domain is all real numbers greater than or equal to 0, because the car did not have a value prior to the year of its manufacture. The range is all real numbers greater than or equal to approximately $1000, because the function's value starts at approximately $3685, and then drops to approximately $1000 before rising from that point onward.

21. The function has no *x*-intercepts, because it does not cross the *x*-axis. The function has a *y*-intercept of $3685.45, which represents the estimated value of the car in the year 1970 according to the function.

23. The intersection point is about (40, 19,000) so the value of the car will be about $19,000 in 2010.

25. The function does not have a maximum value. Even though the given exponential function has no minimum value, the function as it relates to the problem has a minimum value of approximately 5 in the year 2005.

27. The function increases over the entire domain from the year 2005 to infinity.

29. The intersection point is about (7, 200) so about 200 wild Burmese pythons will be captured in 2012.

1. Answers will vary.

The shark is released into the water after having the device attached. It swims downward to a depth of 5 meters over a two minute period. It remains at this depth for 3 minutes before swimming upward to a depth of 2 meters over the next 3 minutes. Finally, it swims downward past the a depth of 10 meters over the next 2 minutes. The slope in this situation represents the rate at which the shark's depth is changing over time. When the slope is positive, the shark is going deeper. When the slope is negative, the shark is going towards the surface. When the slope is 0, the shark's depth is remaining constant. The slope of part A is $\frac{5}{2}$, the slope of part B is 0, the slope of part C is −1, and the slope of part D is 4. The x-intercept in this situation represents the time at which the shark is at the surface. The only x-intercept is (0, 0) which means the shark was only at the surface at the moment it was released. The y-intercept is (0, 0) and represents the depth of the shark when it was first released. In this case, the depth of the shark was 0 meters when it was released.

3. Answers will vary.

The hiker begins his hike at an elevation of 800 feet and walks uphill 800 feet in the first 2 hours. The hiker walks downhill 1600 feet over the next 4 hours. He walks uphill 1200 feet over the next 2 hours, and then walks downhill 400 feet over the following 2 hours to reach his starting elevation. The slope in this situation represents the rate at which the hiker's elevation is changing per hour. When the slope is positive, the hiker is going uphill. When the slope is negative, the hiker is going downhill. The slope of part A is 400, the slope of part B is −400, the slope of part C is 600, and the slope of part D is −200. The x-intercept represents the time at which the hiker's elevation is 0. The x-intercept is (6, 0), which means the hiker's elevation was 0 six hours after the start of his hike. The y-intercept represents the hiker's elevation at the start of the hike. The y-intercept is (0, 800), which means the hiker started his hike at an elevation of 800 feet.

5. Answers may vary.

Peyton begins by walking 6 miles in the first 4 hours. She then rests for an hour. She then picks up the pace and walks 2 miles in the next hour. She then turns around to head home. She returns home by traveling 10 miles in 3 hours. The slope in this situation represents the rate at which Peyton's distance from home is changing per hour. When the slope is positive, she is walking away from her home. When the slope is negative, she is walking toward her home. When the slope is 0, she is not moving. The slope of part A is 1.5, the slope of part B is 0, the slope of part C is 2, and the slope of part D is 5. The x-intercepts represent the times at which Peyton is at home. The x-intercepts are (0,0) and (9, 0), which means she was at home at the start of her walk and 9 hours after the start of her walk. The y-intercept represents Peyton's distance from home at the start of her walk. The y-intercept is (0, 0) which means she started her walk at home.

7.

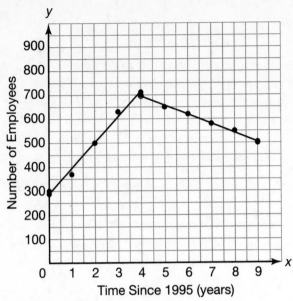

Answers will vary.

Let $f(x)$ represent the number of employees employed by the company x years since 1995.

$$f(x) = \begin{cases} 106x + 288, & 0 \leq x \leq 4 \\ -38.286x + 848.857, & 4 < x \leq 9 \end{cases}$$

9.

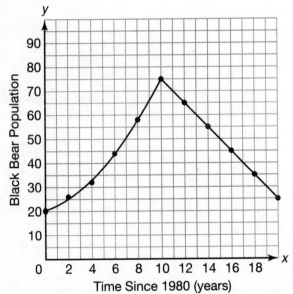

Answers will vary.

Let $f(x)$ represent the black bear population in the county x years since 1980.

$$f(x) = \begin{cases} 0.388x^2 + 1.588x + 20.321, & 0 < x \leq 10 \\ -5x + 125, & 10 < x \leq 20 \end{cases}$$

11.

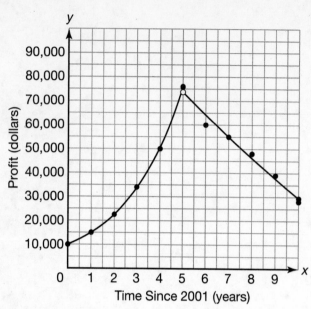

Time Since 2001 (years)

Answers will vary.

Let $f(x)$ represent the bookstore's yearly profit x years since 2001.

$$f(x) = \begin{cases} 10{,}011.384(1.499)^x, & 0 \le x \le 5 \\ 160.714x^2 - 11{,}267.857x + 126{,}000, & 5 < x \le 10 \end{cases}$$